Pharmacy

THE MOLECULAR CONTROL
OF CELLULAR ACTIVITY

The University of Michigan
Institute of Science and Technology Series

THE MOLECULAR CONTROL OF CELLULAR ACTIVITY

Edited by

JOHN M. ALLEN

Associate Professor of Zoology
The University of Michigan

McGRAW-HILL BOOK COMPANY, INC.

New York Toronto London

1962

THE MOLECULAR CONTROL OF CELLULAR ACTIVITY

01200

Preface

The papers contained within this volume are the result of a series of lectures held in Ann Arbor during the Spring of 1960 under the auspices of the Institute of Science and Technology of The University of Michigan.

During the past decade the biologist's concept of the cell has been greatly altered by accumulation of significant new information derived from diverse areas of inquiry. The demonstration of a wealth of structural detail within the cell as a result of studies with the electron microscope has had a major impact in this conceptual alteration.

Closely associated with this morphological advance has been the assignment of biochemical and physiological properties to such structures. Great strides have been made in the relation of the molecular structure of the hereditary material to genetic function, and the "gene" has been subdivided so that we know something of its fine structure from both molecular and physiological standpoints. The means by which the genetic material regulates cytoplasmic activity are now being translated into molecular terms, and it is customary to ponder the means by which molecules derived from the nucleus may control the formation of proteins in the cytoplasm. Indeed, we are close to an amalgamation of morphological and biochemical inquiry in the sense that much of our knowledge of cellular structures is subject to interpretation in terms of macromolecular aggregates.

The progressive comminution of cellular function to finer and finer levels of organization has destroyed many of our older concepts as to how various areas of cellular function are related. We now find ourselves thinking of the regulation of cellular activity in terms of the interaction between metabolic systems and the influence of macromolecular structures upon this interaction. The task of relating this information on molecular interaction into a coherent image of cellular regulation is of major importance. Accordingly, during the planning stages of the lecture series from which these papers are derived, every attempt was made to regard the cell as a totality and with this consideration in mind, to arrange a series of topics that would cover those areas most pertinent to a comprehension of the regulation of cellular activity in terms of molecular action and interaction. It was our desire to examine these areas from a very general vantage point rather than to delve deeply into any particular aspect of the problem of cellular regulation. By this approach, it was hoped that a degree of synthesis might be achieved in terms of our understanding of the molecular control of cellular activity.

I wish to thank the contributors to this volume for giving so freely of their thoughts and of their time. Thanks are also due Dr. M. J. Coon of the Department of Biological Chemistry of The University of Michigan Medical School and Dr. Wilbur Ackermann of the School of Public Health of The University of Michigan for their very considerable role in the planning of this series of lectures.

John M. Allen

Contents

Chapter One

From Cell to Molecule*

PAUL WEISS

The Rockefeller Institute, New York

INTRODUCTION

The privilege of introducing this series of lectures on *The Molecular Control of Cellular Activity* is all the more precious to me because it provides me with an opportunity to recenter the object whose "activities" are to be "controlled" — the cell — from the increasingly off-center, out-of-focus position which it has assumed in current thought. Of the twelve lectures of the series which are to follow, all twelve deal with important fragments of the molecular inventory of cells, and seven alone with nucleic acids. This is a true reflection of current hopes — or illusions — that it might be possible to pinpoint in the cell a master compound "responsible" for "life" — an obvious reversion in modern guise to animistic biology, which let animated particles under whatever name impart the property of organization to inanimate matter. Therefore, lest our necessary and highly successful preoccupation with cell fragments and fractions obscure the fact that the cell is not just an inert playground for a few almighty masterminding molecules, but is a *system*, a hierarchically *ordered* system, of mutually interdependent species of molecules, molecular groupings, and supramolecular entities; and that life, through cell life, depends on the *order* of their interactions; it may be well to restate at the outset the case for the cell as a *unit*. A unit retains its unity by virtue of the power of subordination which it exerts upon its constituent elements in such a manner that their individual activities, instead of being free and unrelated, will be restrained and directed toward a combined unitary resultant. In short, the story of "molecular control of cellular activities" is bound to remain fragmentary and incomplete unless it is matched by knowledge of what makes a cell the unit that it is, namely, the "cellular control of molecular activities."

*Introductory lecture delivered March 1, 1960, in the lecture series on "The Molecular Control of Cellular Activity" of The Institute of Science and Technology, University of Michigan.
Some of the research results used as examples in this address have been obtained in investigations that were aided in part by grants from the American Cancer Society and the National Cancer Institute (National Institutes of Health of the Public Health Service).

It is on this principle then that I shall concentrate here, for it is as poorly understood as it is neglected. Or rather, it suffers not so much from outright neglect as from being frozen into literary symbols (e.g., "control," "organization," "information," "coordination," "regulation," etc.), the resolution of which into objective terms has been bypassed far too long. The problem of the cell as a unitary system may easily escape notice by those whose practical experience is confined to a limited sector of cellular activities, or it may be recognized but relegated to the mental attic as uncomfortable or untractable. Yet unless it is restored explicitly and courageously to a central place commanding universal recognition, it will not receive the concentrated attention and investigative effort which it deserves and without which the concepts of the cell — more broadly, of organisms — will remain an incongruous mixture of solid factual descriptions and vacuous anthropomorphisms.

FROM CELL TO MOLECULE

Analysis — the way from cell to molecule — appears a relatively easy road when one compares it with the uphill task of getting back from molecules to cells. Can what we destroy on the way down be replaced in reverse order and the system resynthesized from its shambles? Retracing such synthetic courses in our minds, we rely on verbal crutches, — "reconstitution," "reintegration," and the like. Do these abstractions have concrete counterparts in our actual experience with living things? Or, phrased differently, is it conceivable that we could resynthesize a cell from its fragments, if we only knew how to put the parts together stepwise one by one; and how to keep the intermediary partial assemblies from collapsing before the culminating self-sustaining state has been attained?

Recent developments in cell biology might seem to encourage positive hopes for an affirmative answer. Less than half a century ago, when I studied biology, something called "protoplasm" was globally endowed with all the properties required for a cell to live and function — reproductive capacity, growth, respiration, excretion, contractility, and excitability. Since then all these performances have been successfully allocated to identifiable components — genes, ribosomes, mitochondria, Golgi nets, acto-myosin threads, and polarized membranes, respectively — and some of them have actually been obtained from the respective components in isolation. What is often overlooked, however, is that in order to obtain performance by an isolated part, the experimenter must provide it with accessories which themselves are products of cellular activity, such as enzymes. Isolation thus connotes by no means the cessation of dependence upon activities of other cell systems. In fact, it is precisely this indissoluble interdependence among its various component operations which marks the cell as an entity in its own right and, as I shall indicate presently, discourages prospects for a "synthetic cell."

In passing, we might examine the reason why this qualifying fact is often overlooked. It lies, I believe, in our stage of scientific development to which future historians of science will perhaps refer as the "age of identification." We are looking for the doer and forget about the deeds. There seems to be some predilection for indentifying agents and charging them with "responsibility" for actions, the mechanisms of which we do not seem to be equally intent on exploring. For instance, we have identified, purified, crystallized, and even synthesized some of the hormones, but how they exert their selective effects on cells of various types has as yet been revealed in no single case. We state that the hormone "controls" a given cellular activity, and we mostly let it go at that. In fact, belief in identification as the real object of research accounts for the presumptuous habit of attaching labels of identity to unknowns which have not even been identified at all. For instance, how often does one hear the gratuitous assertion that in a given unknown mechanism "an enzyme may be involved," without any real evidence that the process does "involve" enzymes, or how it does, let alone which enzymes are involved? Of course, identification is defended as merely the first and indispensable step to understanding, but a first step leads nowhere unless the next step follows, and furthermore, understanding of an activity does not necessarily presuppose knowledge of the identity of the agency, as is well illustrated by the fact that the basic laws of optics were established long before the electromagnetic nature of light waves became known.

Accordingly, unless we follow through with the second step, the historian of the future will rightly blame us for partial blindness. This second step, which we have been slack in taking, is the study of the orderly interdependence of the partial mechanisms of the cell of which the identified molecules or particles are the tools.

Life is a dynamic process. Logically, the elements of a process can be only elementary *processes*, and not elementary *particles* or any other static units. Cell life, accordingly, can never be defined in terms of a static inventory of compounds, however detailed, but only in terms of their interactions — with stress on *inter-*, for as I indicated before, to credit compounds with "actions," "responsibility," "control," and other personifying traits of spontaneity is nothing but old-fashioned animism in disguise.

There is an obvious disproportion between the relative wealth of information about molecular and supramolecular entities as such and the dearth of knowledge about their complex interplay. Undoubtedly, the study of their interactions should command a larger share in the blueprint of future research than is evident in the contemporary scene. But, as the following commentary will indicate, even on the basis of current knowledge, more can be said about those interactions than is commonly made explicit.

In analyzing cell content by progressive fractionation, proceeding downward on the scale of magnitudes, we get from the microscopically visible units (e.g., nucleus, chromosomes, fibers) through submicroscopic particles to macromolecules, and further to simple molecules and radicals, ending up with a selection of the atomic elements, ubiquitous in nature.

Figure 1 exemplifies the scale of sizes of organic units between the cellular and macromolecular levels, which extends across the border zone between living and nonliving systems; even the entities within the lower range have never as yet been proved to be reproducible except through the mediation of a cell. One finds, in fact, the same gamut of units of different size orders represented within each living cell. By physical fragmentation (or its mental counterpart), we can effect, or at least visualize, the decomposition of a cell, or more generally, of units of the upper range, into piles of units having the characteristics of the lower range, that is, being definitely incapable of continued life independently of cells. The question then is this: just what is it that is lost in this degrading process from cells to nonliving constituents, and that would therefore have to be restored if ever one were to get back in ascending order from the elements to the whole ?

There has been no loss of mass, the total of the fragments equaling the mass of the unfragmented cell. The number and proportions of atomic elements contained in both have likewise remained the same. What has been lost are some of the specific kinds of combinations and constellations in which the fragments had existed in the living cell and which are vital for those specific interactions on which the integral existence of the cell depends. This network of interrelations between components is what is meant by "complexity." Since the interacting components are in themselves of different compositions, complexity at the same time implies "inhomogeneity." And these two attributes are often all one has reference to when one describes a cell simply as "an infinitely complex system of heterogeneous molecular species."

However, this description misses the most important point of cellular organization, which is that the heterogeneous mixture of components combined in the complex system operates within a framework of *order*, the stability of which contrasts sharply with

Diameter or
width X length in mμ

Red blood cells	7500
B. prodigiosus (Serratia marcescens)	750
Rickettsia	475
Psittacosis	270
Myxoma	230 x 290
Vaccinia	210 x 260
Pleuro-pneumonia organism	150
Herpes simplex	130
Cytoplasmic virus (Tipula paludosa)	130
Rabies fixe	125
Newcastle disease	115
Avian leucosis	120
Vesicular stomatitis	65 x 165
Polyhedral virus (Bombyx mori)	40 x 280
Influenza	85
Adeno	75
Fowl plague	70
T2 E coli bacteriophage	65 x 95
Chicken tumor I (Rous sarcoma)	65
Equine encephalomyelitis	50
T3 E coli bacteriophage	45
Rabbit papilloma (Shope)	45
Tobacco mosaic and strains	15 x 300
Cymbidium (orchid) mosaic	12 x 480
Genetic unit (Muller's est of max size)	20 x 125
Southern bean mosaic	30
Tomato bushy stunt	30
Coxsackie	27
Poliomyelitis	27
Turnip yellow mosaic	26
Tobacco ringspot	26
Yellow fever	22
Squash mosaic	22
Hemocyanin molecule (Busycon)	22
Foot-and-mouth disease	21
Japanese B encephalitis	18
Tobacco necrosis	16
Hemoglobin molecule (Horse)	3 x 15
Egg albumin molecule	2.5 x 10

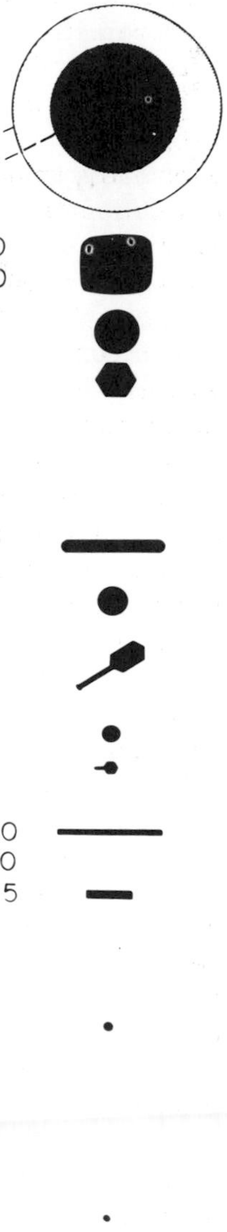

FIG. 1. Size spectrum of organic bodies. (*Revised in* 1958 *by R. C. Williams from W. M. Stanley* "Chemical Studies in Viruses," *Chem. Eng. News*, 25:3786-3791, 1947.)

the potential randomness of the individual component events if these were not subject to some over-all control. This *stability* of order manifests itself in two basic facts — first, that the individual cell as such remains recognizably similar to itself, i.e., essentially invariant, despite the incessant turnover and reshuffling of its content; and second, that the countless specimens of cells of a given kind remain recurrently similar to one another although in detail the content of each has a unique and nonrecurrent fate. Considering the cell as a population of parts of various magnitudes, the rule of order is objectively described by the fact that *the resultant behavior of the population as a whole is infinitely less variant from moment to moment than are the momentary activities of its parts*. Despite the continual flux of components, both as to composition and location, the system *as a whole* preserves its character. Small molecules go in and out, macromolecules break down and are replaced, particles lose and gain macromolecular constituents, divide and merge, and all parts move at one time or another, unpredictably, so that it is safe to state that at no time in the history of a given cell, much less in comparable stages of different cells, will precisely the same constellations of parts ever recur.

By contrast, however, one does not find this uniqueness, hence unpredictability, of the precise state and distribution of components reflected in the resultant total system, whose over-all pattern and behavior (or what one usually refers to as "organization") remain relatively unaltered, hence predictable. This forces us to conclude that although the individual members of the molecular and particulate population have a large number of degrees of freedom of behavior in random directions, the population as a whole is a system which restrains those degrees of freedom in such a manner that their joint behavior converges upon a nonrandom resultant, keeping the state of the population as a whole relatively invariant. It is this property of directive restraints, then, that is the most essential loss a cell suffers in the process of analytical disintegration, and since it is a property of a *collective*, we cannot observe its manifestations when we study the members of the population *singly* in isolation. Examples to illustrate this proposition will be presented later on.

In its more strictly morphological past, biology tended to ascribe the stability of the organization of the total behavior pattern of a cell to a rigid frame of fixed structures within the cell — a cytoskeleton supposedly exempt from the metabolic and motile changes to which the rest of the cell content is constantly subjected. This notion has arisen from the preoccupation with microscopic pictures of fixed dead cells, and even in our day it is still sometimes carried over to the submicroscopic realm of electron microscopy. But as will be explained presently, stable structures that are demonstrable in the living cell, other than chromosomes, have mostly turned out to be secondary derivatives, rather than primary carriers, of cellular organization. Just as the turnover of radioactively labeled compounds has revealed the flux of cell composition on the molecular level, so the microscopic observation of the living cell in action, particularly with the optical speed-up of time-lapse cinemicrography, has revealed such incessant reshuffling of the cell content that even the thought that at least the supramolecular units (particulates) might be linked into a stable framework can be safely dismissed. In motion picture films of single cells in tissue culture (a sample film taken under the phase-contrast microscope was shown at the lecture), one can directly observe how cell contour, intracellular fiber systems, and granules of various descriptions change their configurations and positions continuously, thus ruling out the presence, or at any rate, the relevance, of a consistent three-dimensional cytoskeleton. Two-dimensional continua are present in the various surfaces and membrane systems, but their repeated disruptions likewise fail to impair the essential integrity of the cell.

Yet despite the absence of an orderly static frame, the various activities of all parts remain coordinated in the maintenance of a standard pattern of order in any given cell. It is an order of relations rather than of fixed positions. Lacking a static foundation and barring sham explanations by extraneous vital agencies, we evidently must seek the source of this order in the *population dynamics* of the cellular constituents of various magnitudes. That is to say, the cell (as well as any of its subsystems) is not only made up of heterogeneous parts, but the various segments of this molecular and particulate population are so constituted that they assume the proper mutual space and functional relations simply by virtue of their own activities, rather than by passive allocation within a fixed framework. Some of the interacting subsystems are in such cooperative interdependence — symbiotically as it were — that neither can proceed without essential contributions from the other; in other cases, the dependence will be unilateral, comparable to parasitism; and in still other instances, there will be mutual interference or incompatibility between adjoining processes. In this dynamic concept, organization rests on properties which, to be sure, are inherent in the individual members of the heterogeneous population, but which can find expression only in collective interaction. By analogy to human populations, one could compare this emergent ordering process with the "self-structuring" of a community — an ecological simile to which we shall return later.

In the light of these somewhat ponderous but relevant prefatory remarks, our earlier question about the possibility of recompounding a fragmented cell must be rephrased more articulately. As the cell is not simply a random array of molecules, but a hierarchy in which molecular groupings are combined into macromolecules, macromolecules into particulates, and particulates into organelles, the question must evidently be posed separately for each level of this hierarchical organization, leading to such specific queries as the following: If we start with a random mixture of selected molecular species, we must ask just how high a system in the ascending scale of order would they be able to build up by sheer free interaction, without the intervention of a living cell or of cell products? This implies a sharp logical distinction between de novo synthesis, i.e., actual compounding, from the atomic level up on the one hand, and recombinations of (or with) compounds which themselves had a cellular origin, on the other. If we start from the opposite end, the intact cell, we must ask just how far can a cell be broken up and yet again be restored to integrity from reassembled pieces? To find the answers to such questions is a purely empirical problem and no longer a matter of abstract speculation. Yet, by the same token, "synthetic" success at any one level does not automatically spell success for any other level, and any generalization remains likewise a matter of empirical tests, rather than just confident assertion. Therefore, to predict whether or not cells will ever be synthesized from scrambled molecules is in that generality not only an idle but a logically unsound undertaking with more emotional and cultural overtones than scientific foundations.

In conclusion, once we have acknowledged that the cell is nothing but the systematically organized community of molecular populations in dynamic interaction, the *dynamic organization* of the system becomes our central problem. And solely by learning more and more about the isolated pieces, we can never hope to gain understanding of the higher degrees of order to which the pieces are subordinated in those collective groupings which we know as cells, and whose continuity as organized systems has been passed down uninterruptedly through the whole course of evolution.

To sum up, even though we have now some fairly good road maps for the analytical trip "from cell to molecule," most of those roads are still one-way, and the reverse trek "from molecule to cell" takes us into uncharted land.

FROM MOLECULE TO CELL

By way of dramatizing our problem, I am showing in Fig. 2, side by side, a 6-day-old chick embryo immersed in liquid, before (Fig. 2a) and after (Fig. 2b) having been homogenized by crushing. As no

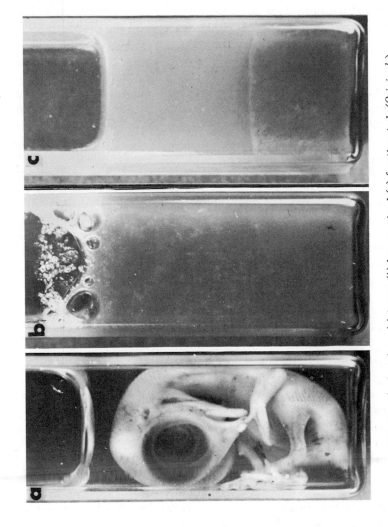

FIG. 2. Chick embryo (*a*) intact (*b*) homogenized (*c*) fractionated. (*Original.*)

9

substance has been lost or added during the procedure, the content
of the vial before and after is the same in weight and composition.
An inventory of molecules, if it could be taken, would likewise re-
veal no change (disregarding, for the moment, mechanical breakage
of some macromolecules, whose fragments are, of course, still
there). What has been lost is structural organization from the highest
level of the organism down to the order of whatever subsystems were
small or consistent enough to have escaped the disruptive force of
our crushing technique and whose ordered heterogeneity has therefore failed to become "homogenized." As pictured here, organs and
tissues have been broken up, so also have the individual cells, their
membranes, nuclei, and cytoplasmic systems. To get from *a* to *b*
was easy. How to return from *b* to *a*—that is our uphill problem.
Of course, if one considers the change from *a* to *b* as nothing but a
general transition from heterogeneous to more homogeneous distribution, a change in the reverse direction can readily be brought about;
for instance, by subjecting the homogenate of Fig. 2*b* to centrifugation or other separatory measures by which the molecular or particulate scramble can be partly unscrambled into distinct fractions,
as shown in Fig. 2*c*. But the result is not a step back toward the lost
old order, but rather a step toward a new and artificial order, which
bears no more resemblance to the original than a neatly stacked as-
sortment of spare parts bears to an intact machine. The different
components are all there, but the specific structural order on which
the functional capacity of the whole assembly depends is lacking.

Now, as stated before, this order comes in hierarchic steps, hence
it needs to be considered separately for each level. The very fact
that cellular subsystems, functionally specialized, are interposed between the levels of organization of the cell and of the molecule has
long been recognized. But it has remained for the electron microscope to resolve the details of those subunits. The examples presented in the following pages will outline certain common properties
of such cell "organelles," as well as their bearing on the problems
of cellular organization.

For practical purposes, one might draw a distinction between continuous subsystems, such as membranes or fibrous networks, and
discontinuous systems, consisting of such discrete units as chromosomes or mitochondria. In some sense, however, this may be misleading, for the real cell is a physical continuum, no part of which
can be considered as truly separate from the rest. Moreover, both
in life and during fixation, continuous structures may break up into
fragments, while conversely, discrete bodies may coalesce. These
qualifications should be borne in mind in the following account.

Our first example shows some of the common implements of

cells (Fig. 3). Surrounding the nucleus (n) concentrically, one observes a system of more or less parallel double-contoured lamellae, called "endoplasmic reticulum" or "ergastoplasm" (e), which per-

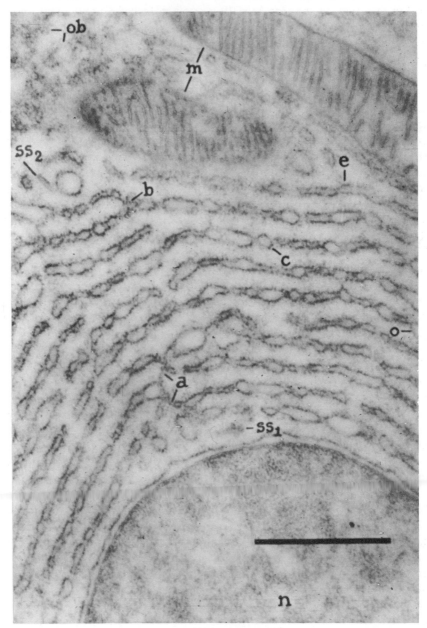

FIG. 3. Electron micrograph of section of gland cell. (*From K. R. Porter.*)

vade the cytoplasm as a branched and anastomosing network. Conspicuousness and dimensions of this system vary greatly, not only according to cell type, but what is more important in the present context, with the age and functional activity of any one cell. This latter fact proves that the lamellar system is not a permanent and rigid fixture formed once and for all, but is a "dynamic" system which undergoes reductions and restorations while nevertheless preserving its basic pattern.

It is the nature of this pattern which concerns us here. One notes at once two salient features, namely (1) the rather strict orientation of the lamellae along well-defined planes, and (2) the tendency for these planes to be equidistant in any one cell. These features can serve as clues to the dynamics of the formative processes to which the lamellar system owes its specific pattern. That is to say, the observed geometric regularity is but an index of some singular constellation of underlying physical and chemical conditions. The presence of an overt lamella in a given plane reveals that prior to the appearance of the lamella that particular plane must have been distinguished as a uniquely favorable site at which lamella-forming elements could persist long enough to become detectable. Just what the locally favored process is will vary from case to case; it may be the synthesis of lamellar material, or the assembling and orderly deposition of material from a dispersed state, or the active inflow of formed material[1] along invisible interfaces — at any rate, some process which is responsive to the physical constellation of its environment. The formed lamellae thus become the visible traces of the configuration of an invisible field of interactions, figuratively comparable to the iron filings which trace the lines of force of a magnetic field.

Accordingly, the fact that the planes occupied by the lamellar system are separated by a standard distance (e.g., 1,300 A in Fig. 3) can be taken to signify that some such processes as the following are involved: either (1) the material itself is produced in rhythmic waves spreading at a constant rate from a few basic planes (e.g., the nuclear surface); or (2) the material occurs ubiquitously, but once a layer has formed it inhibits the deposition of a like layer within its range of action, comparable to the phenomenon of rhythmic Liesegang rings; or (3) the ground substance of the cytoplasm, appearing structureless under electron microscopic inspection, may in reality be composed of shells or laminae of a given thickness of which the lamellar system would outline the borders. Alternative (1) seems to be ruled out by the frequent branchings and intercalations (e.g., at points *a* and *b* and at the asterisks, respectively, in Fig. 3). No decision can be made at present between points (2) and (3). Both are equally conceivable, although they differ crucially in that the former assumes direct interaction among the folds of the lamellar system itself, while the latter refers the lamellar pattern back to a lamination of the ground substance. This issue is a fundamental one and will recur in our later discussion.

A similar rhythmic pattern on a small scale is encountered in the internal structure of the mitochondria (m, Fig. 3), whose diagrammatic interpretation by Sjöstrand is given in Fig. 4. As in the preced-

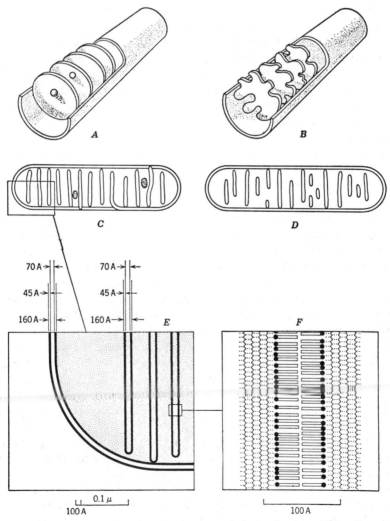

FIG. 4. Interpretation of the fine structure of mitochondria. (*According to F. Sjöstrand.*)

ing case, the matrix, which is enclosed in a double-contoured sheath, contains, in its interior, lamellar plates and folds, called "cristae." The distances between these lamellar plates are again relatively uniform, indicating that there is either mutual interaction or an underlying periodic structure in the matrix. The double contour of the lamellar walls (Fig. 4E, F) has been explained quite plausibly as resulting from the self-arraying of mixtures of protein and lipid molecules by virtue of the latter's hydrophilic and hydrophobic ends — a principle well demonstrated by the formation in vitro of polar monomolecular layers of stearates and proteins (according to Langmuir and others) and first applied successfully to biological systems in the interpretation of the lamellar fine structure of the myelin sheath of nerves. In our present context, however, it must be stressed that even though the molecular basis of the fine structure of the individual lamellae be known, this does not of itself lead to an understanding of the higher organization of a mitochondrium as a whole. Observations of living cells have shown mitochondria to be highly mobile and morphologically unstable units, given to subdividing, coalescing, branching, and anastomosing [2]. In view of this lability, it would seem impossible to account for the structural regularities noted in the electron micrograms of fixed cells otherwise than on the premise that they are but momentary records of formative dynamics which continuously remakes and adjusts the structural details, while maintaining the integrity of the mitochondrial pattern as a whole.

Once this fact has been realized, a series of new questions comes to mind, for which no answer is as yet available, partly because the questions have never been raised explicitly. For instance, what determines and maintains the average distance between the cristae? Mitochondria, though varying in length, seem to be of fairly uniform diameters for given cells and conditions; to what equilibrium condition do they owe this relative stability of girth? Why does their growth stop when standard unit size has been reached? Within what limits does the unit size adapt itself to metabolic and functional conditions, and by what means? Some of these questions touch on a most basic problem of morphogenesis, which is: Why are discrete subunits of cells produced in quantal steps, rather than in a continuous spectrum of sizes? Does not this fact itself suggest a dynamics of the integral higher system of such a kind that at a particular size range a singularly stable state for the whole assembly of subsystems would be reached?

Another example of cell organelles with lamellar fine structure are the chloroplasts of plant cells (Fig. 5a), which show further specialization in the fact that at certain points the lamellae are compacted into more tightly packed "grana" (two of which are seen in

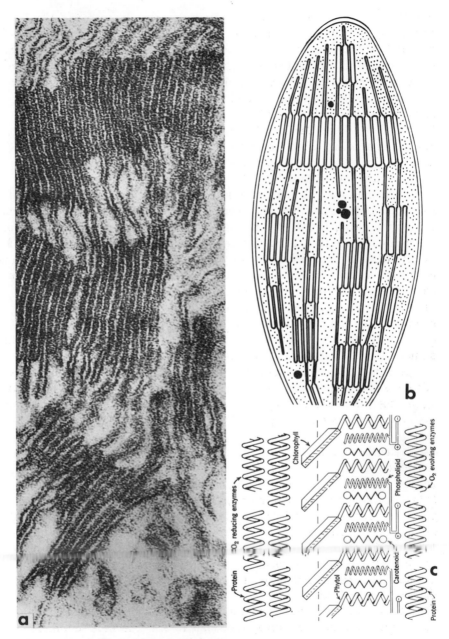

FIG. 5. Fine structure of chloroplast. (*a*) Electron micrograph. (*Courtesy von Wett-stein.*) (*b*) Diagrammatic reconstruction of the lamellar arrangement. (*After von Wett-stein.*) (*c*) Hypothetical molecular organization of the lamellar system. (*After Calvin.*)

the illustration). From combined electron-microscopic, biochemical, and X-ray studies, a hypothetical concept of the molecular composition and architecture of the individual lamellae has been constructed (Fig. 5c) which, regardless of validity in detail, indicates the degree of orderly complexity which one must postulate for even the elemental constituents of this structure. But as with the mitochondria, the supraelemental order remains to be explored and explained. Why, for instance, do all the lamellae of a given group change suddenly along a sharp line from the loose to the compact packing, or why does a chloroplast, on reaching a liminal size level, subdivide instead of keeping on to enlarge?

Sometimes the cell surface itself contains specialized subunits of rather constant size. For instance, the underside of larval amphibian epidermis cells, illustrated in Fig. 6, shows the plasma membrane of the cell dotted with regular bobbin-shaped bodies, each consisting of two lipid-rich discs connected by a hydrophilic neck, which, according to experimental evidence, serve as adhesive devices [3]. As one can readily see, both their dimensions and spacing are so regular as to raise again the question of how the shape, size, and arrangement of such complex supramolecular entities are regulated to a standard norm. The question is all the more cogent, since this is one of the instances in which the lability of the pattern could be directly demonstrated: in a cell which has been mobilized by wounding the skin, the adhesive discs undergo resorption, but once the cell has settled down again, the discs are formed anew in the same typical size, shape, and distribution as before. The conditions for the formation of this surface pattern are, therefore, ever present in those cells.

As another surface differentiation of unit character and fleeting existence, I may cite certain filamentous projections which are observed in electron micrographs of single cells cultured in vitro (Fig. 7); these projections from the cytoplasmic margin are supported by one or several rather rigid core filaments ("microspikes") of variable lengths, but of a standard diameter of slightly less than 1,000 A. Since in these highly motile cells the margin changes its composition and configuration incessantly, it must be taken for granted that the microspikes are continually renewed, yet always of the same unit width.

Many of the more permanent structures subserving specialized cell functions likewise display unit character. The most common examples are cilia and flagella. All of them, whether of protozoans, plants, animal tissues, or spermatozoa, are built alike. Even the visual elements of the retina contain abortive cilia, presumably homologous to the light-sensitive spot of flagellates, which is likewise a modified cilium. Cilia, shown in cross section in Fig. 8, con-

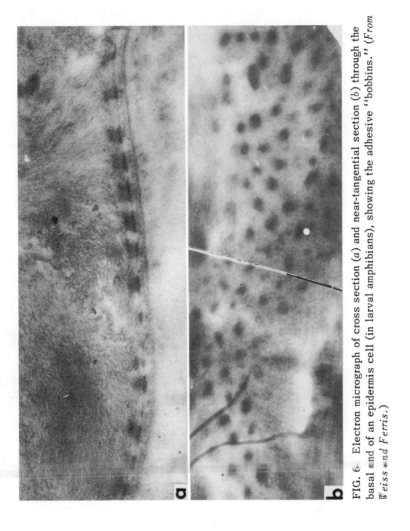

FIG. 6. Electron micrograph of cross section (*a*) and near-tangential section (*b*) through the basal end of an epidermis cell (in larval amphibians), showing the adhesive "bobbins." (*From Weiss and Ferris.*)

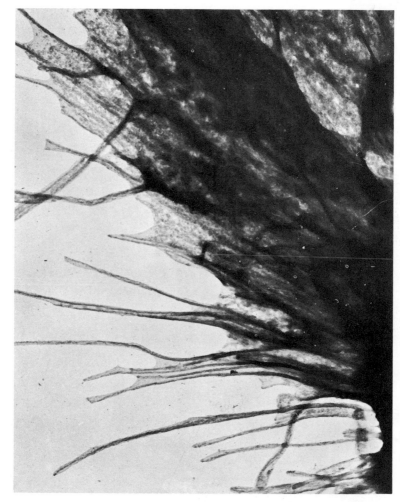

FIG. 7. Electron micrograph of free margin of single cell grown in tissue culture. (*Original, Weiss and Robbins.*)

18

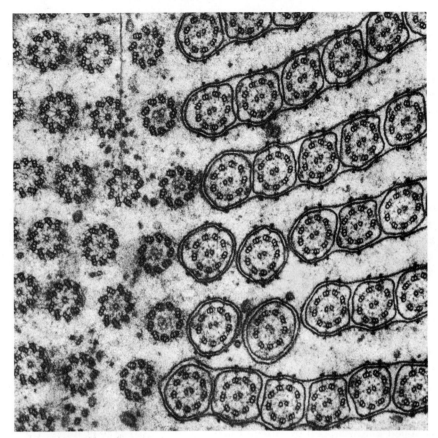

FIG. 8. Electron micrograph of cross section through the ciliary field of a proto-zoan. (*Courtesy I. Gibbons.*)

sist of a matrix, which is enclosed in a cylindrical sheath and con-tains in the interior invariably eleven parallel fibers, of which two lie in the center, while the other nine are rather evenly distributed about the periphery; in some types, each of the nine is a doublet, sometimes with an additional odd appendage. The basic pattern is remarkably constant. Over the whole range of species, cell types, and stages, measurements of the diameter of individual cilia, of the order of about 0.2 micra, seem to vary by no more than a factor of two. The occurrence of the number 9 is puzzling and unaccountable by ordinary rules of symmetry; in favorable cases (Fig. 8), they can be seen to be arranged pinwheel-fashion, rather than in a plain circle, while the two central fibers define a plane of bilateral symmetry for each cilium, the planes of symmetry for all cilia of a given tract ap-pearing to be essentially parallel. Each cilium grows forth from a basal body localized beneath the cell surface, but just how this takes place is still quite obscure. Depending on whether these production sites are spaced at random or are themselves arranged in definite patterns, the resulting ciliary fields are either irregular or ordered in grids, as exemplified in Fig. 8. A cell can repeatedly re-form a ciliary field of the typical pattern after resorption or loss of a primary field (e.g., after the fission of ciliate protozoa); consequently, the conspicuous morphological features of ciliation must again be viewed not as singular products of some single occurrence in the developmental history of the cell, but as the tangible manifestations of an ever-present and active dynamics of the cell.

It should have become abundantly clear by now that this dynamics operates hierarchically: macromolecules are linearly linked to filaments, filaments are laterally compounded to fibers of definite diameter, fibers in fixed numbers (9 + 2) are combined with matrix in a fixed proportion and distribution to make up a sheathed cylindrical cilium of fixed diameter, and rows of cilia compose a ciliary field. Each level of this hierarchy is thus characterized by its peculiar constants of composition, dimensions, proportions, and configuration [3a].

As a second example of an intracellular system of great structural regularity, we may cite the contractile apparatus of the cross-striated muscle fiber. Its major elements on the molecular level are chains of the proteins myosin and actin which are combined with other components of the muscle cell (sarcoplasm) into myofibrils, which in turn are assembled into muscle fibers, which then are grouped and wrapped by fibrous sheaths into still larger units, the muscle fascicles, a given number of which constitutes a muscle. For every one of these unit classes, the sizes, numbers, and arrangement of its subunits seem to be held within such close statistical limits that one must conclude that each one is subject to a separate regulatory mechanism. Little is known beyond the sheer fact that such an order exists, and only on the two lowest levels have studies of the fine structure presented us with some details on the degree of order. According to those studies, leaving aside all controversial interpretations, each myofibril is a tandem array of identical segments ("sarcomeres") cemented together by transversal discs. Each segment consists of large numbers of parallel protein filaments (Fig. 9a) extending from one cementing disc to the next. In the middle portion of each segment, another protein (presumably myosin) appears in close association with the continuous filaments and so exactly in register among all the molecular chains of the sarcomere as to give rise to the sharp "anisotropic" band of microscopic "cross striation." To this strict sequential order along the axis of each com-

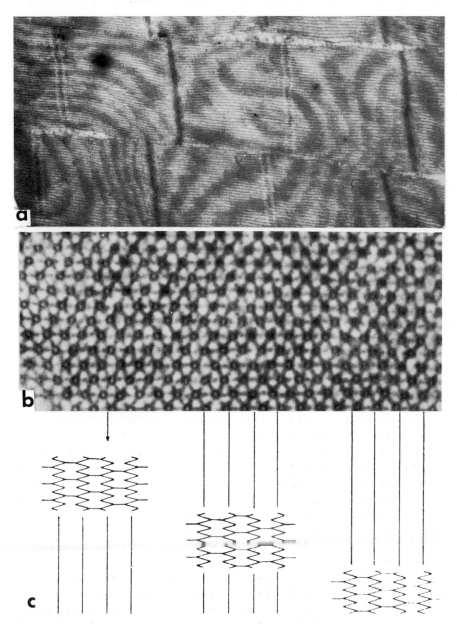

FIG. 9. Structural and functional organization of a myofibril of cross-striated muscle. (a) Electron micrograph of longitudinal section, X23,500. (*From A. Hodge.*) (b) Electron micrograph of cross section. (*Courtesy A. Hodge.*) (c) Phase coordination of contractile wave. Polar displacement of a liquid "plasma" strand. (*After Frey-Wyssling.*)

pound molecular chain is then added a higher intermolecular order
in the lateral direction, of which the register within the anisotropic
band is probably a collateral expression. In cross section (Fig. 9b),
each individual compound molecular chain appears as a circle, of
which the light center has been assumed to be the actin core, with the
dark ring around it representing the myosin jacket. As one can see
from the picture, these elements, without being stacked in direct lateral contact, are spaced in a regular hexagonal grid pattern.

Although the dynamic basis of this pattern is still obscure, it
points to a strong lateral group interaction between the component
filaments, hence it is of decidedly supramolecular order. The same
inference is reached on physiological grounds, for the effective contraction of a muscle fiber presupposes that the contractile wave be
synchronized for all the constituent chains. If contractility is based
on the propagated alternation of the folding and unfolding of protein
chains, as has been contended, all the elements of a unit at any given
transverse plane would always have to be in the same phase, as indicated in the diagram of Fig. 9c. If, as others have proposed, contraction results from a lengthwise slippage of chains relative to one
another, this likewise would have to be cross-synchronized. Either
theory requires strict lateral coordination among units which are
separated by distances of several hundred angstroms. This functional
cross linkage may be mediated by structural cross connections [4],
but such periodic cross structures themselves must have been pre-
ceded by a process which staked out the respective planes in the first
place.

The muscle cell is particularly impressive in demonstrating the
inexhaustibility of the faculty of cells to produce substructures of invariably the same pattern. The "hypertrophy" observed in muscles
as a result of exercise or endocrine stimulation involves in the main
the enlargement of individual muscle fibers by the production from
within their cytoplasm of additional myofibrils, built exactly like the
old ones, with which they are made to line up. The basic property of a
muscle cell, therefore, is not its possession of a given complement of
myofibrils, but its capacity to produce and reproduce myofibrils almost indefinitely.

Many more similar examples could be listed. Undoubtedly the
rapid expansion of fine structural research will enlarge the list at a
phenomenal rate. As a result the facts and problems of supramolecular order will become more familiar and attractive. But even the
scanty evidence thus far available, as sampled in the foregoing, permits us to draw a few general conclusions as guides to our thinking
and further research as follows:

THE HIERARCHY OF ORDER

Any description of cell constitution and cell behavior couched
solely and directly in molecular terms misses the basic fact of the
existence of intermediate supramolecular entities of unit character.
To be fully consistent, one might as well assert that a cell consists
of atoms in various combinations, which of course is true but meaningless. As different atoms are compounded into molecules with
specific chemical properties, so cells contain, besides free molecules, larger units in which diverse species of molecules are combined in definite numerical ratios and specific mutual space relations to yield composite structures of rather uniform dimensions,
proportions, and architecture. Although the de novo origin of these
supramolecular subcellular entities has not yet been observed directly, the empirical fact that cells can keep on producing and reproducing them proves that they can be formed whenever and
wherever conditions are right. The more complex the units are, the
more specific prerequisites must evidently be fulfilled in the same
place at the same time in order that the crucial event of complexing
be able to take place.

The fact that each kind of these supramolecular units appears
mostly in characteristic uniform dimensions at all cell ages indicates strongly that the particular molecular assemblies composing
a given unit can exist solely in that single unique combination and
configuration, and that partial or intermediary combinations are too
unstable ever to be discovered. This is the obvious explanation of
the fact that no one seems ever to have seen a fractionally completed mitochondrion, cilium, or sarcomere. Plainly, unless the
conditions in a given spot at a given time are absolutely correct for
all the components of such a unit to fall into their proper places in
the right numbers and proportions all at once, no structure is formed
to leave a record. Consequently, such structures are known only in
quantal units, as it were, and in their multiples, but are never found
in fractions.

On the other hand, in stressing uniformity of size and proportions
of such composite units, one must remain aware of the degree of latitude left to the individual specimen. Although there are no comprehensive measurements and statistical data available on the actual var-
iances among the dimensions of different cilia, mitochondria, or
comparable subunits, the fact that they are subject to some degree of
variation is clear from ordinary observations. That is to say, the
microprecision of molecular composition ascribed to biological macromolecules (e.g., amino acid composition of proteins; nucleotide composition of nucleic acids) does not prevail at higher organizational
levels. The numbers and ratios of macromolecules going into the

formation of an organelle are unquestionably not exactly identical in each instance, but are merely kept within a certain standard range. This only strengthens our conclusion that the unit size of the complex is not the passive outcome of the stacking up of a preassigned number of molecules but rather that some *equilibrium level for the unit as a whole* determines the approximate number of subunits that it can accommodate.

Let us consider, for example, a cilium. Whether each of the nine peripheral filaments is a bundle of exactly the same number of molecular chains is not known, but it is highly doubtful. The dimensions of the two central filaments definitely indicate a composition different from the peripheral ones. As for the amorphous matrix, the number of constituent molecules is decidedly an open one, as one can readily see from the fact that as the cilium grows forth from its basal body, the matrix increases steadily. By contrast, however, the number of filaments is rigidly fixed. As for the distances between them, only the average value seems constant, leaving the individual measurements to fluctuate about that value. The diameter of the whole cylindrical structure again seems to be far more constant than one could expect in view of the indefiniteness of the mass of the amorphous matrix, which raises the possibility that the circumference of the sheath may be the critical equilibrium value which secondarily determines the amount of matrix as that quantity which it can hold within its confines. And going on to the spacing of the individual cilia in a ciliary field, it is quite evident that however regular the rows and distances of their generative basal bodies may appear on the supramolecular scale, it would be absurd to assume that this could be due to their being separated always by precisely the same number of molecules.

In summary, patterns of supramolecular order result not directly from freely interacting *molecular* units, but from the interactions of *supramolecular* entities of various degrees of complexity and various orders of magnitude, which behave as relatively constant units. Such unit groups possess properties and faculties that are characteristic of the particular collective, but are not manifested by the individual components in the unassembled state. Although the rules of the dynamics of such group behavior are still largely unexplored, much could be learned about them from a proper evaluation of their resultant morphological expressions.

This presupposes that we consistently cultivate the mental habit of viewing morphological patterns, such as microscopic or ultramicroscopic structures, as merely indices and residues of the patterns of processes by which they have been formed — rhythmic structures, of processes with periodicity; polar structures, of polarizing processes; etc. Dynamic process is the foundation of static form, rather

than the reverse. Processes are not visible, only their effects are.
Which brings to mind the words of Robert Louis Stevenson:

> Who has seen the wind?
> Neither you nor I.
> But when the trees bow down their heads,
> The wind is passing by.

FROM THREAD TO FABRIC

In the realization that the way "from molecule to cell" leads
stepwise through a hierarchy of levels of increasing ordered complexity, we can now turn to examining on which of those levels the
compounding of higher units from a free mixture of lower-order
constituents has been observed, or better still, has actually been accomplished outside of cells. Each step, as stated earlier, presents
a problem of its own. Since the study of the origin of cellular subunits is in its infancy, our case will have to rest on scanty evidence.
We shall not consider here subunits of the so-called "self-reproduc-
ing" kind, where a new unit springs directly from a preexisting unit
of the same level of organization, although they grade over into the
category of "replications after a model," on which we shall touch
later. Rather we shall concentrate on the crucial case in which, by
the sheer free interaction of elements, a more complex unit of a
higher order is synthesized even in the absence of a corresponding
model unit, that process referred to earlier as true "compounding,"
as molecules are compounded from ions.

As the simplest instance, one could cite the formation of linear
polymers, the self-stacking of mixtures of polar molecules along
interfaces, and the three-dimensional self-sorting and ordering observed when polar molecules combine into coacervates. In all these
cases, what started out as a random mixture of molecules ends up
in a less random condition, manifested as segregation, orientation,
alignment, and the like, attained either solely by the mutual interaction of the molecules concerned or with the aid of physical guidance
from the environment, as will be discussed further below. All of
these are still relatively primitive systems, not confined to the organic, but illustrating at least in rudimentary form the principle of
emergent order in groups.

Going on to the specifically biological objects, however, one finds
oneself at a loss for truly crucial examples to cite, except for one
outstanding phenomenon — fibrogenesis, especially of collagen. The
formation of the collagen fiber has been one of the very few processes
whose analytical study has been driven far enough to document both
the fact and the manner of the compounding of genuinely biological

fine structures [5]. The main conclusions seem to be sufficiently firmly established, even though some of the detailed assumptions on which they rest are still hypothetical and in part controversial.

The elementary molecule of collagen, "tropocollagen," is a protein of a molecular weight of about 300.000; it consists of a triple-stranded chain of amino acids with a particularly high ratio of glycine and hydroxyproline. The length of this macromolecule has been determined as about 2,600 A and its width as 14 A. In the body, the molecules are known only as polymerized chains, "protofibrils," which in turn are bundled up into larger fibrils. Electron microscopy and X-ray analysis of native collagen fibers have revealed a characteristic axial periodicity in the fibrils (Fig. 10), with a major cross band repeating itself every 640 A and minor cross bands spaced in an aperiodic sequence in between (see Fig. 11), resulting in a definite morphological polarity of all segments. The fact that a fibril, which is an aggregate of hundreds or thousands of molecular strands, shows these over-all regularities, proves that the molecules have not aggregated at random, but in a definite linear and lateral order. Since the serial order of the minor bands is the same in all segments, polymerization must have taken place with the head end of one monomer always linking up with the tail end of the next throughout the whole chain. The cross striation of the assembled fibril in turn reveals that the constituent molecular chains have become joined laterally in such a way that the homologous fractions of all chains have come to lie in strict register; any slippage out of register obviously would blur the band pattern. The current view is that there are only four possible equilibrium positions in which the protofibrils can join up laterally and that the typical band pattern (Fig. 11) is the result of the statistical summation of the four staggered positions — each period of 640 A representing the ends of one fourth of the population of unit segments 2,600 A long. As we shall elaborate presently, a further element of order lies in the fact that many fibers fall into definite size classes, reminiscent of the more elaborate subcellular units discussed in the preceding chapter, which means that in the cases concerned there is a finite upper limit beyond which lateral aggregation of protofibrils cannot continue. So much for the collagen fibers encountered in the body.

Yet under appropriate conditions, precisely the same type of organized fiber can be compounded from the component molecules outside the body in vitro. Nageotte had discovered that collagen from connective tissues (e.g., tendon) can be brought into molecular solution by treatment with weak acids. Upon adding salts to this solution, or better, by dialyzing against salt solutions, a colloid precipitate would form that had all the then known properties of native collagen.

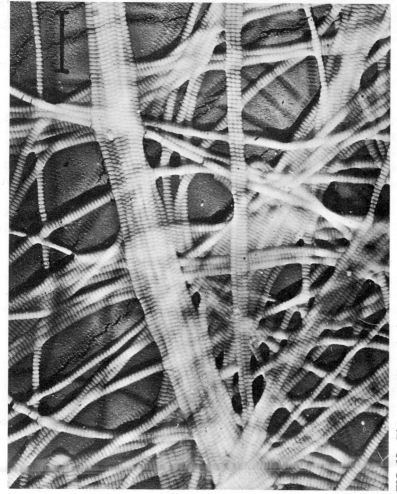

FIG. 10. Electron micrograph of metal-shadowed collagen fibrils showing the native axial repeat period at 640 A. (*From F. O. Schmitt.*)

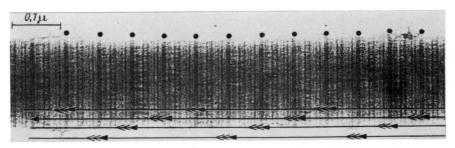

FIG. 11. High-resolution electron micrograph of a collagen fibril reconstituted in vitro, showing the major periodic bands at 640 A (at the dots) and the aperiodic minor bands. (*Courtesy A. Hodge.*)

It was this observation which the subsequent electron-optical, X-ray, and biochemical studies were signally successful in elaborating. Fibers reconstituted from such solutions in vitro showed electron-microscopically (Fig. 11) the typical 640-angstrom periodicity, and in several other critical tests gave every evidence of being the equivalent of the native fibers from which the molecular solution had been derived. As in the native structure, the molecules had become polymerized in correct polar order into protofibrils and the protofibrils had aggregated in register to form cross-banded fibers.

These results are a patent documentation of the fact that when identical molecules of given constitution come together in an appropriate environment they do not remain a random pile, but snap into mutually compatible group arrays, which are characterized by common orientations, alignments, and size rules of higher degrees of order than were present in the original molecular scramble. Here then is a crucial case in point to substantiate the thesis of "order emerging in compounds," which we have set out to test.

The issue gained a novel and even more exciting aspect when it was shown that the native collagen array (with the 640-angstrom periodicity) is only one among several possible group constellations which collagen molecules can assume, including some quite artificial patterns not known — or at least not yet observed — in nature. By allowing the dissolved collagen molecules to precipitate in different ionic and otherwise altered environments (e.g., in the presence of adenosine triphosphate), the following modifications in the form of aggregation in vitro could be obtained: (a) fibers without periodicity (abolition of lateral register); (b) fibers with 200-angstrom repeat pattern (abnormal staggering); (c) fibers with a 2,600-angstrom periodicity, but with polarized segments (Fig. 12; only a single instead of four possible stacking arrays); (d) fibers with a 2,600-angstrom periodicity but with symmetrical banding patterns within each segment.

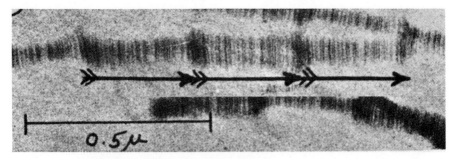

FIG. 12. Electron micrographs of aberrant assemblies of collagen reconstituted in vitro, forming periodic segments of a length of 2,600 A. (*From F. O. Schmitt.*)

These are the facts. It must be admitted that the detailed nature of the energy relations and force constellations that limit the combination of macromolecules to just a very few specific group configurations is scarcely known and awaits further analysis. But in the spirit for which I have been pleading, the acceptance and exploitation of these facts for the explanation of biological structure formation is not necessarily contingent on a final resolution of that problem, and we may take it for granted from here on that the kind of self-ordering of macromolecules in groups, which we have illustrated here, is a reality, whatever its physicochemical basis may turn out to be.

Proceeding from this foundation, we can now take a further step in our ascending course, which leads to an even higher degree of ordered complexity. It concerns the process of ossification, or more generally, of mineralization of tissues [6]. Bone is a tissue which derives its mechanical strength from the incrustation of its organic matrix with the inorganic crystals of hydroxy-apatite. The matrix, as in all varieties of connective tissue, consists of a base of muco-polysaccharide interlaced with collagen fibers of the native type just described. If the crystals were simply scattered freely through the ground substance, they would be no more than grit; to act as reinforcements for the fibrous framework they must be firmly linked with it, like microbraces. This is achieved by having the crystals incorporated in the collagen fibers. Since these fibers form prior to the mineralization process, one may expect the pattern of crystallization to be guided by the collagen pattern. In confirmation of this expectation, it was actually observed [7] that at the onset of osteogenesis in the embryo, the first deposits of crystals visible in electron micrographs appeared along the collagen fibrils at constant intervals corresponding to the 640-angstrom repeat period of the fibrillar cross bands (Fig. 13a). Evidently some specific condition prevailing at those particular sites of the collagen fiber initiated or enhanced

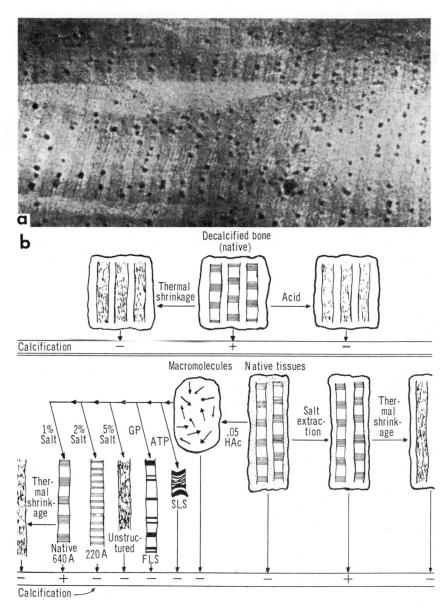

FIG. 13. Localized combination between collagen fibrils and hydroxyapatite crystals in ossification. (a) Electron micrograph, showing crystal deposition (dark dots) at periodic repeat bands of collagen fibrils in the initial stage of embryonic bone formation. (*After S. Fitton Jackson.*) (b) Diagram summarizing the success (+) or failure (−) of calcification of different varieties of collagen in metastable solutions of calcium phosphate. (*From Glimcher.*)

either the formation or the early growth of the crystals. In their later stages, the elongate crystals are found to lie, on the whole, parallel to the axis of the fibrils with which they are associated, thus revealing a continued directive dependency.

It was at this point that the success in reconstituting collagens of various forms in vitro offered a promising, and as it turned out, most profitable approach to a more penetrating study of that dependency. The task was to find out whether collagen in vitro could actually induce the formation of apatite crystals in a metastable solution of calcium phosphate. And this did take place if reconstituted collagen fibrils of the native 640-angstrom periodicity were used as inducers, even when the particular collagen had been extracted from normally not calcifying tissue, such as tendon, skin, or swim bladder. The crystal germs reappeared at sites corresponding to the 640-angstrom segments of the fibers so the conclusion was compelling that some peculiar configuration of the fibrillar structure at those levels, in contact with the ambient solution, initiated the formation of crystal nuclei. But not until collagen patterns of other than the 640-angstrom variety were tested could the degree of specificity of this effect be assessed. As was mentioned before and is diagrammatically represented in Fig. 13b, the same molecular solution of tropocollagen can be made at will to yield in vitro fibrils of either the native type with the 640-angstrom repeat period, or several other types of fine structure. Now, in exposing each of these varieties, as well as variously treated native tissues, to metastable calcium phosphate solutions under otherwise identical conditions, it was established that crystal nucleation occurred only in the presence of fibrils showing the 640-angstrom repeat period, and in no other combinations (Fig. 13b). Since neither the simple tropocollagen molecules, nor their linear polymers, nor any larger aggregates of other than the native stacking pattern has ever led to nucleation, it is evident that the effect depends strictly on the specific group arrangement which characterizes the macromolecular collective in the native-type fibril.

There exists thus a matching relationship between certain steric properties of the native collagen aggregate on the one hand and the crystalline state of the hydroxyapatite on the other, which predisposes these two systems to combine in a definite space pattern and thereby to "compound" a new system of higher-order complexity. The fact that native collagen from ordinary connective tissue will become calcified in vitro, but not in the body (except under certain pathological conditions), points to crucial differences in the local microenvironments of the fibrils at different tissue sites, only some of which would be favorable for crystallization; but this is another matter. The basic lesson to be drawn from this remarkable story is that the principle according to which two otherwise unrelated and heterogeneous components can be conjugated into a higher-order union if there is some steric or other specific correspondence between them is not confined to intermolecular reactions, for which it has been generally acknowledged, but is equally valid in the realm of large supramolecular systems. The discovery that virus particles, which consist of a nucleic acid core and a protein jacket, can be dissociated into these two components, and that if the two separate fractions are mixed again, they will combine again in the proper spatial arrangement [8] points to the same conclusion of "complementarily prematched systems."

Whether or not this is to be interpreted as a veritable "missing link" in the chain "from molecule to cell" is something we shall consider later. For the moment, it serves to illustrate that in order to become integrated into a higher-unit system, the elements that come together must have properties that prefit them for each other; then, if they are of proper fit, they apparently fall into place instantaneously. The mutual fitting may be based, as in this last example, on some configurational correspondence; but it may also reside in the fact that the time courses of the two component events are harmonious ("resonance"). Since the configurational model is the simpler one, we shall take the next step in our ascent from there.

COMPLEX ORDERED FABRICS

If the foregoing has acquainted us with properties of a multimolecular complex, the collagen fibril, we now pass on to consider a system of higher order, in which the fibrils are assembled to fibers of rather uniform size, and the fibers are arranged in a definite geometric pattern in a continuous matrix, or "ground substance," of mucopolysaccharide. This dual composition at once raises the question of whether, as in the simpler case of calcification, the structural order might not be a conjoint product of both component systems — in this case, collagen and ground substance.

The issue is presented most clearly by the basement lamella of the larval amphibian skin [9]. This is a membrane which lines the underside of the epidermis and separates the latter from the subjacent loose connective tissue. As can be seen in Fig. 14a, it is a laminated structure. Notwithstanding certain variations according to species, age, and body region, its basic construction is essentially constant, consisting of an electron-optically amorphous sheet of matrix, about 4 micra thick, in which the collagen fibers lie embedded, like steel cables in reinforced concrete. A higher-power electron micrograph (Fig. 14b) illustrates the regular geometric pattern which the courses of these fibers describe, as well as other constant fea-

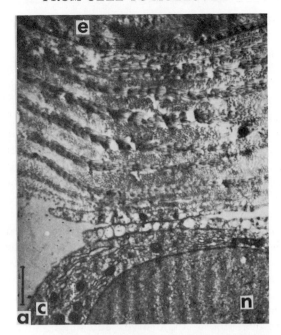

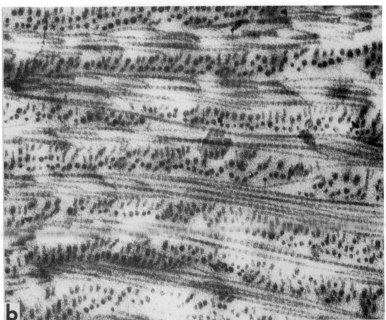

FIG. 14. Electron micrographs of cross sections of the laminated basement lamella of larval amphibian skin. (a) Low-power view (ca. 10,500X); e, epidermal cell; n, nucleus, and c, cytoplasm of fibroblast. (b) Part of the lamella at higher magnification (ca. 27,000X.) (*Originals.*)

tures, as follows: (1) The fibers run in layers of about 2,500-angstrom width each. (2) All fibers within a given layer are parallel. (3) The direction of the fiber axes alternates between adjacent layers by an angle of 90°; that is to say, fiber orientation is the same for all even layers, as well as for all odd layers, and a surface projection makes the fibrous fabric appear as an orthogonal grid, while a favorable transverse section, such as that of Fig. 14b, shows the fiber systems alternately in side view (as beaded strings) and in cross sections (as circular dots). (4) Along the trunk, the two systems of fibers run diagonally with regard to the main body axis. (5) The individual fibers are cylindrical, with relatively uniform diameters of 500 to 600 A. (6) The fibers are not densely packed and may be separated by distances of several hundred angstroms (control experiments have excluded the possibility that this separation might be a hydration artifact arising during fixation of the tissue). (7) Despite the lack of lateral contact between fibers, the periodic bands of all of them within a given layer appear to be in register, defining thus a periodic system of parallel planes perpendicular to the fiber axes.

We are faced here with a fabric of great over-all regularity, in which the individual fibers, themselves supramolecular units, function as subordinate elements. Evidently, such an object affords a unique opportunity for studying the manner in which higher-order patterns develop. We used for this study the process of wound healing (Fig. 15a). Small holes made in the skin, which penetrate the basement lamella, are quickly covered by epidermal cells moving over the lesion. The gap in the underlying basement lamella is repaired more slowly, so that its stepwise reconstruction could be followed. At first the gap is filled with a structureless exudate of undetermined nature. Then fibroblasts appear underneath and deposit collagenous material in this matrix. The precise mode of fibrogenesis is still debated; but the prevailing view is that the fibroblasts extrude fibrous precursors, which on interaction with the outer medium become polymerized and aggregated into fibrils. At any rate, the young fibers in the wound in the vicinity of the fibroblasts already show the typical periodic banding of native collagen. Significantly, however, they show no preferential orientation whatever and lie helter-skelter in the matrix, like cordwood dumped from a delivery truck (Fig. 15b). Moreover, these fibers are much thinner than the mature collagen fibers and, of course, much sparser. The hole in the old basement lamella is thus filled at first by a primitive patch of ground substance containing an irregular feltwork of matted immature collagen fibers. This, incidentally, corresponds to the terminal stage at which the development of the lamella is normally arrested in certain areas of the body surface.

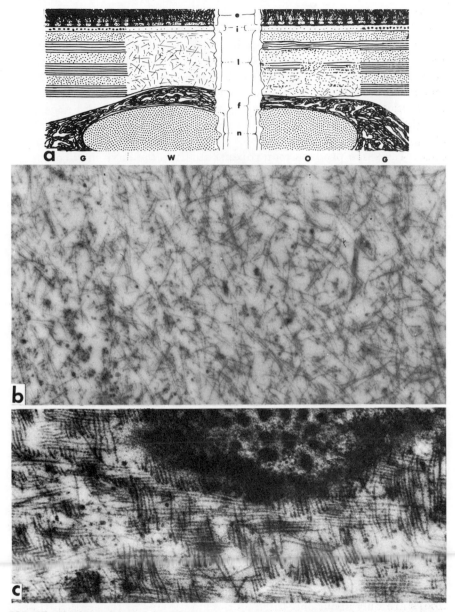

FIG. 15. Healing of wounds in the basement lamella. (*a*) Diagram (cross section) of restoration of lamella (*l*, only six layers are represented). G, old intact region; W, O, wound region during first and second week of healing, respectively; *e*, epidermal cell; *f*, fibroblast. (*b*) Electron micrograph of cross section of wound region with unordered early fibers. (*From Weiss and Ferris.*) (*c*) Electron micrograph of tangential section through wound region adjacent to epidermal underside (island dotted with "bobbins") in second week of healing, with beginning ordering of fibers. (*From Weiss and Ferris.*)

Secondarily, however, this erstwhile irregular texture is super-seded by the typical architectural order described above, which is characteristic of most skin regions. The ordering process starts from the epithelial surface and sweeps downward. It manifests it-self in a marked reorientation of the fibers nearest the epithelial underside; instead of the earlier random directions these assume orientations (a) in a common plane parallel to the epithelial sheet, and (b) parallel to one another within that plane, their axial direction being determined by the stumps of the old fibers at the former wound edge. The same process then repeats itself in the next subjacent layer, but with axis orientation perpendicular to that of the preceding layer. Then a third layer appears, and so on down, always with alter-nation axis orientations (Fig. 15c), until the whole lamella has again become laminated. At about the same time, the fibers acquire ma-ture dimensions.

The unexpected lesson from these observations has been that the imposition of geometric order upon the fabric is a secondary process, or rather a series of processes: preexisting fibrous units are being rearranged and restacked, comparable to the orderly crosswise layer-ing of cordwood from a dumped heap. This is expressing the matter in oversimplified terms, especially since there may be a recasting of fibers involved, comparable to recrystallization, that might have es-caped detection; yet basically, the simile is correct. The question then arises whether such a physical reordering process can be ac-counted for in terms of interactions among the structural components. A closer study of the disposition of the fibers during the early phase of rearrangement furnished some clues, as can be seen from the ex-ceptionally favorable tangential section pictured in Fig. 15c. The section lies in a plane roughly grazing the underside of the epidermis, a sliced-off cap of which (with bobbins) is seen on top. The basement lamella having been hit at a very low angle, the consecutive layers of fibers in it appear almost side by side, with only partial overlap. Thus seen in surface view, the following details could be discerned: (1) Each layer contains as yet one row of fibers only. (2) Within each layer, the fibers have already assumed a common parallel orientation and, most significantly, with their periodic bands aligned in lateral regis-ter, just as in the original undamaged membrane. (3) The individual fibers are only about one-third as thick as fibers of the mature tis-sue, but they are regularly spaced at lateral distances from center to center of 500 to 600 A. (4) The fibers of each layer intersect the pro-jections of those of adjacent layers approximately at right angles (making allowance for distortion during fixation). Since the lateral distance between the fiber axes is of the same order as the axial re-peat (~ 600 A), the projections of overlapping adjacent orthogonal

sets of fibers describe squares, many of which are plainly evident
in Fig. 15c.

The fact that the segments of the parallel fibers within any given
layer lie in register despite the lack of lateral contact calls for some
principle of alignment operating across the intervening spaces of
several hundred angstroms. One can conceive of two different hypotheses both of which would satisfy this condition. The first is outlined
in the diagram of Fig. 16. It goes as follows: The eventual consoli-
dated fiber grid bears the same relation to the earlier random mat-
ting, which it supersedes, as does the crystalline to the amorphous
state of a substance. The "crystallinity" of the ordered system would
consist in the fact that certain critical constellations of the collagen
fiber, morphologically expressed by repeat bands, could become stabilized only at equidistant points, roughly 600 A apart. The first
row of fibers, laid down in a plane defined by the epidermal underside
and polarized by the linear extensions of the "crystal" axes of the
severed old fibers around the wound, would then constitute a grid with
a square pattern that would serve as foundation. A second story of
fibers would then be set on top, and if we assume again an equilibra-
tion distance of some 600 A, we arrive at a cubic system of nodal
stabilization points. There are two line systems to define the short-
est connection between these points on the second story of the lattice
(Fig. 16), one parallel (A) and the other (B) normal, to the basal
grid. If one assumed that symmetry relations would make B su-
perior to A energywise, the orthogonal alternation from row to row
would be explained.

In all of this, the geometric order of the final fabric would be a
result of the self-positioning of the fibrous units relative to one another into a distribution and orientation which would be the only permissible one for a collective body of the given constitution in the given
physicochemical environment. In this version, the hypothesis would be
but a logical extension to the next higher level of the principle underlying, for instance, the formation of the orderly aggregate of a fiber

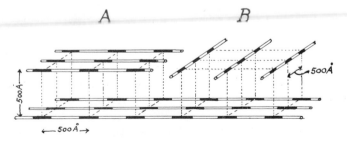

FIG. 16. Hypothetical cubic lattice for the stabilization of collagen fibers in the basement lamella. (*From Weiss.*)

from a pool of free molecules. The fibers, by virtue of their interactions with each other and with their environment, would determine a field of forces with energetically distinguished equilibrium points spaced in the indicated cubic lattice pattern. The pattern of the emergent system of higher order thus would result from the fact that the interacting units themselves have a distinctly nonrandom, patterned constitution. At any rate, in this view, the active role in the performance is ascribed to the collagen units.[10]

However, an alternative hypothesis, which also deserves serious attention, would assign a much more crucial role to the ground substance. It would attribute the requisite property of crystallinity with a cubic lattice and a lattice constant of around 600 A to the ground substance, and it would postulate that the nodal points are sites where physicochemical conditions are singularly suited for the linkage between ground substance and collagen. In other words, the periodic collagen chains would settle on grids of lines staked out by acceptor sites of the matrix which coincidentally are spaced in the same steric pattern. The resulting higher order would then be based on a property of neither the ground substance alone, nor of collagen alone, but on the fact that both systems share a fundamental steric property. This, as one realizes now, would truly tie this case conceptually to the lower-order one of mineralization discussed before, and more generally, to the broader biological thesis of specificity as based on the interaction between systems mutually attuned by pairwise matching properties.

This latter hypothesis assumes that the supposedly "hyaline" ground substance in reality possesses definite structural order analogous to "crystallinity." This assumption might seem gratuitous in view of the fact that the electron microscope, at least after the conventional procedures of tissue fixation, has as yet disclosed no direct evidence of fine structure in the matrix. But there are some observations that ought to caution us against accepting the negative evidence of the electron microscope as conclusive. Two of these observations pertain directly to our present object — the basement lamella — hence, will be related here. A third one, more involved, will be dealt with later.

It will have been noted in Fig. 14a and b that the boundaries between the domains of consecutive layers of the lamella are absolutely sharp and straight, even though the planes one can lay through the outermost row of fibers in each layer are quite erratic; to visualize this, one need only connect the dots marking fiber cross sections in Fig. 14b. This in itself suggests that the lamination is a feature of the ground substance, notwithstanding the absence of clear optical delineations between laminae.

But there is more direct proof that the ground substance is actually built of discrete layers, plywood fashion. At metamorphosis, the cell-free larval membrane is suddenly invaded by mesenchyme cells from the underlying connective tissue. As these cells move in, they do not drill through the lamella in arbitrary directions, but can be seen to extend preferentially along invisible cleavage planes between the individual layers, wedging lamina from lamina. A cross section through the exfoliating membrane at this stage (Fig. 17a) shows quite clearly that each lamina is a cleanly separable slab. Because cells have been known to prepare invasion routes by trail-blazing enzymes lytic for ground substance, and because the matrix in our object could by analogy be judged to be a mucopolysaccharide of the hyaluronic acid class, we tried to duplicate the metamorphic exfoliation by placing larval skin directly into hyaluronic acid. As Fig. 17b shows (by comparison with Fig. 14b), this treatment actually dissolved the ground substance between the collagen fibers (causing the latter to become more densely packed in between), but as in metamorphosis, the enzymes spread faster and more effectively in the planar direction and along the invisible borders between adjacent layers (in the horizontal sense in the illustration).

Thus there is concrete evidence of a planar pattern of organization in the ground substance; that is, there are structural discontinuities which set off layer from layer, although these have become discernible only in biological tests, not in electron optical inspection. On the other hand, our hypothetical proposition of an additional structural order in the third dimension, as presented above, can derive from these tests, at best, some logical, but surely not yet actual, support; it is still highly speculative, as is much of this excursion into obscure and uncharted land.

Yet there is one recent instance which positively implicates the ground substance in the determination of architectural features of tissues. This case deals with the development of cartilage by chondrogenic cells in vitro. At a certain stage of their development, mesenchymal blastemas destined to form cartilage, which have been removed from the embryo and explanted into nutrient media, will continue to develop in vitro and form skeletal pieces characteristic of the embryonic sites from which they were taken [11]. Thus mesenchyme from avian limb buds, grown in vitro, will form limb cartilages; that from the ventral midline, sternum; that from the eyeball, sclera; each with the characteristic site-specific architecture. Later it was found [12] that when cells of embryonic limb mesenchyme were separated from one another by trypsin treatment and the suspension was placed in a culture medium, the reaggregated cells would develop into cartilaginous nodules. The identification of the develop-

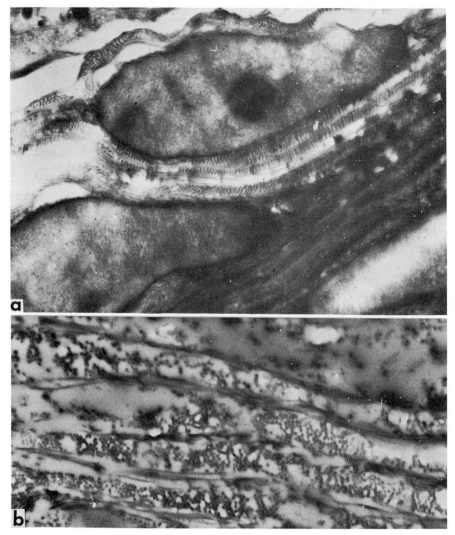

FIG. 17. Signs of laminated structure of ground substance of basement lamella.
(a) Invading mesenchyme cells. Two nuclei, one with dark nucleolus, are seen in
section; cytoplasm, extremely thin and indistinct, split the lamella along preformed
cleavage planes. (*From Weiss and Ferris.*) (b) Electron micrograph of cross section
of larval lamella, fixed after immersion of live skin in hyaluronic acid, showing faster
dissolution of ground substance in the horizontal than in the vertical direction.
(*Original.*)

mental result rested largely on the appearance of intercellular ground
substance typical of normal cartilage, in which the cells became en-
trapped. Evidently the faculty of generating specific cartilaginous
ground substance was inherent in each individual cell of the poten-

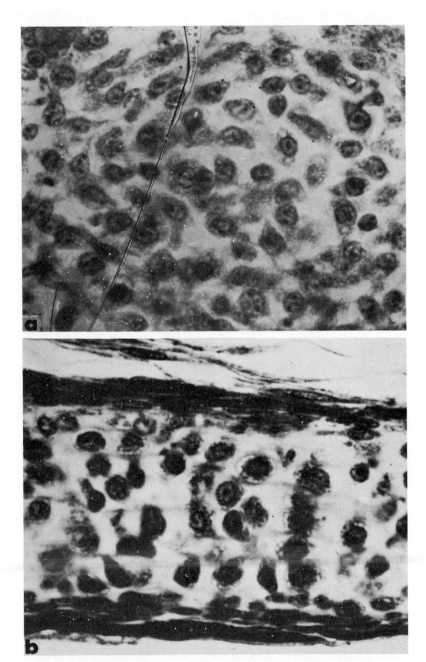

FIG. 18. Transverse sections through cartilages formed in vitro from dissociated and reaggregated chondrogenic blastemas of limb bud (a) and sclera
(b). (*From Weiss and Moscona.*)

tially chondrogenic tissue, rather than in some property which only the integral blastema would possess.

But a further extension of the cartilage experiments indicated a far more differentiated architectural role of the ground substance. As just indicated, cartilages allowed to develop in vitro from undisrupted chondrogenic blastemas bear certain distinctive features characteristic of their original destinations. Thus limb cartilage, *in situ* as well as in vitro, tends to grow rather massively in concentric whorls, whereas scleral cartilage in both conditions is laid down in the form of a slab of rather uniform thickness. It was surprising to find [13] that these distinctions were still clearly displayed by cartilages developed from blastemas that had been broken up completely into their component cells. Mesenchyme cells from the limb bud and from around the eye, respectively, dissociated, scrambled, reassembled, and then cultured under identical conditions, produced two distinctly different kinds of cartilage, which, as one can judge from Fig. 18, are readily recognizable as of the massive whorllike limb pattern (Fig. 18*a*) and of the flat plate-shaped scleral pattern (Fig. 18*b*), respectively.

This is no longer just a sign of the ability of chondrogenic cells to secrete a generalized cartilaginous material — chondroitin sulfate and collagen — but is an index of far subtler properties. For obviously, although it takes a multitude of cells to build collectively either a nodule or a slab, each individual cell of either tissue must have "known" how to contribute its distinctive share to the erection of its special type of cartilage structure when it became rejoined to other cells of like character. Contrary to man's technology, where culverts or cathedrals can be built from the same kind of bricks, the cellular bricks for different skeletal structures are differently constituted and carry, as it were, the blueprint for the respective construction procedures within themselves.

This is, of course, a matter difficult to visualize and even harder to translate into analytical terms. However, in order to make at least a beginning, I have suggested that perhaps each cell type produces a ground substance of different "crystalline" characteristics, which would determine the specific mode of its accretion in the different dimensions of space, with the radial direction dominating in the case of the limb, but a two-dimensional extension in the case of the sclera. The cells, enclosed in their own product, would then assume conforming positions within this framework, and the architectural integration of the "compound" would thus be completed. There seems to be sufficient variety in the family of mucopolysaccharide ground substances [14] to make such a hypothesis at least reasonably possible. In combination with the preceding account of the architecture of the basement lamella it assumes even greater plausibility. If confirmed, it would bring the evidence for the "compounding" of higher-order systems by the free interaction of lower-order units clear up to the level of tissue structure. Let it be remembered, however, that in all these instances the integrated pattern of the group interaction is prepared — built in, as it were — in properties of the interacting units, which, as observers who know the outcome, we recognize as anticipatory in character.

SOME ORDERING PRINCIPLES

From this survey of ordered or regulated interactions of units at all levels from macromolecules to tissues, one can extract a number of general conclusions which are instructive in two respects: in one sense, they give greater precision to our initial thesis about "the cellular control of molecular activities," and secondly, they lead to the posing of more concrete and succinct questions to which research on "cellular organization" could be directed than would be feasible from the worm's-eye view of molecules alone. It is for the purpose of setting the sights, rather than with any presumption of finality or comprehensiveness, that I venture to set forth the following somewhat arbitrary selection of thoughts on the subject.

One result which emerges clearly from a survey of our illustrative examples is the almost commonplace realization that the operation of a system cannot be inferred from its composition. A description of composition is a static record of the content of a given unit: a catalogue of all the items in it, whether they operate or not. No matter in what terms we list the component items, whether as molecules or higher complexes, no item as such ever "acts." It can only "interact" with another item [15]. Yet such interaction is, of course, contingent on the opportunity of both to come together. If we are dealing with a body in which all components can move freely and at random, the probability for any two of them to meet is merely a matter of time; homogenization is a device to approximate this condition. However, in any system whose components are restrained in their degrees of freedom of motion, there will be correspondingly fewer probabilities for interaction from unguided pairwise collisions. In other words, of the total number of possible constellations and combinations that could conceivably be formed from the elements of a given inventory, were they free, only a very limited fraction has actually a chance to materialize within the framework of an organized unit system. One could vaguely compare the static chemical equipment of a cell to a chemist's store with chemicals on shelves confined in bottles: the mere presence of the bottles on the shelves as such has no effect whatever. However, when by design and choice some are uncorked and their contents mixed, predictable reaction products are obtained — as the outcome of "organized behavior." Homogenization, by contrast, is comparable to the smashing of all bottles, spilling and mixing freely the contents of them all.

Therefore, unless the listing of the content of a system ("composition") is supplemented by a description of the set of conditions which limit the opportunities for the occurrence of random interactions, the operation of the system remains incomprehensible. Although a plain truism, this rule is so commonly ignored that it deserves to be reiterated.

Two recurrent mistakes may illustrate the point. One is the tacit conversion of enzymatic "activity" observed in a living cell into terms of enzyme "concentration." Evidently, any enzymes bound to specific sites (hence not distributed ubiquitously throughout the cell) can be "active" only in proportion to their accessibility to substrate and to the fraction of active groups actually exposed to the substrate, and in reference to the physicochemical environment at that particular microsite. Collision frequencies between enzyme and substrate molecules, which are what we register as "activity," are further reduced if substrate cannot diffuse freely but is channeled into limited compartments. For any given localized group of fixed enzyme molecules, on the other hand, "activity" will be enhanced if all of them are oriented alike so as to expose the maximum number of reactive groups to the passing stream of substrate, particularly as parallel orientation would also permit the closest stacking, hence the accommodation of the maximum possible number of enzyme molecules per unit of available surface. Again, we encounter structure, in the broadest sense, as one of the major factors "controlling molecular activities" in the cell, so that homogenates, unleashed from its restraining influence, can never portray truly the operation of the structured system.

A second related set of errors arises from inadequate attention to barriers of penetration by agents to which a cell or cell part is exposed (e.g., hormones, antibodies, drugs, etc.). Such situations are often dealt with as if the ability of the agent in question to permeate the cell and all its compartments could be taken for granted. Admittedly, the barrier of the cell membrane is rather generally respected, but it is not equally well recognized that every interface, microscopic or submicroscopic, must be considered to be a potential screen for the passage of substances or the transmission of influences. Moreover, there is nothing to justify the expectation that any given agent that can pass through a given cell compartment will emerge from it in the same form as it has entered. For instance, in

order for a chemical externally administered to an embryo to be able
to alter the genic response of certain cells, and hence to cause developmental alterations, it must reach the genes. But in order to
reach them, it must pass through cells, intercellular spaces, body
fluids, and finally in the target cell, through cytoplasm, nuclear
envelope, nuclear "sap," and chromosomal matrix — a complicated
journey through spaces metabolically far from inert, during which it
is more likely than not to suffer some alterations. The same is true
of the traffic in the reverse direction, from genes to body products.
This is not to say that substances may not get to distant destinations
without essential changes, as often they will, but merely to caution
against assuming such inertia as a matter of course.

These two examples serve well to illustrate the sort of structural
limitations of the degrees of freedom of interaction which distinguish
the organized system from its randomized homogenate. The constructive side of this principle lies in the fact that as it restrains
ubiquity of interaction, it also creates uniquely favorable conditions
for special reactions to occur at now restricted sites. I have already
referred to the potentiation of the effectiveness of enzymes resulting
from their adsorption from solution, where they had n degrees of
freedom of orientation, to an interface, where they are stacked in
parallel. In general, structural organization will be effective only to
the extent to which, in restraining wasteful ubiquity and randomness,
it establishes guides for optimal utilization of the available energy;
just as a combustion engine turns explosive energy into useful work.
In the cell as in the machine, structural provisions route energy from
random, undirected, dissipation into useful channels.

A common morphological expression of such directive guidance,
as well as one of its major tools, is a uniform (or at least nonrandom)
orientation of polar elements. As we shall show below, tool and product are here in a reciprocal relation, which is perhaps most simply
illustrated by the grooving action of water flowing downhill — the river
fashioning its bed and the bed confining the river. Processes oriented
in a given direction (e.g., shear, hydraulic, or electric flow) can result in structural orientation, which then, in turn, will channel further
flow. Orientation, therefore, is a device for, as well as an index of,
increased efficiency.

In this general perspective, it seems highly doubtful whether a
living cell could operate efficiently if substance traffic in it depended
chiefly on the relatively inefficient process of free diffusion, particularly in view of the narrowness of the capillary spaces involved. Just
as higher organisms have expedited intertissue traffic by the institution of circulatory systems, so intracellular traffic may be enhanced
by convection currents much more widely than is commonly envisaged.

Aside from the rather conspicuous streaming observed in cell bodies of radiolarians, amoebae, plant cells ("cyclosis"), and fish eggs, the possibility of "directed traffic" inside the cell has received no more than casual attention, and certainly no systematic study. In a speculative mood, one might add that such "traffic direction" need not be confined to the familiar device of channeling and pumping liquid flow, but that the interfaces of linear bodies in liquid pools may also be able to propagate substances down their length faster than would be feasible by free diffusion in the pool, hence, would act like everted channels. This would be particularly pertinent if oriented molecular chains should turn out to have the faculty of acting as "bucket brigades" in conducting electrons or protons down the line at rates far in excess of those attainable in solution [16]. If this should come to pass, one might be led to conclude that all the truly relevant directive processes in a living system are carried out by molecular arrays that form a continuous, though labile, network with the properties of a solid, rather than by the liquid diffusion pools, which are subject to random agitation.

However, to return from these conjectures to familiar ground, there are enough established facts to argue for the dominant role of molecular orientation as one of the basic principles through which biological organization becomes effective. The following primitive models, which I presented a decade ago, may serve to symbolize some elementary ordering processes in this category. They are to convey the realization that even processes that give an aspect of elementariness, like "molecular orientation," may still be truly composite, occurring in several steps "controlled" by different and often quite unrelated factors. The fact of such compositeness makes explicitly clear why, as was postulated in the preceding sections, there must be "integration" of all those unrelated factors on a higher level if they are to be rendered interrelated for the conjoint act of constituting and preserving a higher unit system.

Figure 19 shows the progressive ordering of a linear array. We start at a, with a random pile of filamentous macromolecules (e. g., of a fibrous protein) with different polar end groups. On introducing (in b) an appropriate linkage, we obtain a linear polymere chain (in c) with polarized segments, but neither straight nor oriented (ignoring, for simplicity, attractive and repulsive forces between side chains). To straighten the chain, we introduce an external force, for instance, mechanical tension (in d), which if applied to a whole group of chains, turns all of them into a common direction (in e), thus imparting common linear order to the collective. In this situation, further order emerges from the interactions among the formerly separated elements, which as a result of their parallel orientation have been brought into closer proximity, hence, mutual lateral interaction, conducive to aggregation into larger bundles (ignoring, again for simplicity, more complicated group configurations such as the formation of tactoids). An ulterior ordering step ensues if some equilibrium condition for the group prescribes that the ends of the monomeres of neighboring chains be as closely approximated to one another as possible, which would cause them to slip from random axial positions (e) into strict register (f). It will be noted that this series of steps is essentially a portrayal of such phenomena as the collagen fibrogenesis described above.

Let us now proceed to a model of planar order. For this, the model experiments of Langmuir and of Harkins on monomolecular layers can serve as a point of departure. They show the orderly adsorption from solution of macromolecules with polar end groups along an interface dividing media of different affinity for the respective end groups. For instance, molecules with a hydrophilic group at one end and a hydrophobic group at the other, when entering the boundary between oil and water, will form a picket fence, the ends of whose stakes are each immersed in the medium appropriate to it (Fig. 20b). On such a polar monolayer, a second, inverted, layer can then be deposited; on this a third layer, and so forth. In other words, the exposed ends of an adsorbed monolayer act like a new interface. Consequently, a hydrophilic protein can be deposited on top of the hydrophilic face of a lipid layer, and in this manner, a mixture of both species (Fig. 20a) can be segregated as a double foil (Fig. 20c). For practical examples, we need only refer to our earlier description of some lamellar systems within cells (Figs. 4 and 5b). As one can see, this scheme could be extended to allow for much more specific and exclusive affinities as determinants of the molecular combinations to be accomplished than is possible by the mere binary choice among the terminal charges on a dipole. Once a ground layer has been established of molecules with end groups of specific steric configuration, all of which stick out into the medium, these would function as acceptors or traps for any passing molecules that have a complementary configuration, thus leading to the building on of a second layer of different composition. And if these latter molecules were then to act, on their part, in a similar manner, still a third molecular species with affinities to the exposed ends of the second would be fished out from the common medium (Fig. 20d).

As one can sense, in deriving the rationale for this model of "stacking according to steric correspondence," I have leaned on the phenomena of immunology. The model is as hypothetical as is the steric basis for antibody-antigen binding, but not much more so. If it should prove untenable, some other model for the building up of

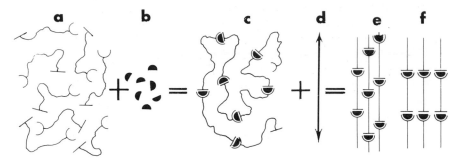

FIG. 19. Diagrammatic model of stepwise ordering of linear array of macromolecules. (*From Weiss.*)

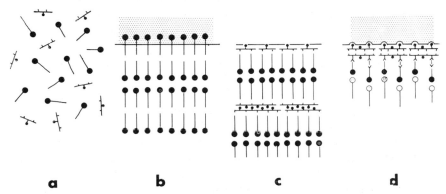

FIG. 20. Model of progressive ordering and stacking of macromolecules along interfaces. (*From Weiss.*)

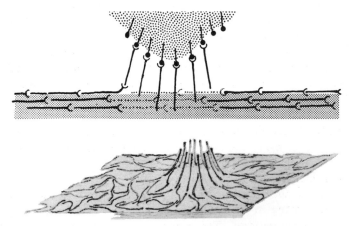

FIG. 21. Hypothetical generation of surface breaches and leaks as a result of molecular reorientation toward a specific stimulus. (*From Weiss.*)

the third dimension in an organized system would have to be invented. For one important consideration that must be taken into account in explaining three-dimensional organization of supramolecular systems is that the interior of such systems initially is often liquid, hence randomized. The only spatial patterns of sufficient stability to provide firm bearings for any subsequent organized consolidation of the interiors, therefore, reside in the boundary layers, which by virtue of their interfacial positions act as two-dimensional solids. As such, in contrast to the liquid contents, they can hold in position space mosaics of diverse molecular populations in a typical nonrandom mapping.

Given such primary surface mosaic, interactions of its settled molecules with the disordered content would then secondarily extend order into the interior, vaguely comparable to the erection of a building on its orderly foundation. For instance, I proposed long ago that the basis for the localization of the first differential steps in embryonic development is to be sought in a surface mosaic of areas with specifically different molecular populations, blocked out in the cortex of the egg, and all the experiences gathered since have strengthened this concept. It would seem plausible to broaden it by assuming that the organization of other cell and subcell systems likewise resides primarily in planar patterns. Growing support for this assumption comes from the prominence of smectic systems in the cell (myelin sheath, cell membrane, endoplasmic reticulum, etc.) revealed by the electron microscope. The secondary elaboration of a planar pattern in depth adds not only body to the system, but most significantly, a further dimension of order in the progressive chemical diversification along the new third axis, much as primary differences in soil composition find secondary expression in the pattern of vegetation.

For further details of these concepts, I must refer to earlier accounts [17]. Indeed, without such supplementary commentary the static frame of the system described in the preceding pages would seem to be incompatible with the lability and flux of structural organization emphasized in the earlier sections of this paper. First, I labored the fact that outer and inner membrane systems of the cell are in a state of continual flux and remodeling, and now I have introduced a topographic mosaic of conventional stability as the fixed basic reference system from which further organization is to proceed. Let me, therefore, briefly summarize the formula by which I have in the past attempted to reconcile the two propositions. It is implicit in what I have termed the concept of "molecular ecology" [18].

It considers molecular populations in the living cell essentially analogous to populations of organisms which are adjusted to their ecological environment. Each kind of population is capable of exist-

ing and surviving only in an appropriately fitting set of external conditions, comprising chiefly the physicochemical milieu and the activities and products of other populations in the joint territory. We know
that macromolecules of the kinds to be found in living systems require for their formation and maintenance highly specific constellations of metabolic conditions, such as the adequacy of concentration,
proportions, and local availability of the requisite building blocks, of
the energy supply, of essential catalysts and other cofactors, of the
right temperature range, pH, and so forth, as well as the sort of kinetic enhancement by proper alignment and orientation which was mentioned above. The more complex the molecular species in question,
the more particular are its existential prerequisites, and the more
factors must combine cooperatively at a single site in order to satisfy them. Once formed, a given macromolecular species still can only
lodge at a site compatible with its continued survival, where it is
protected against metabolic extinction. Conversely, it will be positively concentrated at a site for which it has chemical affinity.

Because different molecular species with different requirements
must coexist and function in a common space without being insulated
from one another by preformed mechanical compartments, the activities of each are of critical concern to the survival of its neighbors.
Any localized chemical activity in a given spot inside a cell consumes,
transforms, and gives off substances and energy in a characteristic
time course and thus constitutes part of the fluctuating environment
of other centers in the vicinity, just as the activities and products of
the latter reciprocally impinge upon the former. In this dynamic in-
terdependency, no localized system can become established and persist unless what the neighboring systems are doing is in every respect
compatible with it. The inner organization of a cell thereby becomes
"self-organization," which becomes stationary whenever the various
chemical domains have assumed a distribution relative to one another
such that maximum mutual harmony and complementariness of operation are guaranteed. The crucial point is that this state is brought
about and actively maintained by the interacting subsystems themselves, rather than by their fixation in a rigid mechanical framework —
their grouping being the result of the dynamics of the populations involved, rather than of passive allocation to given positions by outside
forces.

In all of this, different macromolecular species may appear either
in cooperative, mutually supporting ("symbiotic") roles or in competitive relations. Consequently, when a mixed molecular population
is faced with a variety of possible sites for adsorption, or chemical
combination, or otherwise preferential location, it will sort itself
out into its separate components, as each species occupies the site

most appropriate to its kind. In preempting that site, it automatically excludes other species from it. If either a site or a species residing there changes in character, some other species, previously barred, suddenly acquires thereby favorite status and consequently crowds out the original occupant. The patterns of relative distribution, segregation, and localization among the different segments of a mixed molecular population thus sustain themselves dynamically as a result of the "ecological" conditions which the various species create for one another in a bounded physical space. In this sense, structure and ordered activity appear again as merely different phases of the same phenomenon, as the "primary" structural patterns of localization in surfaces, to which we ascribed above a guiding role in cell organization, presumably originate, themselves, from the dynamic self-sorting and territorial segregation of molecular species in competitive interaction.

Although stated in this generality, these concepts of molecular ecology must sound rather vague, they could be liberally documented but for the lack of space. Nor is it as important for the moment to be convincing as it is to introduce the ecological point of view into the molecular realm, where it can overcome serious conceptual barriers to an objective treatment of biological organization. Needless to say that in line with the hierarchical scheme of organization, there also will have to be created a macromolecular ecology, an ecology of supramolecular units, of organelles, of cells, and of cell populations.

As will be shown later, the ecological scheme is, in fact, a more concrete version of the more formal "field" concept in so far as it endows geometric field parameters such as "central," "peripheral," "marginal," "axial," etc., (as well as references to "position" or "distance") with physical meaning in terms of differential effects of forces and limiting conditions. I mention this in the present context because our earlier discussion of molecular orientation as a dominant ecological factor in the regulation of molecular behavior is a case in point. I have indicated its bearing on structure formation and on enzyme efficiency. To this I shall add a bried remark on its instrumental role in cellular selectivity and specificity.

Cells possess the discriminatory capacity of selectively admitting or excluding specific physical stimuli, chemical agents, and traffic with fellow cells (e.g., in permeability, food ingestion, drug reactions, hormone responses, parasitic infections, immune reactions, fertilization, virus penetration, sensory perception, or nerve excitation). While it has been generally assumed since Ehrlich's days that in at least some of these phenomena the specificity resides in the interlocking of molecules of matching configuration between the two interacting partners, the relation between the specificity and the dynamics of such interactions (transfer of substance and energy, current flow, cementing, and so forth) has remained undefined.

As a tentative approach to the problem, I have recently [19] proposed a "dualistic" hypothesis based on the following assumptions. (1) A major fraction of the cell surface is occupied by a network of filiform macromolecules in essentially planar (surface-parallel) array, barring substance passage ("barrier position"); (2) certain of these molecules have end groups of specific configuration as selective acceptors for complementary groups; (3) carriers of complementary end groups approaching the cell from the environment, in attracting and combining with matching surface groups, thereby turn the respective molecules from their erstwhile tangential into radial ("open-gate") positions (Fig. 21); (4) for molecules with an axial (length:diameter) ratio of 100, this reorientation implies the uncovering of 99 per cent of a formerly covered surface site, in other words, the opening of local "breaches" or "pores" as channels for secondary outflow or inflow across the surface; (5) local electrostatic disturbances produce surface "leaks" in similar, but unspecific, fashion.

According to this concept, specific molecular interactions at a surface serve merely to unlock passage for less specific and dynamically more powerful transport and transmission mechanisms. What has been said for the cell surface applies, of course, equally well to other membrane barriers within the cell. Although the validity of the idea remains subject to further tests, the main point in presenting it on this occasion is to focus attention on the crucial role of macromolecular orientation in the ecology of the cell and its subunits. It is noteworthy that this type of effect would remain concealed to ordinary chemical determinations, as it involves no change in the composition of the molecular population concerned.

DIFFERENTIATION

Our considerations thus far have been confined to a cell which can be regarded as stationary, immutably maintaining its essential character as a whole despite the incessant variations of content, distribution, shape, and behavior of its constituent elements (other than perhaps the genes). This is permissible as long as we contemplate only a relatively short sample period of its life span. A new class of problems along the way from molecule to cell emerges, however, as soon as we widen our scope to encompass the full life cycle of the individual cell, including its growth, differentiation ("cytodifferentiation"), and possibly its transmutation, and aging; or broader still, the development of the whole protoplasmic continuum of many cell generations, of which the individual cell is merely a small probing sample. Again, at the hurried pace of this cursory survey, I can do no more than sketch the gist of the problem [20] as follows:

As indicated above, in molecular terms one can ascribe the progressive specialization of the interior of a cell to the competitive segregation of selected molecular species into various and separate "ecological niches" favorable to their kinds, followed by a series of interactions between these settled species and those of the still roaming population; the nature of the interactions varies with the nature of the species which have monopolized the critical positions. It does not matter in this context whether or not the particular key species exercise their master functions as clusters of enzymes or as nucleation sites (or anchoring points) on which to build structural elements. The salient feature is that one can understand in principle how an orderly mosaic of chemical properties, once it has been initiated in the cell, can be progressively elaborated to yield the specialized equipment displayed by the "differentiated" cell, examples of which have been given in an earlier section. I have also indicated before that the master positions of given segments of the population need not be permanent; but that if conditions change, some ruling groups could be supplanted by totally different ones, entailing rather thorough modifications of the behavior, products, and appearance of the whole cell [21]

This picture of cytodifferentiation, which is restricted to the individual cell during its individual life span, presents nothing new that could not be fundamentally covered by our ecological cell model. Yet if we turn from the cell individual to the family of cell lines, the problem of differentiation becomes truly vexing. For then the problem arises of how two cell strains, derived from one common ancestral cell — or to put it more pertinently, derived from two cells of exactly identical composition and constitution and fully interchangeable — can acquire the radically different properties which characterize them in later stages of development, often irreversibly. Considering the contingencies of cell life, random differences between two originally equivalent cells could arise and then be transmitted, and even be amplified in their transmission, to the descendant cells. It is not difficult to visualize how in this manner a cell population could undergo random diversification. In fact, this is apparently what takes place among cell strains cultivated in vitro for prolonged periods. However, in the organism the diversification is not fortuitous, but specific as to time and place, and this requires an extension of our cell model. We must assume that if two cells are destined to give rise to different kinds of progeny, this is achieved by inducing a different set of compounds in each to occupy the critical master positions, thus initiating radically different sequences of subsequent interactions in the two lines.

Figure 22 illustrates diagrammatically an extreme case, in which such a differential dichotomy between two equivalent cells is induced by their exposure to different environments whose molecules are prematched to different complementary key fractions in the cell. In this case, the discriminate response is of the "resonance" type. Supposedly, however, there are other instances in which the same dichotomy of cell fate can be evoked by environmental differentials of less specific character (e.g., different metabolites favoring different members of competitive pairs of metabolic processes). What conditions determine the switch in one direction or the other must be decided empirically for each separate instance of cell-type differentiation. It also remains an empirical task to determine whether the course of events following the initial critical dichotomy will or will not deprive a given cell of its faculty to return, in response to changed conditions, to the state at which it was at the time of the original dichotomy and thereafter to transform into something else [22].

In ascribing the primary dichotomies of cell lines to the differential effects of outside conditions, we do not intent to obscure the fact that the differential courses of cell development thus initiated from the cell periphery will, at the central end, result in differential reactions and activations of genes, with telling effect on the subsequent transformation of the cell and of its progeny into a given specialized type. In line with our earlier comments, however, the genes are rated as reactive rather than active participants in differentiation. The studies of experimental embryology and developmental genetics have furnished abundant and compelling evidence to support this view.

The total repertory of reactions and productions a given cell could possibly display at a given stage is limited and defined not only by its initial physicochemical endowment, but by all the modifications through losses, gains, transformations, and dislocations, which this endowment has undergone in the prior ontogenetic history of that cell. Yet of the remaining faculties only a very limited fraction is ever given a chance to materialize, depending on which portion of the molecular population attains controlling dominance, as symbolized by our model, in response to conditions outside the cell. It cannot be emphasized too strongly that the critical "conditions" in question — which are popularly referred to as "inductive" — are different for each specific type of differentiation, and that tendencies to discover and identify a single universal "inductive agent," or at least a common class of such agents, are not only illusory, but in outright contradiction to many established facts of development. On this point,

FIG. 22. Molecular model of the induction of dichotomous differentiation among cells of the same kind. (*From Weiss.*)

the actual concrete phenomena of development, as they have become known through the disciplined and precise studies of the past, are in marked contrast to some current notions of development as an abstract generality. This cautionary remark seems necessary in view of the express danger that the growing and enthusiastic collaboration modern cell biology is receiving from the physical sciences might be misdirected toward some false and fictitious notion of a cell and of what really is involved when cell fate is turned in one direction rather than another.

Perhaps because of this ambitious search for an illusory over-all master solution, there is as yet hardly a single case in which we have detailed factual information on, let alone control of, how a given cell with alternative reactive potencies is actuated to take one specific course to the exclusion of another. There are certain hopeful beginnings, but that is all. One case in this category deserves mention here because of its exemplary simplicity and clarity. Epidermis of the chick embryo, explanted into a medium of blood plasma in vitro, produces the usual stratified epithelium of skin, the outer layers of which transform into typical keratin. But if the medium is enriched with vitamin A, the cells take an alternative course and form a columnar epithelium, which secretes mucus; and even a brief bath in vitamin A, followed by rearing in unenriched medium has the same modifying effect on the cells that have been exposed [23]. Although the intimate mechanism of this spectacular deflection of a cell line from one course into another is still unknown, here at least is one instance in which the initiation of the conversion can be linked directly with a known difference in the molecular environment [24].

This whole line of argument, however aptly it may apply to the progressive orderly diversification among cells, does not, of course, answer the familiar question of how the first critical differentials may have come about when the egg was still a single cell, uniformly exposed, as it is in many cases, to an environment devoid of the kind of systematic differentials to which one could ascribe a differentiating effect. For an answer to this problem, one must turn to our earlier statement that there are major regional differences in the molecular composition of the egg surface, which, in being parceled out directly among the cleavage cells, leaves them, right from the start, with specifically different endowments in accordance with the particular parcel of egg surface each has acquired [25].

Despite their sketchiness, these remarks on differentiation should have sufficed to indicate that in development, as in the stationary mature cell, more catalogues of what is present in the cell, and what *might* come of it, can yield no understanding of the orderly sequence of actual events, that is, of just what part of the inventory becomes operative, when and where; and what really *does* take place in the system. That understanding presupposes knowledge of the principles which govern the nonrandom, typically patterned, distribution and discriminative activation of specific segments of the inventory. Unfortunately, such knowledge is still very scanty. It might grow faster if more attention were paid to problems of this sort. And perhaps more attention would be focused on the problems if they were stated in explicit, rather than symbolic, terms. The models presented in the foregoing should be regarded in this spirit — more as aids in the phrasing of questions, than as answers.

GROUP DYNAMICS

The key theme of our entire discussion has been the extent to which the order observed in a unit of higher order can conceivably be derived from the ordered group dynamics of its interacting elements of lower order. We have encountered this issue at levels of all magnitudes, from the complexing of macromolecules to the cooperative building of typical tissue architecture by randomly aggregated cells. If it were not for the fact that the level of the cell was set as arbitrary cutoff mark for the topic of my address, the theme could readily have been further expanded upwards to the order-determining group dynamics of organisms, populations, and species, which is the subject of the discipline of ecology. The fact that its basic tenets are formally so similar throughout the whole range of biological magnitudes, has led me to the concepts of "molecular ecology" and "cellular ecology," as well as earlier to a "field" theory of development [26]. Of course, labels like these do no more than identify the problem and point to its nature; its resolution still depends on our success in determining precisely the rules of interaction that mark the patterned effect of group activity as of a higher order than the sum total of the effects of the individual constituents operating separately. So what is needed is not a new set of noncommittal terms (and I include among them the much misused symbol of "information"), but factual descriptions of how specific kinds of interactions among elements in given environments can yield order in the group. Carried out methodically, such studies should lead to a consistent science of "dynamic morphology," which could subsume under a common principle, such phenomena as, for instance, the dendritic patterns of electric discharges, of snow crystals, of nerve cells, of lichens, and of trees. As yet we do not even have a nucleus for such a systematic science. But in order not to dwell on abstractions, I would like to refer briefly to two concrete examples.

The first one is a phenomenon which I have called the "two-center effect." It appears in situations in which two separate centers of activity reside in a common medium in relative proximity. In such cases, the radial symmetry of the field of possible effects emanating from a single center is distorted in the direction of the connecting line between the two centers so that there emerges, instead of two partly overlapping radial patterns, a single novel pattern with axial symmetry, as illustrated in Fig. 23. In this manner, the independent scalar and undirected actions (e.g., chemical emanations) of each of the two centers yield, by virtue of the fact that they operate in a common matrix, a vectorial effect with unique geometric features of great consequence; in the place of the isotropic spaces around the independent centers, we now find a structured space connecting the two centers directly, establishing a preferential channel of traffic between them, hence terminating their former independence.

This description has deliberately been kept in the most general terms so as to be applicable to a wide variety of manifestations of the "two-center" principle. The practical case from which it was first derived concerned the interaction between two separate tissue fragments cultured in a common blood plasma medium [27]. The chain of events went like this (Fig. 23): Growing tissue dehydratized its colloidal environment (syneresis); water was lost from the

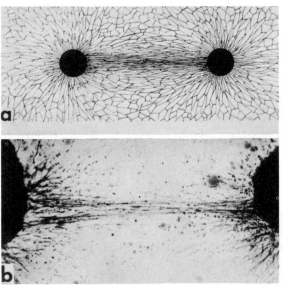

FIG. 23.   Two-center effect. (a) Diagram of orientation of molecular chains in the fibrous matrix around two active centers. (b) Cell bridge formed between two explants (spinal ganglia) in thin plasma membrane. (From Weiss.)

plasma-fibrin sponge; the fibrin net therefore contracted, engendering radial tensions; two centers of radial tension in a common net
produced maximum strain along the connecting line; fibrin chains
consequently became oriented in this direction (Fig. 23a); cells mi-
grating from the centers thus found a preferential oriented track; as
a result, not only did the two centers become connected and united
by a cell bridge (Fig. 23b) but the continued syneretic activity of
these growing cells amplified the effect progressively in positive
feedback fashion. The point is that once the asymmetry has been
initiated, it becomes further accentuated automatically by the chain
of sequelae. One can readily extrapolate the picture to the simultaneous activity of more than two centers. Evidently the effects will not
just summate arithmetically, as would be the case if only stoichiometric chemistry were involved, but they will create characteristic
patterns (see Fig. 24 for three centers). Thus, in conclusion, we have
a practical case in which order of a sort emerges demonstrably from
the interaction of separate independent bodies.

This is only one example from among many obeying the same underlying principle. Let me just mention one other variety. Supposing a
cell emanates some agents which can affect the surface constitution
of other cells. Naturally, unless other cells are present in the vicinity to serve as indicators, the effect cannot manifest itself. But if
two cells are present in close vicinity, a polarizing group effect may
emerge, as the accumulation of the agent on the inner side of the pair
sets up a steady differential of concentrations to which the cells are
exposed on their inward and outward facing sides. In liquid media,
there is a critical distance above which no such surface asymmetry

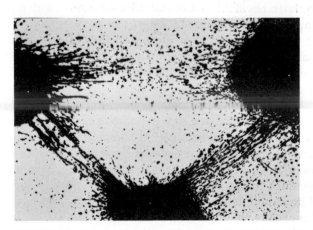

FIG. 24. Two-center effect exerted pairwise between
three separate cultures. (*From Weiss.*)

could develop because of the leveling action of thermal agitation. But
below that threshold distance, cells can mutually polarize each other
by their products. The functional result of this polarization will vary
depending on whether the agent in question softens or stiffens the surface, resulting in the protrusion of cell content toward the opposite
cell or away from it, respectively. In the former case, one may observe an extension of cell processes or actual movement of the cells
toward each other, and in the latter case a movement of the cells
away from each other [28]. It is important to bear in mind that even
very slight and inconspicuous but systematic asymmetries of this
kind can establish differentials which in the course of subsequent
chains of interactions are not only perpetuated, but amplified. The
two-center effect in its various expressions illustrates one general
principle of morphogenesis which prevails from the tissue level down,
presumably to the subcellular units (e.g., mitotic spindle), and perhaps lower. Its salient feature is the emergence of novel patterns
from interactions within the confines of the group of elements without pattern-determining directives from outside the group, in other
words, "self-organization" [29].

The second example to be cited is of even broader application,
although less well documented. It has to do with the emergence of
crucial differentials within a mass of initially fully equivalent units,
producing patterns in which the kind of reaction manifested by a
given unit is demonstrably related to the position of that unit within
the whole group. Such "position" effects have been observed at various levels, from the position of a gene in the chromosome to the
position of an embryonic cell within the germ. As indicated earlier,
"position" evidently signifies the prevalence at that particular site
of characteristic physical and chemical conditions, which depend
upon and vary with, the constellation of the whole system.

In order to instill some concrete sense into this abstract formulation, I shall give an elementary example of how equal units can
suddenly become unequal, depending on their position within the
group. Let us take a system the existence of which depends on an
equilibrated exchange with its environment along a defined boundary
(Fig. 25a). Let us then have a small number of such units, regardless of whether the multiplication has come about by division
or aggregation (Fig. 25b); every one of these components still shares
in the surface along which the exchange takes place, though in a
smaller measure than the original body, hence perhaps quantitatively
restrained by having become part of a collective. But carrying the
numerical increase (by division or aggregation) still further, a condition abruptly arises (Fig. 25c) in which some elements are no
longer in contact and communication with the outside medium, but

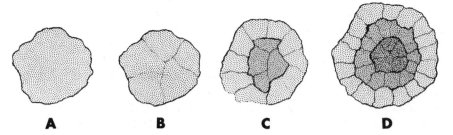

FIG. 25. Diagrammatic illustration of the emergence of differentials in groups of equivalent units. (*a*) Undivided unit (*b*) subdivided unit (*c*) further subdivision, yielding inner and outer units (*d*) increasing complexity by interaction of outer and inner units. (*Original.*)

are completely surrounded by their former fellow units, which henceforth act as mediators and screens from and to the outside medium. Among the units which initially were all "outer," a new positional category has sprung up, which now is "inner." Cut off from their former medium, they are suddenly deprived of all interactions with it, and become instead subject to a new set of interactions, namely, those with their new envelopment — the girdle of outer units. A simple example of such a positional differentiation is the separation in the solid blood island of the chick embryo of the outer cells, which form the endothelial tube, from the inner cells, which become blood cells. Now, let us increase the number of units still further so that a belt of units intermediate between the former outer and inner units emerges (Fig. 25*d*). Then these will obviously come under a dual interactive influence from both adjacent layers, as a result of which they will become a third variety [30]. In this manner, it is possible to conceive of progressive diversification of units in accordance with a relatively invariant over-all pattern of distribution and proportions irrespective of absolute size and dimensions [31].

Considerations like these may at least point the way in which an abstract "field" concept could be translated into operational terms. The actual translation, however, remains to be carried out in yet a single practical case. This is a program for the future. Basic to it is the realization that in a body composed of identical and interchangeable units, the reactions of individual units and hence their future fates, can be crucially different depending on where they are located in the body, whether in the surface or in the interior, or for that matter nearer or farther relative to the source of any agents with which they can interact. It has been the historic merit of the gradient theory of Child to have claimed a dynamic basis for geometrical "position" effects. It fell short of the goal by unnecessarily confining the dynamics chiefly to a single monotonic scale of values of metabolic intensity; for in doing so, it ignored the specificity and selectivity of intermolecular reactions which we now recognize to be among the foundations of organized structures and processes. And for this same reason, the crude scheme of "field" differentials presented above would lose its meaning unless it is coupled with a concept of "ecology of reactive elements," which makes the specific qualitative response of any element a determinate function of the constellation of physical-chemical conditions in its microenvironment at that particular locus; that is, of its coordinates within the integral field. Just what those conditions are which can evoke or suppress a particular response from among alternative responses, will vary for macromolecules, for macromolecular complexes, for cell organelles, and for cells, and within each level, will vary from type to type.

If this seems like a forbidding task for study, it becomes even more formidable when one remembers the introductory proposition about organized systems, which specified that all elementary events, however much they may fluctuate individually, must be so coordinated and controlled that their total combined effect does not impair the integrity, unity, and relative invariance of the system of which they are the constituents. Therefore, molecules can contribute to the "control of cellular activity" only insofar as "cellular control" prevails over their individual activities.

In order to illustrate concretely, once more and lastly, the fact that this "control" is not exercised by a single monopolistic master agent, but is reinsured by a multiplicity of cooperative and synergistic devices — many more than Spemann or Lehmann had envisaged when they spoke of "double insurance" or "combinative unitary performance"[32] — let me briefly refer to one means by which cells seem to exert control over one another's growth.

GROWTH CONTROL

It had become apparent that the growth of different body parts is regulated not only by the gross conditions of space, accessibility to nutrients, activity, and the like, but by much subtler and more specific means of harmonization. The hormone system constitutes one such device. But it, in itself, might be only an evolutionary specialization of a more general chemical control system inherent in the growth process. Proceeding from this general premise and a number of specific facts, including the experience that the artificial reduction of the cell population of a given organ system (e.g., liver, kidney, blood) is followed promptly by an automatic compensatory growth reaction of the residual part of the very same population, no matter how dispersed, I proposed a molecular "control" mechanism operating as follows [33] (Fig. 26):

1. Each specific cell type reproduces its protoplasm, i.e., it grows, by a mechanism in which key compounds that are characteristic of the individual cell type (symbolized by large circles and triangles in Fig. 26) act as catalysts. The postulated cell-specific diversity of compounds is the chemical correlate of the differentiation of cell strains. Growth rate is proportional to the concentration of these intracellular specific catalysts (or "templates") in the free or active state. Under normal conditions these compounds remain confined within the cell, where some become switched into nonreproductive differentiation products (stippled in Fig. 26).

2. Each cell also produces compounds ("antitemplates," small full circles and triangles in Fig. 26) which can inhibit the former

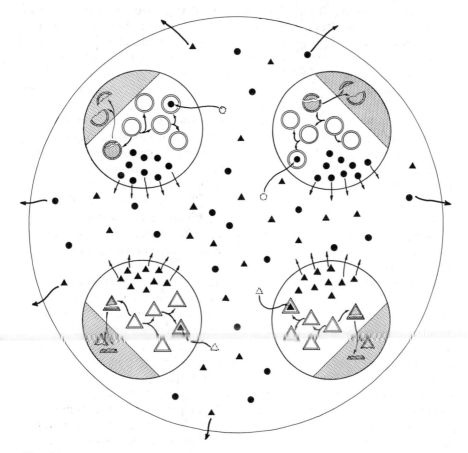

FIG. 26. Model of organ-specific molecular control of organ growth. Explanation in text. (*From Weiss and Kavanau.*)

species by combining with them into inactive complexes. These may be turned out as direct by-products in the process of protoplasmic reproduction or may be secondary differentiation products. They may be steric complements to the former or matched to them in some other fashion. The only prerequisites are that (a) contrary to the specific templates, they can leave and reenter the cell and get into the extracellular space and into circulation; (b) that they carry the specific tag of their producer-cell type, which endows them with selective affinity for any cell of the same type; and (c) that they are in constant production so as to make up for their extracellular katabolic decomposition and final excretion.

3. As the concentration of antitemplates in the extracellular medium increases, their intracellular density, hence inactivating effect on corresponding templates, will likewise increase; in short, growth rate will decline in all cells belonging to that particular strain bathed by the common humoral pool. When stationary equilibrium between intracellular and extracellular concentrations is reached, incremental growth will cease. This mechanism results in a sigmoid growth curve for the total mass of each organ system, and the familiar sigmoid curve for the whole organism is then essentially an aggregate of similar curves for the individual constituent organ systems.

This general concept of a "negative-feedback" regulation of growth offers a rational explanation both for the self-limiting character of normal growth in a confined medium (organism or culture), and for the homologous organ-specific growth reactions after experimental interference or pathological alterations. As can readily be seen, each interference or alteration will have to be examined in a dual light as to its effects on the concentration of both templates and antitemplates, since it is the ratio of both that determines growth rate. The following conclusions can immediately be deduced from this scheme:

A. Removal of part of an organ system removes part of the sources of corresponding types of templates and antitemplates. Since the former, according to our premise (1), have been in intracellular confinement, neither their former presence nor their recent loss can be noticed as such by other cells of the system. This is not so for the antitemplates, which are in circulation and a reduction of whose production source would soon register by their lowered concentration in the extracellular pool. According to points (2) and (3), this would shift the intracellular ratio of templates to antitemplates temporarily in favor of the former, causing automatic resumption of growth till a steady state is restored, resulting in a "compensatory" growth reaction.

B. Addition of a part should have opposite effects, depending on whether or not its cells survive, or rather on the ratio of surviving to disintegrating cells. If all cells survive, the net effect would be an increased concentration in the circulation of the particular anti-templates, hence a reduction in growth rate of the corresponding host system, provided it is still in a phase of growth. If all cells disintegrate, they release into the extracellular space a contingent of specific templates that would otherwise never have escaped. Assuming that these, according to point (2), combine with, or otherwise trap, homologous antitemplates, their presence in the pool will entail a temporary lowering of antitemplate concentration, hence again a spurt of growth in the homologous cell strains of the host. The simultaneous release of antitemplates from the disintegrating cells would have to be assumed to be insufficient to cancel this effect because of their faster metabolic degradation, point (2c). An alternative possibility is that the templates freed from cracked cells are directly adopted by homologous cells, where they would temporarily increase the intracellular concentration of growth catalysts, hence growth rate [34]. In either scheme, the release of cell content would accelerate homologous growth by increasing the intracellular ratio of templates to antitemplates — in the former case, by reducing the denominator, in the latter case, by increasing the numerator. It can be seen that in terms of this interpretation, partial necrosis of an organ will have the same effect as partial removal, and that implantation of a fragment, followed by some degeneration, as well as the injection of cell debris, are merely further variants of the same procedure.

When the mathematical formulation of this theory was subjected to quantitative tests, it reproduced with accuracy the observed time course of normal growth (e.g., Fig. 27); but above all, when electronic computers were programmed to derive from our equations the time course of changes to be expected in a given system after artificial reduction or augmentation of its mass, the records showed not only the automatic return to the original equilibrium mass, but its attainment by a series of damped oscillations, as is characteristic of systems with negative feedback regulation [35].

If further substantiated, this theory would lead to the conclusion that organ-specific features of molecules (e.g., organ-specific antigenicity) are not only products and indicators of differentiation, but are instrumental devices for the maintenance of intercellular balance and harmony in a multicellular system [36]. It might well be that the concept could also be scaled down to apply to intracellular regulation carried out by complementary pairs of molecules, one compound fixed to structures (analogous to the cell-bound template system), the other freely mobile in the liquid spaces (comparable to the freely

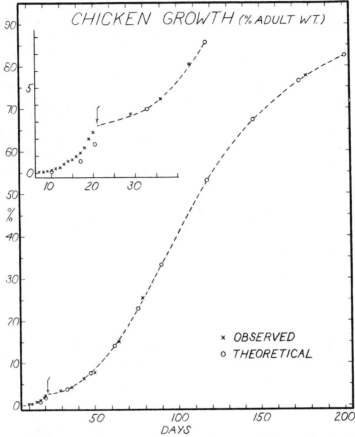

FIG. 27. Growth curve of fowl in embryonic and postembryonic phase. Crosses represent observed values according to Schmalhausen and to Landauer; circles are values calculated from mathematical growth model of Weiss and Kavanau.

diffusible inhibitors). This would bring us back to the vital interplay between the two interpenetrating systems of the cell emphasized in an earlier section — the ordered solid-state arrays and the liquid diffusion pools bathing them. But this is treading on wholly unexplored ground.

EPILOGUE

With these remarks on growth control, we have arrived at last at a point which comes rather close to what might be defined as "molecular control of cellular activity," only to discover that the "controlling" molecules have themselves acquired their specific con-

figurations, which are the key to their power of control, by virtue of
their membership in the population of an organized cell, hence under
"cellular control." And this indeed has been the whole purpose of my
long discourse; to document by practical examples that the distinction
between molecular control of cellular activity and cellular control of
molecular activity is based on the semantic ambiguity of the term
"control," hence fades in the light of true understanding of the phenomena involved. A cell is nothing but the population of component
entities that constitute it. But these entities are not just of molecular
rank, nor can their ordered behavior in the group be fully appreciated
and understood solely by studying them in isolation, out of context.
As I have tried to carry the principle of self-organization of higher
organizational units by the free interaction of elements of lower
order as far as present factual evidence — not hopes, nor beliefs —
would honestly entitle us to do, I had to add at every turn that elements endowed for such ordered group performance have always been
prefitted for it by properties previously imparted to them as members
of just such an organized group unit, whether cell parts, cell, or germ.
This circular argument contains one of the most fundamental truths
about the nature of organisms, and as one can readily understand,
does not augur well for an eventual affirmative answer to our introductory question, in its naïve form, of whether a cell will ever be
synthesized de novo without the active intervention of another cell.

On the other hand, I have also tried to document the fact that
there are now available practical and constructive approaches to the
gradual replacement of symbolic references to "organization" by
true insight into the dynamics involved. Our knowledge of the dynamics is rudimentary and spotty. But it is consistent enough for us
to realize that almost every mechanism in a living system employs
a combination of dynamic principles, rather than just a single kind.
There was a time, not long ago, when biologists would proclaim mo-
nopolies for certain forms of energy as key to life: electrical, mechanical, and chemical theories vied for primacy. The modern uni-
fied concept of energy makes this sound obsolete, and so it is. Of
itself, scalar energy cannot define, in the sense of a precise description, a single process in a living system (except perhaps its disintegration). While energy input is needed to create and maintain nonrandom diversity, the difference between just *any* nonrandom state
on the one hand, and the repetitive and conservative order of diversity
in organisms on the other, is not spelled by the scalar values of energy, but by the vectors of its channeling; just as it is the ordered
channeling that makes a given amount of energy fed into a machine
yield useful work, instead of dissipating itself in an explosion. If en-

ergy is needed for a cell to move, what makes the difference between this coordinated effect and merely a diffuse warming up? And this is where the old questions of forms of energy involved are still as fully pertinent as ever. The answers no longer select favorites, but by experience have come to admit all forms as being used in various combinations, depending on the specific mechanisms concerned. No generality can exempt us from the effort of determining the workings of each mechanism — including "control" mechanisms — separately in its own right.

How often do we hear in the discussions of biological problems pronouncements to the effect that this or that event is "biochemical." Such statements are platitudinous unless they are accompanied by indications of how the particular reaction is conditioned by the physical setting in which it occurs and how its effects, in turn, modify the physical settings for subsequent reactions. In this broader perspective, ordering process and ordered structure become a single continuum, determining and limiting each other in endless sequences of activities, so that as a given chemical event may control (that is, condition) the appearance of a particular physical array or "structure," the latter then will go on to control (condition) the next chemical transaction, which in further consequence may again alter the prior structure, and so forth almost *ad infinitum*.

Since examples of such chains are scattered throughout this text, there is no need of belaboring the point further. But one important lesson should be reemphasized. Although the word "structure" evokes primarily a picture of such gross mechanical functions as are subserved by tension cables, weight supports, confining envelopes, cross ties, etc., we must not let this limited aspect dominate our thinking. In extrapolating into the future the picture I have presented, one can foresee the ever-growing importance that structure will assume in furnishing the chemical systems of the cell with expediting channels or inhibiting barriers, creating or abolishing, respectively, opportunities for interactions.

More work along this line is badly needed. Not only more work, but also more penetrating thinking about the problems of cellular organization in unfragmented, undiluted, uncorrupted form — the real problems, not some sham versions — so that our minds may gradually acquire a mature and soundly structured concept of cellular organization, as a guide to well-directed further exploration and interpretation of the phenomena of cellular control that make the cell the integrated operating unit it is, and that at the present time are still in deep obscurity.

NOTES AND REFERENCES

1. H. S. Bennett, Membrane flow. *J. Biophys. Biochem. Cytol.*, Suppl. 2, 99-103 (1956).
2. This is, for instance, strikingly illustrated in the motion picture made by F. Frédéric and M. Chèvremont, *Arch. Biol.*, 63:109 (1952).
3. For the evidence, see P. Weiss, *Harvey Lectures, 1959-1960*, Academic Press, Inc., New York, 1961.
3a. Recently, a most stimulating discussion of structural hierarchy, extrapolated from studies of the ciliary system, has been published by C. F. Ehret, *Science*, 132:115 (July, 1960), which in many respects is closely related to the topic of this lecture and, but for lateness, would have deserved a more explicit review in this place; readers interested in our points of contact would do well to consult the original article.
4. K. R. Porter and G. F. Palade, *J. Biophys. Biochem. Cytol.*, 3:269 (1957) have proposed transverse extensions of the endoplasmic reticulum as coordinating communication system.
5. The following brief account is based for the most part on the work and interpretations of F. O. Schmitt and his group (see *Rev. Mod. Physics*, 31:349, 1959) at the Massachusetts Institute of Technology, although, of course, many workers and laboratories have had a share in this success story.
6. The following discussion rests essentially on the excellent review of the subject by Glimcher, *Rev. Mod. Physics*, 31:359 (1959), who has also made some of the most spectacular advances in knowledge of this virgin field.
7. By S. Fitton-Jackson, *Proc. Roy. Soc.* (London) B 146:270 (1957).
8. See, for instance, Fraenkel-Conrat, *The Viruses*, F. M. Burnet and W. M. Stanley, eds. Academic Press Inc., New York, 1959, p. 429.
9. Only the features most relevant in the present context are reviewed here. For details and literature, see P. Weiss and W. Ferris, *Proc. Natl. Acad. Sci. U.S.*, 40:528 (1954).
10. Some observations on primitive higher-order patterning among fibers of collagen reconstituted in vitro (J. Gross, *J. Biophys. Biochem. Cytol.*, 2: Suppl. 261, 1956) would seem to encourage such a concept.
11. H. B. Fell, *Arch. Exp. Zellforsch*, 7:390 (1928). P. Weiss and R. Amprino, *Growth*, 4:245 (1940).
12. A. and H. Moscona, *J. Anat.*, 86:287 (1952).
13. P. Weiss and A. Moscona, *J. Embryol. Exp. Morphol.*, 6:238 (1958).
14. Karl Meyer, E. Davidson, A. Linker, P. Hoffman, *Biochem. Biophys. Acta*, 21 21:506. (1956).
15. Oftentimes our impression of "action," even spontaneity, signifies merely that we have inserted ourselves as observers into the process too late to recognize its prior inception from "interaction."
16. Some of these possibilities were contemplated in an unpublished joint conference of biologists and solid-state physicists, held at the Rockefeller Institute in 1959; the growth of a systematic trend in this direction is documented by the recent conference series bearing on the subject held at the Department of Biology, Massachusetts Institute of Technology (Fast Fundamental Transfer Processes in Aqueous Biomolecular Systems, June, 1960).
17. For instance, P. Weiss, *J. Embryol. Exp. Morphol.*, 1:181 (1953).
18. P. Weiss, "Differential Growth," in: *Chemistry and Physiology of Growth*, A. K. Parpart, ed., Princeton University Press, Princeton, N.J., 1949, p. 135.
19. P. Weiss, *Proc. Natl. Acad. Sci. U.S.*, 46:993 (1960).

20. For a fuller discussion see P. Weiss, *Yale J. Biol. Med.*, 19:235 (1947); *Quart. Rev. Biol.*, 25:177 (1950); *J. Embryol. Exp. Morphol.*, 1:181 (1953).

21. I have designated as "modulations," in *Principles of Development*, Holt, Rinehart and Winston, Inc., New York, 1939, the various expressions which a cell can assume with the same basic molecular equipment by virtue of the alternative functional dominance of different portions of that equipment, in contradistinction to true differentiation, which connotes unidirectional changes—gains or losses—of equipment. Both the distinction and the term have proved useful in articulating the problem of differentiation more precisely, and consequently, have been rather widely adopted.

22. It is remarkable to note the manner in which this fundamental problem of the degree of reversibility and irreversibility of "differentiation" is often slighted in current literature. If differentiation were an objective scientific term with identical connotations to all its users, the solution of the problem would, of course, be simply a matter of finding the facts. However, since the term means different things to different authors, which they often do not bother to specify, we are treated to a display of quite discordant and contradictory professions of faith, rather than statements of fact, pertaining to a common word—"differentiation"— which, since it covers such a wide array of disparate phenomena, lends itself readily to sham arguments based on semantic confusion. For example, one common source of misunderstanding is the outdated, though not yet outmoded, habit of equating the state of differentiation with features discernible under the microscope, thereby confining the living object to the limited detecting power of a particular instrument. As a constructive step toward clarification, I have made a modest effort to identify and list the various kinds of processes and phenomena that one hears usually referred to as "differentiation" (*J. Embryol. Exp. Morphol.*, 1:181, 1953), but despite some success in engendering a more critical and realistic attitude toward the issue, the matter is still often dealt with as an article of faith rather than as a subject for sober evaluation of facts. In factual terms, the question of whether "differentiation" is or is not reversible is plainly nonsensical. All depends on what sort of "differentiation" the questioner has in mind. There is reversibility and there is irreversibility in cellular processes, and nothing short of determining just when, where, and how much of either is connected with a given transformation, will ever make scientific sense.

23. The original experiment by Fell and Mellanby (*J. Physiol.*, 119:470, 1953), in which skin fragments were cultured in a vitamin A-enriched medium, was later modified by Weiss and James (*Exp. Cell. Res.*, Suppl. 3, 381, 1955) in that a suspension of separated skin cells was merely given a brief exposure to the vitamin. But the question of whether the metaplastic effect was produced entirely during the actual exposure or as a result of residual traces of the vitamin absorbed by the cells, has not been crucially decided.

24. Other pertinent examples of recent date are the deflection of prospective muscle cells into a cartilaginous course by influences emanating from the spinal cord (C. Grobstein and G. Parker, *Proc. Soc. Exp. Biol.*, 85:477, 1954; H. Holtzer, in *Regeneration of Vertebrates*, C. S. Thornton, ed., University of Chicago Press, Chicago, 1956, p. 15), and of ectoderm cells into true pigment cells by exposure to a pigment precursor (C. E. Wilde in *Cell, Organism and Milieu*, D. Rudnick, ed., The Ronald Press Company, New York, 1958, p. 3).

25. For a basic discussion of these embryological problems see P. Weiss, *Principles of Development*, Holt, Rinehart and Winston, Inc., New York, 1939; *Analysis of Development*, B. H. Willier, Paul Weiss, and Viktor Hamburger, eds.,

W. B. Saunders Company, Philadelphia, 1955; C. H. Waddington, *Principles of Embryology*, George Allen & Unwin, Ltd., London, 1956; C. P. Raven, *An Outline of Developmental Physiology*, McGraw-Hill Book Company, Inc., New York, 1954, among others.

26. My first explicit reference to a "field" principle in development was made in regard to phenomena of regeneration (*Naturwiss, Jg.*, 11:669, 1923), but was soon extended to encompass embryology as well (*Morphodynamik. Abhandl. z. theoret. Biol. H.*, 23, 1926, *Morphodynamische Feldtheorie und Genetic. V. Intern. Gen. Congr.*, Berlin; *Z. Indukt. Abstammungsu. Vererbungslehre* II, 1567, 1928); for a summary see P. Weiss, *Principles of Development*, Holt, Rinehart, and Winston, Inc., New York, 1939.

27. First described in 1929 (P. Weiss, Roux' *Arch. Entwicklungsmech. Org.*, 116; 438, 1929), the phenomenon was further analyzed in later work (see *Chemistry and Physiology of Growth*, A. K. Parpart, ed., Princeton University Press, Princeton, N.J., 1949, p. 135), and definitely discounted as possibly due to "chemotaxis" (P. Weiss, *Science*, 115:293, 1952).

28. Such polarization effects have actually been observed. Protoplasmic protrusions oriented toward each other by cells have been reported in rootlet formation of seaweed eggs (D. M. Whitaker, *J. Gen. Physiol.*, 20:491, 1937; D. M. Whitaker and E. W. Lowrance, *J. Gen. Physiol.*, 21:57, 1937); and in the outgrowth of nerve fibers from a circle of neuroblasts (A. Stefanelli, *Acta Embr. Morph. Exp.*, 1:56, 1957). Movement of cells away from each other (giving the illusion of "repulsion") has been recorded for pigment cells in vitro (V. C. Twitty and M. C. Niu, *J. Exptl. Zool.*, 125:541, 1954). Similarly symmetrical spindle cells, when making mutual contact with their ends, blunt and immobilize each other on the near sides so that they assume turnip shapes, pointing in opposite directions, and move apart (P. Weiss, *Intern. Rev. Cytol.*, 7:391, 1958; M. Abercrombie, M. L. Johnson, and G. A. Thomas, *Proc. Roy. Soc.* (London), B136:448, 1949).

29. If it were within the scope of this article to enlarge upon supracellular organization, one of the most dramatic manifestations of the "field" principle in the "self-organization" of organs would be dealt with in this place. It concerns the ability of a scrambled suspension of single cells from a fairly advanced embryonic stage to reconstitute themselves without specific "inductive" guidance from the environment, into amazingly complete and harmoniously organized organs; e.g., liver, kidney, feathers, of the typical morphology and functional activity (P. Weiss and A. C. Taylor, *Proc. Natl. Acad. Sci. U.S.*, 46:1177, 1960) and considerably beyond the histiotypic reorganization previously reported (e.g.,A. Moscona, *Proc. Soc. Exp. Biol. Med.*, 92:410, 1956; C. Grobstein, *J. Exp. Zool.*, 124:383, 1953).

30. This model becomes even more pertinent if one takes into account the existence of activity gradients and cellular response thresholds (see Figs. 8 and 9 in P. Weiss, *J. Embryol. Exp. Morphol.*, 1:181, 1953).

31. Since every compound structure requires a certain minimum number of component units for its execution, it is obvious that a completely proportionate and harmonious organization of form can be achieved only above a critical size minimum (e.g., N. J. Berrill in *Analysis of Development*, Willier, Weiss and Hamburger, eds., W. B. Saunders Company, Philadelphia, 1955, p. 620; G. Andres, *J. Exp. Zool.*, 122:507, 1953; C. Grobstein, *J. Exp. Zool.*, 120:437, 1952).

32. See H. Spemann, *Embryonic Development and Induction*, Yale University Press, New Haven, Conn., 1939; F. E. Lehmann, *Einführung in die physiologische Embryologie*, Birkhauser Verlag, Basel, 1945.

33. The general proposition, based on experiments on the effects of antibodies (P. Weiss, *Anat. Rec.*, 75: suppl., 67, 1939) or organ transplants (P. Weiss and H. Wang, *Ant. Rec.*, 79: suppl., 52, 1941) on the growth of the corresponding embryonic organs, was first set forth in a symposium in 1946 (P. Weiss, *Yale J. Biol. Med.*, 19:235, 1947), later expanded by further experimental evidence (P. Weiss in *Biological Specificity and Growth*, E. G. Butler, ed., Princeton University Press, Princeton, N.J., 1955, p. 195), and finally formalized in a workable mathematical model (P. Weiss, and J. L. Kavanau, *J. Gen. Physiol.*, 41:1, 1957; J. L. Kavanau, *Proc. Natl. Acad. Sci. U.S.*, 46, 1960).

34. Intriguing evidence for this view has been brought forward by Ebert in *Aspects of Synthesis and Order in Growth*, D. Rudnick, ed., Princeton University Press, Princeton, N.J., 1954, p. 69.

35. See P. Weiss and J. L. Kavanau, *J. Gen. Physiol.*, 41:1 (1957); J. L. Kavanau, *Proc. Natl. Acad. Sci. U.S.*, 46:1658 (1960). Experimental support for the theory is accumulating (see A. D. Glinos in *A Symposium on the Chemical Basis of Development*, W. D. McElroy and B. Glass, eds., Johns Hopkins Press, Baltimore, 1958, p. 813).

Chapter Two

Nucleic Acids and Cell Morphology in Dipteran Salivary Glands

HEWSON SWIFT
Whitman Laboratory, University of Chicago

INTRODUCTION

Nucleic acids form integral parts of complex cellular structures —
the chromosomes, nucleoli, and the diverse aggregates of ribosomes
and lipoprotein membranes of the cytoplasm. One of the most difficult aspects of nucleic acid biology concerns the position of these
macromolecules in the intricate morphological framework of the
cell. Yet until this is successfully determined our knowledge of the
processes of gene action and protein synthesis will be inadequate
and incomplete.

A number of generalizations concerning nucleic acids are now
widely accepted. It is usually agreed that DNA is an essential component of the gene, and that RNA is required for the manufacture of
proteins. Often repeated, but based on less clear evidence, is the
concept that RNA is also a "transfer" material, carrying information stored in the chromosomes out to regions of protein synthesis
in the cytoplasm. In our attempts to define general principles such
as these it is easy to ignore the complexities of cell structure to the
point where we confuse basic concepts with oversimplification. It is
equally possible, however, to become so involved with the morphological intricacies of the cell, particularly as revealed to us by the
electron microscope, that we lose sight of fundamental facts in a
mass of comparatively trivial detail.

THE DNA CONTENT OF THE CHROMOSOME

The giant salivary gland chromosomes of *Drosophila* and other
flies afford an excellent opportunity to study the chemical components of the nucleus in relation to chromosome structure. It is true
that these cells are highly specialized, and certain aspects may not
readily apply to other tissues. They are like other cells in terms of

73

their major nucleoprotein components. They are unlike them in that, from the time the first gland primordium is formed in the embryo, they do not divide. Thus the larval salivary gland contains a constant cell number from before the time of hatching until its degeneration in the early pupa. The growth of the gland is then entirely through cell enlargement, and as the cell enlarges, the chromosomes enlarge also (Sonnenblick, 1950).

In forming giant cells of most insects the chromosomes do not increase in size with cell growth but instead increase in number. In the salivary glands of the water strider, Geitler (1937) was able to show, by counting the condensed chromosomes, that chromosome number increased with cell growth in a 2N:4N:8N:16N...progression (polyploidy), with successive steps of chromosomal synthesis. The salivary gland of the land snail *Helix* apparently also undergoes a similar process of successive chromosomal doubling. This is supported by measurements made on the amounts of DNA in individual nuclei of this tissue, using the Feulgen reaction and microphotometry. In our measurements (Swift, 1953), all DNA values fell in sharply defined classes in a 2:4:8:16... series, probably representing nuclei with 2N:4N:8N:16N... chromosomes (Fig. 1) (but also see Leuchtenberger and Schrader [1952] where such clear-cut classes were not obtained).

In the salivary glands of *Drosophila*, and apparently of flies in general, chromosome number does not increase as the cell grows. This is apparently associated with the unexplained property of fly chromosomes to undergo "somatic pairing," that is, for homologous chromosomes to remain closely associated through interphase. Nevertheless the DNA amounts per nucleus are much as in *Helix*, indicating that the DNA undergoes a progressive doubling to produce nuclei with 2:4:8:16... 1,024 times the haploid DNA value (Fig. 1). Thus the giant or "polytene" chromosomes of *Drosophila* are probably bundles of up to 1,024 strands, each of which may resemble the tiny chromosomal strand found in a normal diploid cell. The polytene chromosome also grows in length as well as width (Beermann, 1959). This may be because the individual strands "unravel" or stretch with the increasing thickness or synthetic activity of the chromosome bundle.

These studies, and others like them on a variety of plant and animal nuclei, have led us to the hypothesis that in most cells there is a constant relation between the DNA content and the number of chromosome "sets" it contains (Ris and Mirsky, 1949; Swift, 1950a, 1950b, 1953). Also, when new DNA is synthesized, it results in a doubling of the preexisting amount, otherwise the definite classes shown in Fig. 1 would not be obtained. Since such measurements are

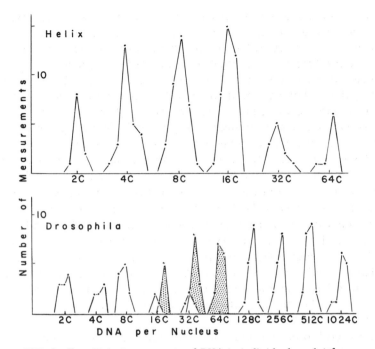

FIG. 1. *Top:* Relative amounts of DNA in individual nuclei from the salivary gland of the land snail *Helix pomatia.* Six DNA classes are shown, with means in a 2:4:8:16:32:64 series. Measurements were made on Feulgen-stained tissue sections with a microphotometer (*Swift,* 1953). *Bottom:* Relative amounts of DNA in individual nuclei of *Drosophila melanogaster.* Values at left (2C to 32C) from anlage and duct tissues, shaded portion from fat body, and values at right (128C to 1024C) from salivary gland. Note that the abscissa is logarithmic, so that each DNA class averages approximately twice the preceding class. (*Redrawn from Rasch and Swift, in Alfert,* 1954.)

only accurate to plus or minus 5 per cent, however, small DNA fluctuation about the mean value could occur unrecognized. The DNA "constancy hypothesis" obviously fits our concept of a DNA template gene, capable of acting, without itself undergoing chemical change; undergoing periodic replication, rather than irregular fluctuations in amount.

An obvious exception to DNA constancy has been found in the flies *Rhynchosciara* (Breuer and Pavan, 1955; Rudkin and Corlette, 1957) and *Glyptotendipes* (Stich and Naylor, 1958), where an abrupt increase in the DNA of certain special chromosome regions ("puffs") has been described, not involving the chromosome as a whole. We were anxious to study this phenomenon by microphotometry, since it seemed to

us that if such a process occured in *Drosophila* we would have found
it in our measurements. *Rhynchosciara* is not readily reared in the
laboratory, but flies of the related genus *Sciara* have been grown for
many years (Metz el al., 1926; Crouse, 1943). The *Sciara coprophila*
also shows these localized increases in DNA (Figs. 6 and 7 part 1,
pp. 91, 95). These occur in at least four specific regions of the
chromosomal set, beginning just before pupation, when the larva becomes quiescent, and the digestive glands fill with a greenish secretion. The salivary glands become bloated at this time, with the lumen
filled with secretion; apparently this is mucoprotein cement substance for the adherence of the forming pupa case to the substrate.

Up to this time the DNA behavior of the *Sciara* salivary gland parallels that in *Drosophila*. The DNA classes of the late fourth instar
larva, found by microphotometry, again fall into a geometric series
of classes, indicating that DNA has probably been synthesized in a
2:4:8:16 . . . progression, in this case apparently up to 4,096 times
the haploid value in a few of the largest nuclei (Fig. 2). After the
DNA puffs have arisen in the prepupal stage, the DNA classes are
still evident, but the distribution of values is skewed to the right by
the "extra" DNA.

It seemed to us that chromosome-puff formation might involve
continued DNA replication, but only of certain bands, while the rest
of the chromosome remained unchanged. If this were so we might
expect that measurements on the puff areas alone, excluding the rest
of the chromosome, would show a stepwise pattern of DNA values.
In Fig. 3 photometric measurements are graphed for two puffs in
chromosome 2, each compared with an adjacent nonpuffed region,
during three stages of the pupation process. The DNA increase of
these two puffs showed no evidence for any stepwise pattern, although
it is possible that such steps may occur, but in an unsynchronized
manner.

Patterns of DNA synthesis may also be followed by radioautography. DNA-puff formation in *Rhynchosciara* has been followed by incorporation of tritiated thymidine into puff DNA (Ficq and Pavan,
1957; Pavan, 1959). In our studies excised *Sciara* salivary glands
were placed for one hour in *Drosophila* Ringer's (Ephrussi and
Beadle, 1936) containing 25 μc/ml tritiated thymidine. Glands from
active fourth instar larvae contained either unlabeled nuclei or nuclei in which all chromosomes were labeled (Fig. 7 part 2, p. 95).
This was expected from definite classes of amounts of DNA per nucleus found in the photometry of similar glands. In salivaries from
prepupae some cells showed a similar total labeling of all the chromosomes, indicating that the replication was continuing in these later
stages, as also shown by photometry. In other cells only the puffs

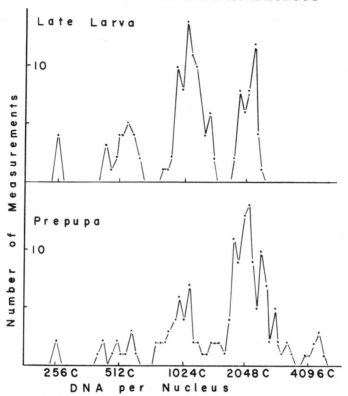

FIG. 2. Relative amounts of DNA in individual nuclei of *Sciara coprophila* salivary glands. Values for late fourth instar larvae above (before the formation of DNA puffs), and for prepupae below (after puffs have appeared). In addition to synthesis of puff DNA, which increases the spread of the higher values to the right of the mean, a new polytene class (4096C) appeared in prepupal salivary glands. (*Measurements by E. Rasch.*)

were labeled (Fig. 7, part 3, p. 95), again indicating that synthesis can take place in these areas alone without involvement of the rest of the chromosome.

Since these DNA puffs showed what we may call an "anomalous" pattern of DNA synthesis, in relation to the rest of the chromosome, it is naturally of interest to know whether they possess any other recognizable differences. In most cases, when they are fully formed, their appearance in the microscope is of an irregularly granular mass rather than the compact bands of other regions (Figs. 6, parts 1 and 3, p. 91). Also, the chromosome stretches more readily at sites of DNA puffs when chromosome smears are made, the stretched regions showing both filamentous and granular components (Fig. 6, part 4). These are rough indications of some difference in consistency of these areas.

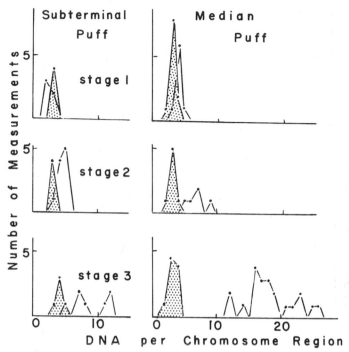

FIG. 3. Amounts of DNA in individual DNA puffs and adjacent regions in *Sciara coprophila*. Subterminal puff (near centromere end
of chromosome 2) at left, median puff (in chromosome 2) at right.
DNA values for three stages in the puffing process are shown (from
late fourth instar larva, early prepupa, and late prepupa). Measurements on puff regions are unshaded; shaded portions indicate
values for adjacent unpuffed regions. All measurements were made
on chromosomes in class 2048C. (*Measurements by E. Rasch.*)

These differences are at least superficially similar to those of the
heterochromatic areas of *Drosophila* chromosomes, areas that coalesce to form the chromocenter in the salivary glands (Fig. 8, part 2
p. 99). It is interesting to note that there is at least a suggestion of
anomalous DNA behavior in these areas in *Drosophila* also, although
quantitatively of a different type than in *Sciara*. In the dorsal ganglion
of *Drosophila* larvae, most diploid interphase nuclei contain one large
chromocenter that comprises much of the volume of the nucleus (Fig.
8, part 1, p. 99). As these cells enter mitosis, this area can be seen to
contain the heterochromatic regions of chromosomes associated with
the nucleolus (Kaufmann, 1934). Certain portions of the ganglion contain larger cells with polytene chromosomes. In many of these cells
the chromocenter is only slightly larger than in the smallest cells.
If we assume that these chromocenters accurately reflect the amount

of heterochromatic material in these nuclei, then it might be concluded that the heterochromatin fails to keep pace with the periodic
replication of the nonheterochromatic, or euchromatic, chromosome
areas. This would be supported by the finding of Heitz (1931) and
Dobzhansky (1944) that the relative lengths of the heterochromatic
regions, as compared with the euchromatic regions, was much
greater in the mitotic figures of the neuroblasts than in the salivary
glands. Also, as frequently emphasized, the genetic-crossover map,
which probably roughly follows the chromosome-length ratio possessed by the oocytes, showed the heterochromatic regions to be
much longer than they appear visibly in the salivary nuclei. Photometric data, however, do not support the conclusion that replication
of euchromatin and heterochromatin are out of step (Table 1). Measurements on *Drosophila* ganglion nuclei show the same stepwise
pattern of DNA values found in the salivary glands. We must conclude either that these visible variations in chromocenter size merely
involve states of aggregation of a fixed amount of DNA, or that they
are associated with DNA changes below the limits of detection of the
techniques used. A possibly similar phenomenon was described by
Schultz (1957) in the nurse cells of the *Drosophila* ovary. The presence of an extra Y chromosome (in XXY females) was found to
produce a discrete heterochromatic body in the nurse-cell nuclei of
the ovary. This inclusion, as in the case of the neuroblast chromocenter, appeared visually to comprise a proportionally smaller

TABLE 1

Amounts of DNA in Individual Nuclei of *Drosophila virilis*
Cerebral Ganglion

DNA class	Number measured	Amount of DNA* per nucleus
2C	12	104 ± 3
4C	8	208 ± 7
4C 8C	2	270
		290
8C	3	404
		429
		432
16C	2	786
		820

*Measured on a Feulgen-stained smear of cerebral ganglion from
late third instar *Drosophila virilis* larva. Means and standard errors
are given for 2C and 4C nuclei, individual values for other nuclei.
The two-wavelength method was used, at wavelengths of 500 and
531 mμ.

amount of the total chromatin as the nuclei increased in size. This hypothesis, however, was also not supported by Feulgen measurements, which demonstrated an approximately even stepwise progression of the type shown in the salivary glands and cerebral ganglia, although, as expected, nuclei with an extra Y chromosome contained slightly more DNA (Freed and Schultz, in Schultz, 1957). Thus in this tissue also, in spite of visible differences in chromocenter size, both euchromatin and heterochromatin apparently followed a regular pattern of DNA doubling.

More work with photometry and radioautography is needed on *Drosophila* before any definite conclusions can be drawn. At present, however, unlike *Sciara*, there is no indication that any changes take place in DNA amounts at localized chromosome regions. All measurements on salivary glands, cerebral ganglia, and nurse cells, indicate a regular replication of DNA involving the entire chromosome set. It seems likely that visible changes in relative size of heterochromatic regions are thus due to factors affecting chromosome "condensation" rather than DNA variation, although the possible occurrence of unmeasurably small localized changes in DNA cannot yet be eliminated.

The regular behavior of DNA synthesis in *Drosophila* can further serve to emphasize the unusual nature of the DNA changes in *Sciara*. In this connection we are faced with an important problem. Do the variations in DNA puffs, now found in the larvae of three species of flies, reflect a basic and widespread property of chromosomes, or is this a rare anomaly of little general significance? Certainly the giant size of *Sciara* chromosomes greatly facilitates the observation of such changes. Comparable events in diploid nuclei might easily go unnoticed. Do they occur in other more familiar tissues?

There is a growing list of tissues where DNA synthesis patterns do not conform to the often accepted scheme of exact interphase replication and equal partitioning between daughter nuclei at mitosis. Descriptions of the loss of "extra" chromosomal material during gamete formation have been published by Giardina (1901) for the water beetle *Dytiscus*, by Bayreuther (1952, 1956) in tipulid flies, and by Tobias (1956) for an African rat-like rodent. Several workers have found that the stainability and DNA content of root-tip chromosomes in a few species of plants is decreased by cold treatment (LaCour et al., 1956; Evans, 1956). However, reports of "metabolic" DNA by Pelc (1958) and Pelc and LaCour (1959) in mouse seminal vesicle and bean roots, appear to have been based on misinterpretation of mitotic index, photometric and radioautographic data (Gall and Johnson 1960; Tschermak-Woess, 1960; Woodard et al., 1961). In spite of disagreements in the literature, enough evidence exists to demonstrate that "anomalous" DNA behavior is not limited to larvae of a few flies.

In addition to these findings involving unusual fluctuation in DNA amounts, there are a few reports that heterochromatic chromosomes or segments possess a different synthesis pattern from the rest of the chromosome. This has been found in grasshopper meiosis (Lima de Faria, 1959), hamster cells in culture (Taylor, 1960), and in bean roots (Woodard et al., 1961). In grasshopper and bean nuclei heterochromatic material was found to be synthesized *later* than the rest of the chromosomes. It was suggested by Taylor (1960) that the formation of DNA puffs in sciarid chromosomes might merely be an example of the late synthesis of heterochromatin. Since the *Sciara* DNA puffs involve far more than a doubling, we would have to imagine that the puff loci undergo little or no synthesis during most of chromosome growth, and then suddenly catch up to the rest of the chromosome in the prepupal stage. This theory has no visible basis in chromosome morphology, since puffs arise from normal-appearing bands, and involve a marked enlargement in chromosome diameter, rather than merely appearing as narrow portions increasing to normal size. (Incidentally the *lowering* of DNA amounts in root tips by cold shock does produce narrow portions of the chromosome, and may well involve the supression of DNA synthesis by the treatment.)

The obvious conclusion to these remarks is, that while the greater part of the DNA in most nuclei shows the constancy and replication process expected of a template, some DNA in some nuclei does not. Many, if not all, of these variable DNA fractions are associated with chromosome regions of atypical consistency and staining properties, i.e., heterochromatin. The functional significance of these regions, although the subject of numerous hypotheses, is still unknown. The genetic properties of heterochromatin, for example, its role in position effects, may well be related to these anomalous patterns of synthesis (see Hannah, 1951 for review). There is as yet a great deal we do not know about the biological significance of DNA.

To summarize the above data on DNA in polytene chromosomes: (1) In *Drosophila* salivary glands DNA is synthesized in a stepwise fashion up to 1,024 times the haploid value. (2) In *Sciara* exactly the same pattern of synthesis was found, up to 4,096 times the haploid value. (3) Just before pupation, however, *Sciara* shows several DNA-puff loci, where "extra" DNA is synthesized; this skews the DNA-class distribution upwards. These DNA-puff loci do not show a stepwise pattern of synthesis. (4) In *Drosophila* cerebral ganglia, regions of high DNA concentration (chromocenters) appear proportionally larger in the smaller nuclei. This was investigated as possibly another case of anomalous DNA synthesis. DNA values fitted into a stepwise pattern as in the *Drosophila* salivary gland, and no evidence for anomalous DNA behavior was found.

DNA AND CHROMOSOME STRUCTURE

We know a considerable amount about the structure of the DNA molecule, but it is surprising how little we know of the way it fits into the chromosome. There have been many theories as to chromosome structure (see Kaufmann, 1948; Alfert, 1954; Ris, 1957; Gall, 1958; Beermann, 1957, 1959; Kaufmann et al., 1960, for reviews), but the gap between the molecular dimensions of the Watson-Crick model and the very much larger chromosome, remains a matter of disagreement and uncertainty. Most theories concerning the relation between nucleoproteins and chromosome structure can be considered in three categories. (1) The "protein-backbone" theories where DNA is thought to be attached to a structural protein. Several types of attachment have been suggested; for example, the alternating of DNA and protein segments arranged end to end (Fig. 4C), or with the DNA molecule attached only at one end to a central protein filament (Fig. 4B) (Mirsky and Ris 1947; Taylor, 1957) or attached at both ends to form a loop (Schwartz, 1958). (2) The multistranded or "rope" theories, in which each chromosome is considered to be a bundle of coiled DNA-protein filaments running the length of the chromosome (Fig. 4A) (Ris, 1957; Steffensen, 1959; Kaufmann et al., 1960). (3) "Differential-coiling" theories, where the chromosome is thought to consist of only one or two strands running the length of the chromosome, but where certain regions are tightly coiled and others not, to produce the beads or "chromomeres" visible in many chromosomes, particularly during the meiotic prophase (Fig. 4D) (Ris and Crouse, 1945; Callan, 1955; Gall, 1958).

Polytene chromosomes. The theories listed above all apply to single chromosomes, as they occur in diploid (2C) cells. In considering polytene chromosomes it is important to remember that their size and DNA content indicate they probably consist of bundles of many individual chromosome units, held together in a giant cable. Each unit may be considered comparable with a single chromosome of a normal diploid cell.

It is often stated (for example, see De Robertis et al., 1960) that the bands of salivary chromosomes are Feulgen-positive, and thus contain DNA, while the interbands are Feulgen-negative and thus do not. A careful look at any well-made preparation will show that this is not true. Interband regions, while certainly much more palely staining, nevertheless contain visible Feulgen-positive material, as mentioned by Heitz and Bauer (1933) in the first published descrip-

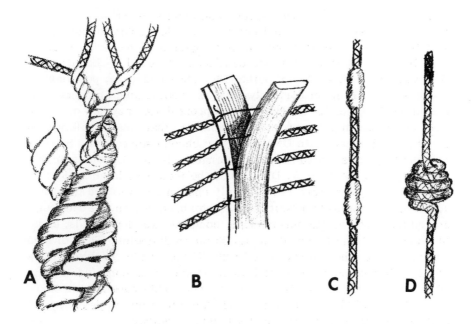

FIG. 4. Hypothetical models of chromosome structure. (*A*) Multistranded or "rope" hypothesis, showing a portion of the chromosome made up of 8 double helices of DNA histone. (*After Steffensen*, 1959.) (*B*) "Protein-backbone" hypothesis, showing a central ribbon of protein, to which DNA-histone fibers are attached laterally. An early stage is shown in the postulated separation of strands prior to chromosome replication. (*After Taylor*, 1957.) (*C*) Model showing alternation of DNA-histone fibers (here greatly abbreviated) and small protein molecules. (*D*) "Differential-coiling" hypothesis showing a single fiber of DNA histone coiled to form a chromomere.

tion of Feulgen-stained polytene chromosomes. The stain in inter-band regions is particularly apparent if the dye azure A replaces basic fuchsin in the Feulgen reagent. This produces an intense blue dye about 3.5 to 4.0 times as sensitive in terms of maximum extinction values than the usual method.

The amount of DNA in interband regions is very small, close to the limits of detection by the azure A Feulgen method. Some faint Feulgen-positive material is detectable, however, in practically all interband regions of both *Sciara* and *Drosophila*. Areas occasionally appear Feulgen-negative on either side of major bands or puffs where the chromosome is widened. In these cases it seems likely that interband strands are held apart, and thus the DNA concentration is reduced below detectable levels. These same regions often appear Feulgen-positive in stretched chromosomes.

From the fact that interbands are Feulgen-positive, but weakly so, we can come to certain important conclusions concerning chromosome structure. First, DNA occurs continually throughout the length of the chromosome. DNA continuity is not interrupted for any detectable length by backbone proteins, as suggested in the model shown in Fig. 4C. This is contrary to the conclusion reached by Schultz (1941). However, the protein "pivot points" for DNA uncoiling, postulated by Frese (1957), might certainly exist in undetectable amounts. The finding by Cavalieri et al. (1959), that proteolytic enzymes decrease DNA viscosity, might support the hypothesis that small protein molecules may alternate with DNA along the chromosome fiber. Second, the rope hypothesis also appears untenable. If each chromosomal unit contained the 32 or 64 DNA double helices postulated by Steffensen (1959), then there is not nearly enough room to put 1,024 to 4,096 such chromosomal units in the interband region. He has suggested that *each* single chromosome contains two chromatids, each of which consists of four filaments 20 mμ in diameter. Each of these filaments is further composed of eight Watson-Crick double helices of DNA. If chromosomes have this structure, each contains eight 20 mμ filaments, or 64 DNA double helices. This ropelike chromosome thus would have a minimum width of about 60 mμ provided the eight 20 mμ filaments were tightly twisted together.

Since *Sciara* salivary gland and surrounding tissues contain 12 DNA classes in a 2:4:8:16:32 ... 4,096 series, the largest chromosomes apparently contain 4,096 chromosomal units. If each unit were 60 mμ in diameter, these would form a dense rod-like structure approximately 4 microns across, assuming the strands were closely packed. One micron of such a chromosomal bundle would contain 8×10^{-10} mg of DNA, assuming $64 \times 4,096$ double helices, each containing a molecular weight of 1.8 million per micron filament.* Such a bundle would be intensely Feulgen-positive (azure A-Feulgen extinction about 0.57), instead of the barely detectable interband staining actually observed.

If we assume that both bands and interbands contain the same degree of strandedness (which seems justified from the DNA values given above) then measurements on the actual amounts of DNA in interband regions are of interest, since they provide an estimate of the actual degree of strandedness of the individual chromosome unit. The amount of DNA per micron for 19 interband areas of the largest *Sciara* polytene chromosomes (2048C and 4096C) are listed in Table 2. The measurements are close to the limit of resolution of microphotometry. They provide only a rough estimate, accurate to about ± 25 per cent. There is considerable variation between values from different chromosomes, particularly influenced by the degree of stretch-

---

*Assuming one turn of the Watson-Crick double helix contains 20 nucleotides with a total molecular weight of 6,000, and that there are 3,000 turns per micron.

ing. It is evident, however, that values fall between one-tenth to one-hundredth of the figure calculated from the 64-strand-rope hypothesis. The lowest figures agree fairly closely with the 1.2×10^{-11} mg of DNA per micron calculated on the assumption that each chromosomal unit is formed from one DNA double helix. Higher values could be considered as due to varying degrees of chromosome contraction, rather than multiple-strandedness.

On the basis of these measurements we have concluded that each individual unit of the polytene chromosome contains only one or two parallel double helices of DNA. Each unit could not possibly contain 64 double helices. It might be argued that the faint interband staining could be due to the smearing of band areas along regions that normal-

TABLE 2

DNA Content of Interband Regions in *Sciara* Polytene Chromosomes*

Polytene class	Chromosome width in μ at region measured	Extinction	DNA content ($\times 10^{-11}$ mg) per μ interband length†
2048C	1.4	0.025	1.2
	2.0	0.026	1.8
	2.2	0.024	1.8
	1.9	0.028	1.9
	2.7	0.021	2.0
	2.2	0.035	2.7
	3.6	0.057	7.2
4096C	2.2	0.028	2.2
	2.9	0.024	2.4
	3.0	0.030	3.1
	3.2	0.028	3.1
	3.8	0.026	3.5
	5.2	0.020	3.6
	4.9	0.022	3.8
	4.2	0.029	4.3
	4.1	0.041	5.9
	4.1	0.053	7.6
Hypothetical 4096C			
Based on 1 double helix 2.0		0.017	1.2
Based on 64 double helices 4.0		0.57	80

*Measured on smear of salivary gland from prepupa, stained with azure A-Feulgen. Measured area 1 μ in diameter, at $\lambda = 590$ mμ.

†Calculated from measurements on 15 diploid rat-liver nuclei stained with azure A-Feulgen, measured at $\lambda = 590$ mμ. These had a mean diameter of 7.1 μ, and a mean E of 0.584, with measured area 4 μ in diameter. Assuming these nuclei contained 6×10^{-9} mg of DNA, then DNA of concentration 3.2×10^{-11} mg would have an E per μ optical path of 0.090. A uniform area containing 3.5×10^{-11} mg DNA per μ^2 thus would have $E = 0.100$. Interband extinctions given here are close to the measurable limits of the instrument, and are accurate only to about $\pm 25\%$.

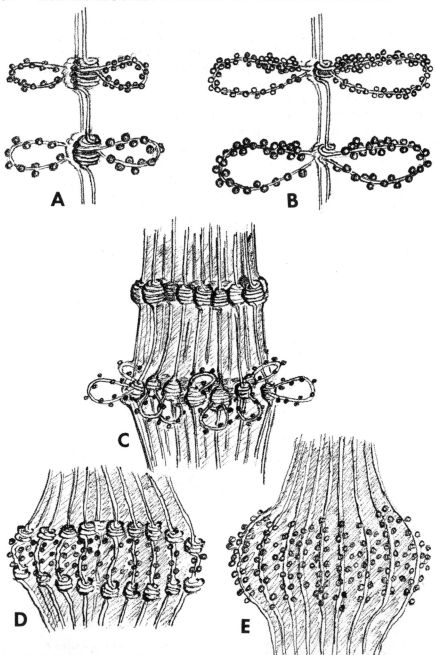

FIG. 5. Suggested structure for "lampbrush" and polytene chromosomes. (*A*) Diagram of lampbrush chromosome structure from amphibian oocytes. A small portion of one of the two bivalent strands is shown, including two chromomeres with loops, connected by interchromomeric strands. Chromomeres are represented according to the hypoth-

ly contain only protein. Thus the low DNA concentrations might result from the irregular distribution of band material among protein interbands. In answer to this it can be said that (1) low but significant concentrations of DNA are characteristic of almost all interband regions; (2) the bands on either side of the interband regions measured were clear and showed no evidence of displacement; (3) as discussed below, interband regions have an equally low quantity of protein, thus bands cannot be "diluted" by interband material. It may also be argued that our estimate of 4,096 strands is inaccurate, and that the degree of polyteny is actually much less. This estimate is based on measurements on a variety of *Sciara* tissues (Rasch and Swift, unpublished) in which twelve clearly defined DNA classes were obtained, each approximately twice the next lowest value. The 4,096 strands assumed for *Sciara* from these measurements falls between the 1024C class shown for *Drosophila* (Fig. 1) and the "approximately 10,000" strands estimated for *Chironomus* polytene chromosomes by Beermann and Bahr (1954).

In the interband regions it seems likely that the DNA fibrils run more or less straight and parallel, although the fact that they withstand considerable stretching may mean the strands are finely coiled and contracted to some extent. The disposition of DNA in the bands is less clear. The increased DNA in the band regions could be due either to side branches as postulated in the Taylor (1957) model (Fig. 4B) or to differential coiling, as suggested for oocyte chromosomes by Callan (1955) and Gall (1958) (Fig. 4D). The behavior of polytene chromosomes during the "puffing" process suggests that the differential-coiling hypothesis is most probable. RNA puffs are formed in both *Sciara* and *Drosophila* by the accumulation of ribonucleoproteins at specific loci, as discussed below.

Bands are capable of *increasing in length* (as measured along the chromosome) during RNA-puff formation, and even disappearing entirely into a faint, uniformly Feulgen-positive area indistinguishable from the interbands (Fig. 9, part 1, p. 101). In Feulgen-stained slides

---

sis of "differential coiling" (cf. Fig. 4D). Ribonucleoprotein particles are shown attached to the lateral loops of the axis DNA-histone fiber. Particles of different sizes occur at different loci. (B) Loops are shown increased in size (with increased rates of oocyte growth) and chromomeres are smaller. (After Gall, 1956b.) (C),(D),(E) Diagrams of the possible changes in a polytene chromosome band during puff formation, based on concepts of lampbrush chromosome structure. (C, above) Inactive band formed from superimposed chromomeres. (C, below) Early stage of puff formation, with presence of small loops on each chromomere, each bearing a few ribonucleoprotein granules. (D) "Doublet" stage of puff formation encountered in some bands, where band splits into two components, bordering an area of ribonucleoprotein particles. (E) Complete uncoiling of chromomere, involving the complete disappearance of discrete DNA-histone band, and the accumulation of numerous ribonucleoprotein particles in the puff region (cf. photomicrographs in Fig. 9 part 1).

chromosomal strands can be traced through such puff areas, as pointed out by Beermann (1952) for *Chironomus*. This "spreading" process of bands during the formation of puffs seems best explained by assuming the DNA fiber has continuity through a band region, but is extensively coiled or folded within it. With puff formation, the folded thread may be partially unfolded, with subsequent increase in the length of the band. This does not completely rule out the possibility that some DNA may exist in the form of side branches, but it does strongly indicate that at least some of the mass of a polytene chromosome band is due to superimposed coiled regions of the chromosomal fibers. This is illustrated in the diagram in Fig. 5C-E.

The DNA banding patterns in polytene chromosomes are, of course, beautifully exact. If bands have their basis in regions of coiling, the coiling process must be equally precise. The factors associated with such coiling of specific regions in the polytene strand are at present completely unknown. They could be sought either in the specificities of DNA structure, or in the variations in the associated proteins.

The electron microscope is also capable of providing information on chromosome structure. The many disagreements in the literature, however, attest to the problems of artifact and micrograph interpretation. The interband regions clearly contain numerous parallel strands, as shown by early studies on smeared whole chromosomes (Palay and Claude, 1949; Yasuzumi et al., 1951), and somewhat less clearly on thin sections (Beermann and Bahr, 1954; Gay, 1956; Kaufmann and McDonald, 1956; Lowman, 1956; Schurin, 1957). Strand number has been computed as between 1,000 to 2,000 for *Drosophila*, and more than 10,000 for *Chironomus*. Strand diameter has been given from about 10 to 50 mμ, the variation probably being in part a function of fixation. As any electron microscopist knows, protein-containing structures may be coarsely or finely precipitated during the fixing process. Also, contaminating nonchromosomal proteins from the nuclear sap, and variable degrees of stretching may further account for the variety of results obtained.

Electron micrographs of *Drosophila* chromosomes first fixed and then smeared are shown in Fig. 12 (p. 107). The chromosomes were then sectioned parallel to the plane of the smear (Gay, 1955). This technique provides the fine fixation of osmium tetroxide, but also allows the chromosomes to be stretched and oriented along the plane of section. We have estimated the number of interband strands to be about 1,000, although not all strands ever appear in one section. Strand diameter appears somewhat variable, since there is some clumping, probably due to fixation. The smallest strands, however, are quite fine, having a diameter of roughly 5mμ. This is another indication that individual units of the polytene chromosome contain only one or at most two double helices of DNA, although the possibility that component strands of individual units fall apart on fixation cannot be eliminated. In pure DNA preparations each DNA double helix has a diameter of about 2 mμ, according to electron micrographs of Hall and Litt (1959). In chromosome-band regions the structure of the fibers is not at all clear. They appear somewhat more electron-dense, and lack the longitudinal orientation. Other and better methods of preparation are required.

Lampbrush chromosomes. All of the major points of chromosome structure discussed above have also been made by Callan (1955) and Gall (1958) for the giant "lampbrush" chromosomes of the amphibian oocyte, which may be up to a millimeter in length. These chromosomes are in late meiotic prophase, and thus they have undergone the chromosomal replication and pairing of homologues characteristic of meiosis. Each chromosomal group, or bivalent, appears to contain two strands, held together only at the centromeres and chiasmata. Each of these strands consists of a string of beadlike chromomeres connected by an extremely fine interchromomeric fiber. Each chromomere contains a pair of lateral loops usually 10 to 50 μ long, along which particles or droplets of ribonucleoprotein are attached (Gall, 1956b). A single chromomere, its lateral loops bearing the particulate material, with its connecting fibers, is diagrammed in Fig. 5*A*. The interchromomeric fibers occasionally appear double in the electron microscope (Guyénot and Danon, 1953). Also in some cases the strand is branched into two substrands, in which case each substrand contains half-sized chromomeres, each bearing a single loop. For this reason it is known that the chromosomal strand, including its component fibers and chromomeres, must be a double structure as drawn here. Thus the total bivalent apparently contains four chromosomal units. This agrees with data of Alfert (1950) on the mouse and Swift and Kleinfeld (1953) on the grasshopper, indicating primary oocytes contain four times the haploid amount of DNA.

Although much too tenuous to give a visibly positive Feulgen reaction, both the interchromomeric strand and the lateral loops contain DNA, since they are readily disrupted by the specific enzyme deoxyribonuclease (Callan and Macgregor, 1958). This is in agreement with the Feulgen-positive nature of the interbands of polytene chromosomes. Also, chromomeres apparently consist of coiled strands of DNA fibers, since as the amphibian oocyte enters its period of maximum growth, the chromosome strands increase in length, the lateral loops increase in size, and the chromomeres become smaller (as indicated diagrammatically in Fig. 5*B*). At the conclusion of synthetic activity the strands shorten and the loops are drawn back. These changes possess obvious similarities with the events occurring at an RNA-puff locus in *Drosophila*. Also, the extreme fineness of the interchromomeric fibril, and of the loop axis as well, again support the concept that the chromosomal unit contains only one or at most very few double helices of DNA. Reports for the diameter of the interchromomeric fibrils vary from about 20 to 40 mμ (Tomlin and Callan, 1951; Gall, 1958). Guyénot and Danon (1953) reported two strands, each 10 to 15 mμ in diameter, although La Fontaine and Ris (1958) feel the connections are many-stranded. Most authors have pointed out the variability produced by different degrees of stretching, and by contaminating materials.

Chromosome strandedness. From the data discussed above, both on polytene and lampbrush chromosomes, we strongly favor the "differential-coiling" model diagrammed in Fig. 4D. Although the data presented indicate the chromosomal unit contains a comparatively small number of component strands, we have been unable to decide whether it contains (1) a single DNA double helix, (2) two helices, or (3) some higher multiple. In the paragraphs below we have reviewed briefly some of the pertinent literature.

In the labeling experiments of Taylor et al. (1957), nuclei that underwent DNA synthesis in the presence of tritiated thymidine had one-half of their DNA content labeled (the newly synthesized DNA) and the old half unlabeled. At the next mitosis the labeled DNA was segregated equally to daughter chromosomes, but at the subsequent division, all the labeled DNA (exclusive of translocation phenomena) was contained in one daughter chromosome, with none in the other. This result could only be obtained were the chromosome *functionally* two-stranded before DNA synthesis, four-stranded after synthesis. It is tempting to equate this functional two-strandedness with the two-stranded double helix. Steffensen (1959) has pointed out, however, how a multiple-stranded "ropelike" chromosome could be constructed, and still follow the demands of the thymidine-labeling experiments. He suggests that the chromosome contains two functional units, but that each is in reality a multiple strand composed of numerous subunits. Space for very many such subunits does not exist in interchromomeric fibrils, or interband regions, as mentioned

---

FIG. 6. DNA-puffs in *Sciara* as stained with azure A-Feulgen. Part 1: Portion of chromosome 2, showing subterminal DNA-puff near centromere end of chromosome, and large medial DNA-puff. Arrow points to position of RNA puff, here shown as a slightly expanded area of low DNA concentration (magnification 1,500X). Parts 2 and 3. Centromere end of chromosome 2 before and after DNA-puff formation (class 4096C). (Magnification 2,200X). Part 4. Median puff of 1024C chromosome, showing filamentous and granular compounds (magnification 2,200X).

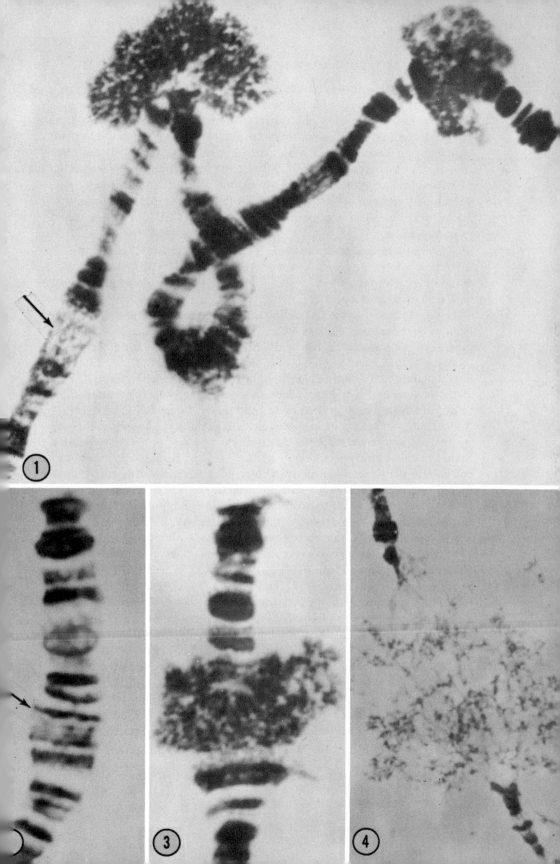

above. Also, this theory postulates that each functional unit of the chromosome consists of a large number of parallel DNA fibers. Such a construction does not agree with genetic data. Crossover maps certainly indicate that genes may be accurately assigned a specific position in a linear series along the chromosome. Thus, if the chromosome is a rope of 64 DNA fibers, each gene must be represented 64 times in each chromosome. Mutations would then exist in a whole series of "strengths" unless one postulates a complex mechanism whereby a change in one strand would spread to all, for which there is no evidence.

Chromosomes are functionally either one- or two-stranded in terms of rejoining phenomena after breakage. Two broken chromosome ends, entering the zygote nucleus in maize, tend to fuse together with a high frequency. Here the chromosome behaves functionally as a single strand. In other tissues (maize microspores and endosperm) broken chromosome ends fail to fuse with one another. Instead, fusion occurs between the two component chromatids within one chromosome (McClintock, 1938, 1941; Fabergé, 1958). Both types of chromosome reunion after breakage produce "bridge" configurations at the subsequent anaphase. Such bridges usually break in late mitosis, producing new broken ends, and the cycle of fusion, bridge formation, and breakage begins again. The factors favoring chromatid fusion in endosperm and gametophyte tissues, and chromosome fusion in most somatic tissues, are at present completely unknown, but should caution us against too easy generalizations concerning the functional-strandedness of chromosomes.

Through most of the mitotic cycle the chromosomes also are functionally either one- or two-stranded in terms of X-ray breakage. The whole chromosome may be broken by a single hit during much of the *Tradescantia* microspore interphase (before DNA synthesis) but half-chromosome (chromatid) breaks are obtained in late interphase and prophase, after DNA synthesis has taken place. Analysis of cells treated in late prophase and metaphase, however, shows that half-chromatid breaks may also occur (Swanson, 1947; Crouse, 1954; Sax and King, 1955). A similar progression was found in lily meiotic prophase, involving chromosome breaks during preleptotene (before DNA synthesis), chromatid breaks until diplotene, and many half-chromatid breaks in diakinesis and metaphase I (Mitra, 1958). Thus the chromosome apparently progresses from a functionally one-stranded state to a two-stranded and finally a four-stranded condition in terms of X-ray breakage, although the interpretation of the four-stranded configuration has been questioned (Ostergren and Wakonig, 1954).

The phenomena of chromosome breakage and rejoining have also been investigated with tritiated thymidine labeling of DNA. In a study of root-tip chromosomes of *Bellevalia*, Taylor (1958) investigated the patterns of exchange between sister strands. It was possible, by the production of polyploid nuclei through prolonged colchicine treatment, to follow the progeny of a single chromosome through two successive divisions. This has demonstrated that "double sister strand exchanges" occur with high frequency, explicable only on the grounds that the exchanges involve *both* the two old (unlabeled) strands exchanging with both new (labeled) strands. Taylor has concluded that his data indicate (1) all breaks and reunions are four-stranded, and (2) the two strands of the chromosomal duplex do not show random exchanges, and thus are not alike. He also considers "a chromosome might be a single double helix" but the possibility that "it is composed of *two* Watson-Crick double helices is certainly eliminated, for these would be identical."

If we accept this conclusion, then on the basis of our photometric data on polytene chromosomes, we may conclude that each chromosomal unit contains one double helix. It seems to us, however, that Taylor's data show only that recombination between strands is under certain restrictions, such that the exchanges will be between two strands separable at the second, and not at the first, subsequent division. This restriction, while an important finding, could just as well be one of proximity, and need not rule out the possibility of the twin double helices. Indeed, one might expect that a strand would be in a more favorable position to exchange with its own recently synthesized product, rather than with the product of its sister. We cannot yet rule out the possibility that the chromosome before DNA synthesis contains two double helices.

There are many observations in the literature of light and electron microscopy suggesting that the chromosome is visibly multistranded. It is certainly true that chromosomes and nuclei in many electron micrographs contain fine fibrous material, varying in width with the organism and means of fixation (and in some cases with the courage of the investigator) from 4 to 50 mμ in diameter (see Steffensen, 1959; Kaufmann et al., 1960, for reviews). In our opinion, none of these micrographs as yet adequately demonstrates the relation between filamentous material and the structure of the chromosome. Although in some cases (for example, Ris, 1959) bundles of parallel fibres are apparent running along the length of a mitotic or meiotic chromosome, whether these are bundles of axial strands or lateral loops flattened along a single axis is impossible to determine. In spite of concerted effort on the part of a number of investigators, we must come to the conclusion that as yet the electron microscope has added disappointingly little to our knowledge of chromosome structure.

Light-microscope evidence for the multiple-stranded nature of the chromosome at present seems more formidable. There are many reports of the visible double-strandedness of chromosomes in somatic anaphase (see Kuwada, 1939; Huskins, 1957; and Kaufmann, 1948, for reviews; Ohno et al., 1958; and Boss, 1959, for recent studies). Such observations present a real dilemma to considerations of chromosome structure. It is difficult to imagine how a chromosome could be visibly double and yet behave as a single strand in terms of X-ray breakage, unless a break at one point somehow induced a break at another. The doubleness is in agreement with the concept of functional two-strandedness of the chromosome presented by thymidine labeling, and chromosome fusion after breakage. But it is in the one-microm range of light-microscope visibility, not in the 2 mμ of the DNA double helix. There are three possible answers to this problem. First, the doubleness may be an optical illusion (Wilson, 1925; Nebel, 1941), or unrelated to the actual plane of chromosome division (Taylor, 1957). Second, the chromosome may be actually four- or more stranded (two or more double helices) but behave functionally as two-stranded. Third, the DNA double helix may fall apart in metaphase or anaphase into two fibers, each containing single-stranded DNA, in preparation for the ensuing synthesis. Single strands, if tremendously contracted, could be visible in the light microscope. There seems no necessity to postulate that the two strands of the DNA molecule uncoil only during the actual process of DNA synthesis. Indeed, such an assumption is difficult to reconcile with the action of DNA replicase enzymes (Atwood, 1960). The concept that the DNA double helix falls apart before DNA synthesis might be the clue to what is responsible for the two types of DNA found in growing rat tissues by Bendich et al. (1953).

Such a theory is at present largely without justification. It also fails to account for a few observations with the light microscope where telophase chromosomes have been described as *four*-partite.

FIG. 7. Chromosomes of *Sciara*. Part 1. The chromosome complement of a salivary-gland nucleus, showing the four chromosomes. Major DNA-puff loci on chromosomes 2 and 3 are indicated by arrows. Parts 2 and 3. Radioautographs made with tritiated thymidine. Part 2 shows characteristic "all or none" labeling of late larval gland. All chromosomes were either unlabeled (right) or completely labeled (left). Part 3a. Subterminal puff on chromosome 2, showing heavy label in puff, very light label in remainder of chromosome. Part 3b. Median puff of chromosome 2, showing heavy label in puff, none in adjacent parts of the chromosome. Part 4. Histone stain, showing strong staining in median puff of chromosome 2. Part 5. Section of prepupal gland, stained with azure B, showing characteristic multiple nucleoli. Arrow indicates DNA puff with two attached nucleoli. Parts 6 and 7. Chromosome smears stained with azure B. RNA puffs are shown at arrows.

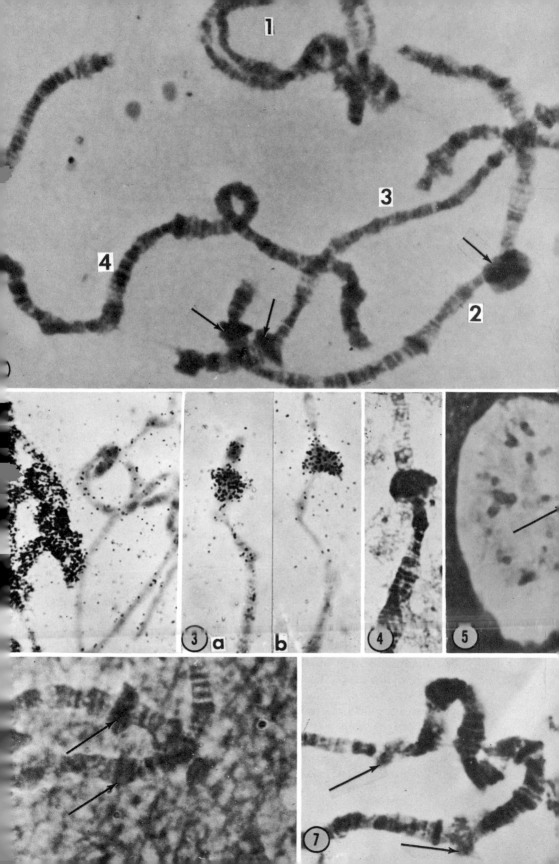

These observations have in some cases been based on chromosomes "uncoiled" by acidic or basic agents prior to fixation (for example, by Nebel, 1941, on *Tradescantia,* and Manton, 1945, on the fern *Todea*). Also, meiotic bivalents clearly contain eight components at first metaphase in the scale insect *Llaveiella,* but occasionally a further split is visible at second anaphase (Hughes-Schrader, 1940). Since pairing and chromosome replication have doubtless occurred by first metaphase, this eight-partite condition is comparable to a two-stranded chromosome at somatic anaphase, but the additional split would indicate a four-stranded condition. Additional indirect indications of multiple-strandedness come from studies on related species or strains, possessing the same chromosome number but differing markedly in the amounts of DNA per nucleus. The sugges- tion has been made, for example, by Alfert and Balamuth (1957) for races of the ciliate *Tetrahymena,* and by Hughes-Schrader and Schrader (1957) for species of pentatomid bugs, that these forms differ primarily in the relative strandedness of their chromosomes. Such studies should caution us against the generalization that all chromosomes contain the same number of component strands. It would be of interest to compare patterns of labeled DNA segrega- tion in such forms.

It is impossible to reconcile the disparate findings in the litera- ture summarized above. Many of the data fit a model of the chromo- some containing either one or two DNA double helices running throughout its length. The chromosome during early interphase is functionally single-stranded in studies on X-ray breakage, and also in the fusion of chromosome ends in certain somatic plant tissues. It must be functionally two-stranded in terms of tritiated thymidine labeling and sister-strand exchanges, and also in chromatid fusion in endosperm and gametophyte. It frequently appears as two-stranded in telophase, under the light microscope. Some light-microscope studies, some electron micrographs, and certain DNA differences be- tween related species suggest a higher degree of strandedness. The multiple-strand concept disagrees with our cytochemical determina- tions on *Sciara.* Differences between the chromosomes of different species may possibly occur.

To summarize this section on DNA and chromosome structure, we have concluded: (1) The polytene chromosome consists of a cable of single chromosomal units, each of which probably resembles the interphase chromosome in a diploid nucleus. (2) Interbands as well as bands are Feulgen-positive, thus there is DNA continuity through- out the length of the chromosome. (3) Calculations based on photome- try and electron microscopy both suggest that each unit contains a single double helix (possibly as many as two, but certainly not as many as 32 or 64 helices) of DNA. (4) Bands increase in length and disappear on formation of RNA puffs, indicating they are formed at least in part from superimposed coiled or folded regions in the chromosomal fibers. (5) Published data on other tissues, utilizing light and electron microscopy, radioautography, and X-ray treatment, have been discussed. Most, but no all, data support the concept of the chromosome as composed of one or two much coiled or folded DNA helices.

PROTEINS AND CHROMOSOME STRUCTURE

There are three major protein components of nuclei distinguishable with cytochemical techniques, namely the histone and nonhistone proteins of the chromosome, and the proteins of the nuclear sap. The histones are usually defined as relatively low-molecular-weight, acid-soluble proteins, rich in the basic amino acids arginine, histidine, and lysine. Whether or not they exist as a single protein or a complex class of proteins is still unclear, but some heterogeneity in histones from the same tissue has been reported (Daly and Mirsky, 1955; Crampton, et al., 1957). Several possible functions have been postulated for histones. Since they are apparently intimately associated with DNA, it has been suggested they function as mediators in gene action (Stedman and Stedman, 1950). On the other hand, they could play a more passive role in combining with, and thus "neutralizing," the acid groups of DNA, or possibly in providing structural support or means of attachment between DNA molecules (Wilkins, 1957).

The histones in the *Drosophila* salivary-gland chromosomes parallel the distribution of DNA (Horn and Ward, 1957; Schurin, 1957). When histones are stained with fast green at pH 8.1 (Alfert and Geschwind, 1953) the Feulgen distribution is faithfully followed, so that, except for a slight staining in nonhistone proteins, the two reactions are almost indistinguishable (Fig. 9, part 4, p. 101). The staining reaction is dependent on the high concentration of basic groups (particularly arginine) in histones. The faint background staining probably results from arginine basic groups that occur in much lower amounts in other proteins.

When an RNA puff forms at one particular locus in the chromosome, as discussed below, amounts of both DNA and histone apparently remain unchanged in total amount. Their concentrations fall, however, as the band "spreads" over a wider volume. This behavior is illustrated in Fig. 9, parts 1 and 4, p. 101. Since the relative amounts of DNA and histone appear to be constant during the puff formation, this argues against the concept that histone levels mediate the action of DNA. Small changes, however, below the level of resolution of the method may possibly pass undetected.

While the histones, like the DNA, remain unchanged in RNA puffs, in the DNA puffs of *Sciara* both DNA and histones increase in amount during puff formation (Fig. 7, part 4). Thus in both RNA and DNA puffs, histones follow the behavior of DNA.

In contrast, the nonhistone proteins of the chromosome do not follow the DNA distribution, but are associated largely with the RNA-containing puffs. There are certain technical difficulties involved in studying this fraction. No satisfactory method has been found for its specific demonstration. Acid-dye-binding techniques at low pH also stain histone, nuclear-sap, and cytoplasmic proteins. It is necessary to obtain chromosomes as free of contaminating proteins as possible and then to compare stains for "total protein" with histone stains, to determine regions that are positive only with the former method. In the nucleus, the chromosomes are surrounded by and probably permeated with the nuclear-sap proteins (Buck and Boche, 1938). This fraction is frequently apparent in smears of *Drosophila* salivary glands, stained for total protein. This can make the protein distribution in the chromosome appear uneven and irregular. On the other hand, chromosomes from the same slide that are widely spread, and preferably away from cytoplasmic proteins, appear much more even in stainability. We have chosen the latter, apparently cleaner chromosomes for study, on the assumption that they are largely free of nuclear-sap contamination. Such chromosomes, stained with fast green at pH 2.0 for total protein, are shown in Fig. 9, parts 2 and 3.

Do these preparations demonstrate the presence of a structural "backbone" or "residual" protein? It is of interest that the protein concentration in interband regions is extremely low, probably entirely accountable by the histone fraction alone. In regions of the

---

FIG. 8. *Drosophila virilis* neuroblast and salivary-gland nuclei. Part 1. Feulgen-stained nuclei from smear of larval dorsal ganglion, showing relative sizes of heterochromatic and euchromatic regions (magnification 3,000X). (*a*) Five 2C nuclei, with heterochromatin comprising about half the total DNA. (*b*) Nucleus in class 4C at right, 8C at left, with abnormally large heterochromatic area. (*c*) 8C nucleus. (*d*) 16C nucleus. (*e*) Spread chromosomes from 128C nucleus; heterochromatic region at arrow is only slightly larger that region of 2C nuclei. Part 2. Chromocenter region from 1024C salivary-gland nucleus, stained with Feulgen and fast green at pH 2. Nucleolus has been displaced during squashing. Feulgen positive droplets inside nucleolus are shown by arrow. Parts 3 and 4. Radioautograph of salivary gland made with tritiated cytidine. Part 3. One-half hour after treatment, showing nucleolus labeled, chromosomes essentially unlabeled. Part 4, same as part 3, after four hours of treatment, showing nucleolus heavily labeled, and also a heavy label in portion of cytoplasm shown in lower right. Label in RNA puff at end of chromosome 2 is shown at arrow.

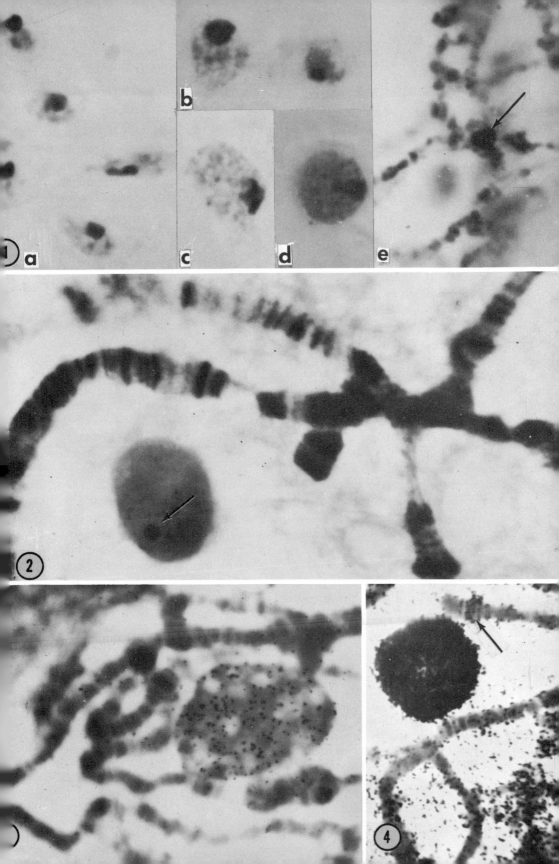

Drosophila salivary chromosome where RNA puffs are absent, the histone stain and total protein stain give similar intensity distributions — heavy staining in the bands, very light staining in interbands. This also parallels the distribution of DNA. However, in the region of RNA puffs, the total protein reaction is obviously stronger than the histone reaction. This is true not only in the immediate region of the RNA puff, but on either side of it as well, possibly because the chromosome is here expanded and possibly still permeated with nuclear-sap proteins.

We have concluded from these studies that nonhistone proteins exist almost exclusively in the RNA puffs, and that proteins of the normal band and interband regions is largely, if not entirely, histone. All of the data obtained so far on *Drosophila* can be explained on the basis of three major fractions: (1) A DNA-histone complex, present in both bands and interbands, and probably responsible for chromosome integrity. (2) An RNA-protein complex occurring at a few specific bands, responsible for swelling out the chromosome at certain loci to form RNA puffs. (3) The nuclear-sap protein, variable in distribution, responsible for irregular interband staining in some chromosomes. Since this fraction is reduced or absent from well-spread chromosomes away from cytoplasmic material, it has been considered a contaminant, and not a structural element of the chromosome (although it may play, of course, an important role in nuclear metabolism).

These observations, although preliminary, argue against the presence of any structural nonhistone protein occurring in the chromosome. They agree with our concept of the chromosome unit as being a fiber or fibers of DNA histone, coiled in the bands, running the length of the chromosome. Other components may obviously occur in the chromosome in presently undetectable levels. Indeed, their presence may be needed as interconnecting links for DNA molecules, possibly as pivot points for DNA uncoiling, and the complex patterns of mitotic condensation. The possibility that any undetected protein plays a major role as "backbone" in polytene chromosome structure, however, seems at present unlikely.

———————————

FIG. 9. DNA and protein distribution in end of chromosome 2 of *Drosophila virilis* (mag. 3,000 X). Part 1. Stages of RNA-puff formation shown on chromosomes stained with azure A-Feulgen. Band before puffing is shown at arrow. Parts 2 and 3. Comparison between DNA (left member, each part) and total protein distributions. Slides were stained with fast green at pH 2, then destained and treated with Feulgen reaction. Note strong protein staining at puff locus (upper arrow), also that areas of low DNA concentration (lower arrows) are also low in total protein. Part 4. Histone distribution, showing faint staining in puff locus, similar to distributions of DNA.

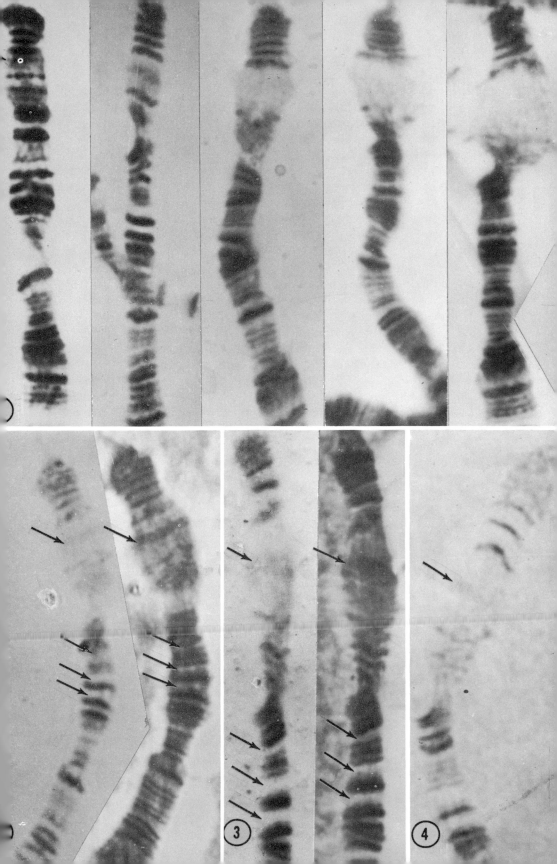

RNA-CONTAINING COMPONENTS

Several types of RNA are distinguishable in salivary-gland cells, on the basis of location, morphology, and incorporation behavior. By the use of basic dye binding or radioautography, it is possible to localize RNA in the chromosomes, in the nucleolus, in the nuclear sap material between the chromosomes, and in the cytoplasm. It is, in all cases, undoubtedly associated with protein. The "soluble RNA" fractions are probably lost during tissue preparation.

Chromosomal RNA. RNA occurs in specific regions of the chromosome. Where present, it usually enlarges the chromosomal width to form an RNA-containing puff. The presence of RNA in the giant puff or "Balbiani ring" of *Chironomus* (gnat) salivary-gland chromosomes was described by Bauer and Caspersson (1948). Since that time many workers have described the presence of RNA in particular chromosome regions (Pavan and Breuer, 1955; Schurin, 1957; Beermann, 1957; Swift, 1959a; Rudkin and Woods, 1959).

The predictable variation in puffing patterns between different tissues, or with different stages in development, has been frequently described (Poulson and Metz, 1938; Beermann, 1952, 1957; Mechelke, 1953; Breuer and Pavan, 1955; Becker, 1959). There can by now be little doubt that such puffs are an expression of the action of specific chromosomal loci, functioning in different tissues in relation to particular stages of development or states of physiological activity. Of particular interest are recent studies where puffing patterns have been experimentally altered, through changing the environment of the cell or nucleus (Becker, 1959; Kroeger, 1960; Clever and Karlson, 1960). Such investigations should provide new insights into problems of gene action and nuclear-cytoplasmic interaction.

The nucleoprotein changes associated with RNA-puff formation may be studied with the basic dye azure B (Flax and Himes, 1952), which, through metachromasy, stains DNA blue and RNA purple. Also, the enzymes deoxyribonuclease or ribonuclease may be used

---

FIG. 10. Nucleic acid distribution in polytene chromosomes of *Drosophila virilis*. Part 1. RNA bands and puffs in the end of chromosome 2 (cf. Fig. 9, part 1). Smear was treated with deoxyribonuclease for 5 minutes, then stained with azure B at pH 4.0. Note similarity of pattern between two different chromosomes. Part 2. Two stages in RNA-puff formation at end of chromosome 2. Both RNA and DNA have been stained with azure B. Part 3. Preparation similar to that shown in part 1, at low magnification, showing the large number of RNA-puffs and bands, and the virtual absence of staining at the chromocenter (arrow). Part 4. Azure B staining for RNA and DNA of nucleus during period of maximum RNA-puff formation. Notice the numerous puffed loci. Chromosomes sometimes tend to adhere at puff loci (arrow). Nucleolus at lower left.

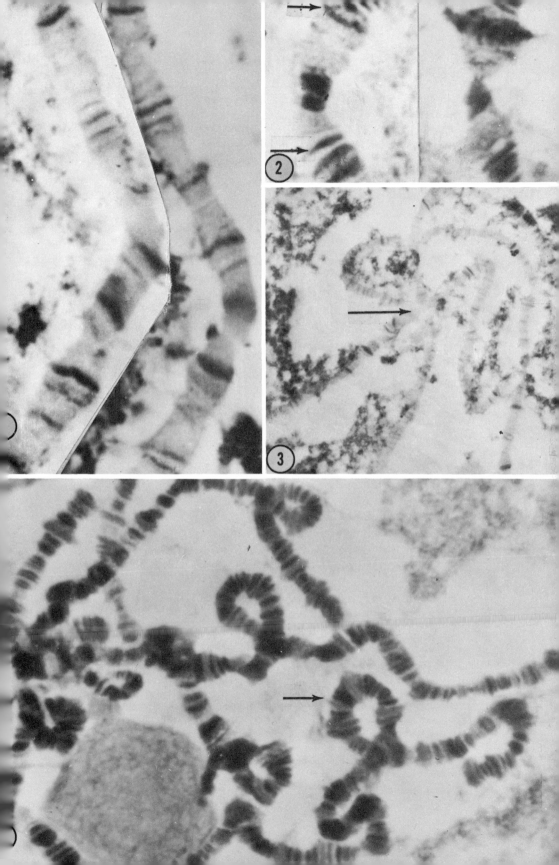

to remove one nucleic acid, leaving the other intact. It is evident, as pointed out above, that puff formation in *Drosophila* involves the accumulation of an RNA-nonhistone protein complex at certain loci. As this material accumulates the band increases in volume, so that the chromosome is "puffed" out in width and also slightly lengthened. During the formation of all puffs in *Drosophila virilis*, DNA and histone levels appear *unchanged*, although their concentration is lowered, since the same amount of material is expanded to occupy a larger volume. These RNA changes, as they occur at the end of the second chromosome of *Drosophila virilis*, are shown in Fig. 10 and are diagrammed in Fig. 5.

Although small amounts of chromosomal RNA are found throughout the third instar larval period, in the few hours prior to prepupa formation most puffs increase markedly in size (Becker, 1959). Chromosomes in this stage are shown in Fig. 10, part 4.

The total number of RNA-containing bands in the late third instar *Drosophila* larva is difficult to determine, since RNA occurs from large puffs down to barely perceptible levels. The RNA distribution may be studied after short treatment of chromosomes with deoxyribonuclease, as shown in Fig. 10, part 1. If enzyme treatment is prolonged the entire chromosome stains heavily, apparently because RNA from the cytoplasm is adsorbed on the chromosome at the sites formerly occupied by the DNA. This heavy RNA staining, that appears only after DNA removal, is thus considered an artifact (Swift, 1953). The chromocenter, or heterochromatic region, although it is intimately associated with the nucleolus, contains little or no diffuse chromosomal RNA within its substance (Fig. 10, part 3) although it may occasionally contain small nucleolus-like droplets.

In *Sciara* chromosomes azure B staining also demonstrates the presence of RNA-containing bands and puffs, similar to those of *Drosophila* in all major respects. (Fig. 7, parts 6 and 7, p. 95). They are somewhat variable in occurrence, and not markedly enlarged in most larvae studied.

The end of the second chromosome of *Drosophila virilis*, as seen in the electron microscope, is shown in Fig. 12, part 1. The major

---

FIG. 11. Part 1. Light micrograph of *Drosophila virilis* salivary-gland cell fixed in buffered osmium tetroxide, embedded in methacrylate and sectioned at $1\,\mu$. The section has been stained with the periodic acid-Schiff reaction for polysaccharides, and also with azure B for nucleic acids. Secretary granules in cytoplasm are intensely PAS-positive. The nucleolus shows inner and outer regions of lower and higher RNA concentration respectively. An area of heterochromatin is above the nucleolus.
Part 2. Low-power electron micrograph of the same material. Heterochromatin area is above the nucleolus. Note the numerous "large granules" in the nucleoplasm between chromosomes.

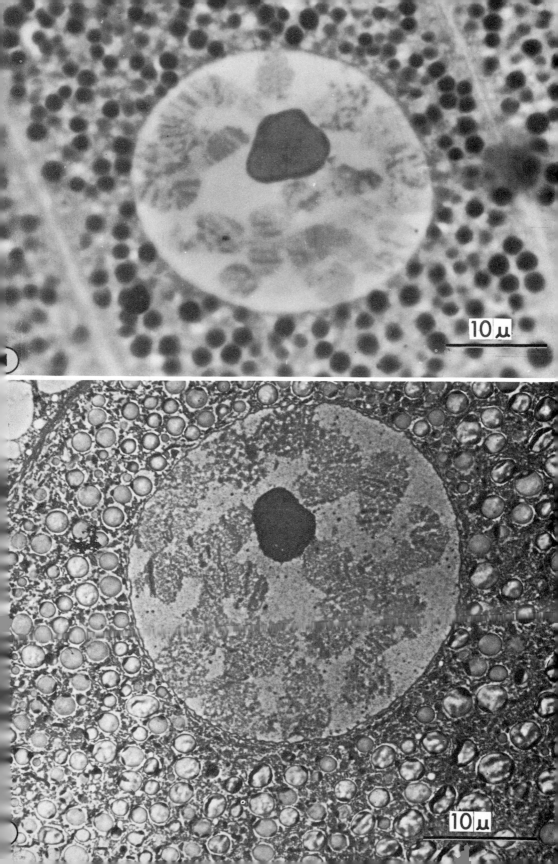

RNA-containing puff is characterized by large granules up to about 40 mμ in diameter (Schurin, 1957; Swift, 1959b). This puff region is shown at higher magnification in Fig. 14, part 3, p. 111. Similar large granules occur free in the nuclear sap, unattached to chromosomes (Fig. 11, part 2, p. 105). These particulates have an appearance suggestive of the inner portion of the nucleolus. They are not obviously made up of fine particles, as is the outer portion of the nucleolus. Other puffs do not contain similar granules; although occasionally a few sparse fine particles may be visible (as in the *Sciara* chromosome shown in Fig. 15, part 1, p. 113).

More study is needed before the fine structure of RNA-containing components of the chromosomes are adequately characterized. Large particles, about 30 mμ in diameter, were reported by Beermann and Bahr (1954) in the large Balbiani ring of *Chironomus*. A granular component was found to be associated with chromosomes in *Triturus* oocytes (Gall, 1956a), and clusters of fine particles about the size of cytoplasmic ribosomes were described from rat-liver nuclei (Swift, 1959b). At least in some cases, these components are morphologically unlike the RNA-containing particles of nucleolus and cytoplasm.

Nucleoli. The nucleolus in *Drosophila* is attached to the chromocenter by a fine Feulgen-positive fiber, and droplets of DNA-containing material occur at the center of the nucleolus (Fig. 8, part 2.) These are apparently portions of the sex chromosomes, although they merit further study.

The nucleolus of *Drosophila* salivary glands, as in many other cell types, is morphologically heterogeneous (Beermann and Bahr, 1954; Swift, 1958, 1959b; Porter, 1960). It contains regions of higher RNA concentration, that usually are more or less peripheral in distribution, and that appear somewhat granular or particulate in the electron microscope; and regions of lower RNA concentration, with a more amorphous fine structure. The differences in RNA concentration are visible in Fig. 11, part 1, and the corresponding difference in fine structure in Fig. 11, part 2 and Fig. 13, part 1. Particles of the nucleolus bear at least a superficial resemblance to the particles (ribosomes) associated with the membranes of the endoplasmic reticulum in the cytoplasm. They are compared in Fig. 13,

---

FIG. 12. Electron micrographs of *Drosophila virilis* chromosomes. Salivary glands were fixed in osmium tetroxide, and then transferred to 45 per cent acetic acid for smearing. They were then embedded in methacrylate and sectioned along the plane of the slide. Part 1. Low-power micrograph of the end of chromosome 2, showing large granules in the puff area (cf. Fig. 10, part 2). Part 2. Region of chromosome stained with uranyl acetate, showing a band (*b*) and interband (*i*) region. Part 3. Enlarged band area, showing presence of filaments not oriented along chromosome axis (arrows). Part 4. Enlarged portion of interband region. Filaments at arrows are 4 to 5 mμ in diameter.

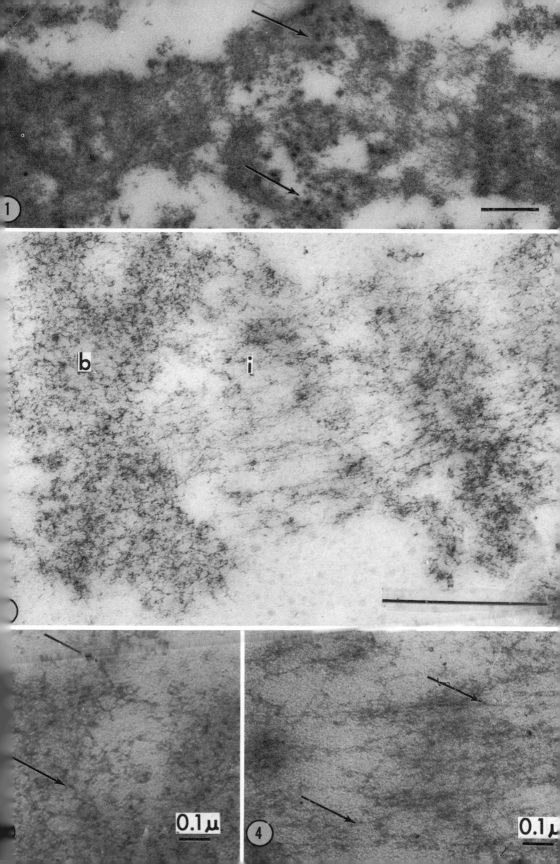

1

b   i

0.1 μ

4

0.1 μ

parts 1 and 2, and at higher magnification in Fig. 14, parts 1 and 2. The nucleolus also contains a number of small vesicles or vacuoles of low density, probably containing nuclear-sap proteins. These frequently lie in contact with the DNA-containing inclusions.

Nucleoli of *Sciara* salivary glands are "fragmented" and occur in up to 20 small bodies scattered throughout the nucleus (Fig. 7, part 5). Most, but not all, of these nucleolar fragments appear to be attached to chromosomes, and in a number of cases to DNA-puff regions. Whether these points of contact between nucleoli and chromosomes represent sites of nucleolar synthesis, or are merely regions of random contact, is not clear, but the nucleoli are readily displaced from the chromosomes when the cells are crushed. In a few cases nucleolar bodies have been observed within the substance of DNA puffs, resembling the chromocenters of *Drosophila* in this respect. Whether or not nucleoli increase in number during the formation of DNA puffs has not been determined.

As in *Drosophila, Sciara* nucleoli contain both particulate areas of high RNA concentration, and more amorphous regions of lower RNA concentration. These are more irregularly distributed than in *Drosophila*, and the amorphous areas are not necessarily surrounded by particulate material (Fig. 15, parts 1 and 2).

Radioautography. Radioautographic studies on RNA components of *Drosophila* salivary glands have indicated that the nucleolus labels rapidly, only 30 minutes after presentation of the labeled precursor. Detectable label appeared in the chromosomes only after several hours. Late third instar larvae were mixed with 20 μc of tritium-labeled uridine in one ml of food, and radioautographs were made on smears of salivary glands collected after 30 minutes, one, two and four hours. At 30 minutes nucleoli were well labeled, but no label was detectable in either the chromosomes or cytoplasm (Fig. 8, part 3). Slight label of chromosomal and cytoplasmic RNA was apparent after two hours, but RNA puffs were not obviously labeled until four hours, at which time a heavy label also occurred in the cytoplasm (Fig. 8, part 4). Similar findings with both P^{32} and C^{14}-adenine were reported for *Drosophila melanogaster* (McMaster-Kaye, 1960).*

Relationships between RNA fractions. The "unitary" hypothesis, that all RNA of the cell originates as a primary gene product, formed

---

*We have recently obtained heavy labeling of puff RNA after only 15 minutes, provided H^3 cytidine is administered during the specific period of prepupal puff formation.

FIG. 13. Nucleolus and cytoplasmic area of *Drosophila virilis* salivary gland. Part I. The nucleolus shows an amorphous (*a*) and particulate (*p*) region. Part 2. In the cytoplasm secretory granules (*sg*) are visible in a variety of sizes, the smaller granules similar to the vesicles of the Golgi material (*g*). Large areas of endoplasmic reticulum (*er*) and a few mitochondria (*m*) are also shown.

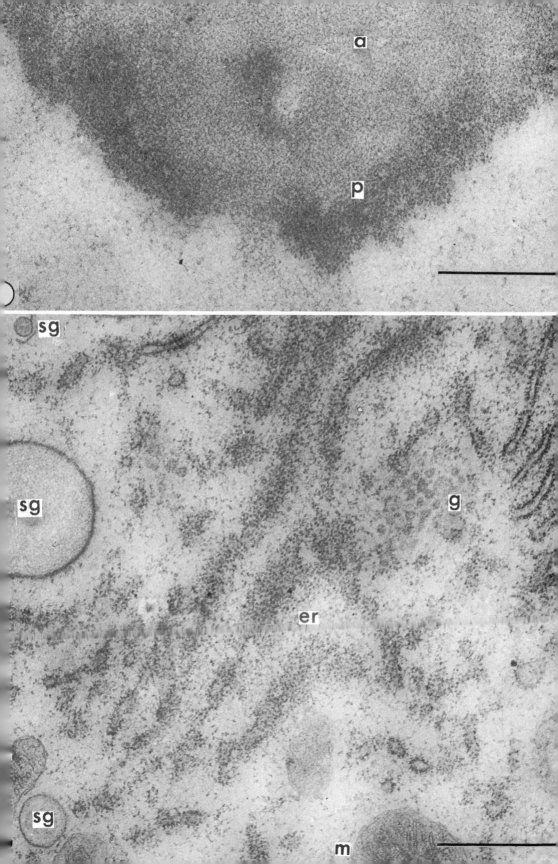

on the chromosome, collected in the nucleolus, and transferred to the cytoplasm, has been popular for a number of years. In the face of the current findings of a number of investigators, this probably must be discarded as too simple. In its place we must substitute a more complex concept, involving a multiplicity of RNA fractions, recognizable in terms of location, fine structure, and incorporation rates. These are only indirect indications of probable differences in chemistry and function.

We can distinguish RNA-containing components by location in chromosomes, nucleoli, nuclear sap, and cytoplasm. Since certain RNA puffs appear at specific times in larval development, and since bands in some cases may show a characteristic fine structure, "chromosomal RNA" doubtless represents a heterogeneous group of ribonucleoproteins. The nucleolus contains two regions, differing in RNA concentration and fine structure. These may well represent fractions with different incorporation rates, as found by Vincent (1957) for starfish oocyte nucleoli. Nuclear-sap RNA probably de-. rives at least in part from the chromosomes. That RNA-containing particulates may leave the chromosome and enter the nuclear sap seems likely from the occurrence within it of large granules similar to those in the subterminal puff on chromosome 2. Fine particles, also present in the areas between chromosomes, could be related either to chromosomes or to nucleoli. The probable origin of nuclear-sap particulates from the chromosomes in amphibian oocytes has been suggested by Gall (1956a). Cytoplasmic ribosomes, presumably the major RNA-containing component of the cytoplasm, resemble in their fine structure the particulates of the granular portion of the nucleolus. Small-molecular-weight RNA fractions (soluble RNA) are doubtless lost from tissues during preparation. Attempts to preserve their localization within the cell for cytochemical study are obviously needed.

We know next to nothing about the possible interrelatedness of these various fractions. Nucleoli in *Drosophila* salivaries, as in many other tissues, are obviously related to the chromosomes. They form at specific chromosomal regions, and frequently contain Feulgen-positive components in their substance. It was emphasized by Bauer (1935) that the nucleolus-like Balbiani ring of *Chironomus* ex-

---

FIG. 14. Comparison of RNA-containing particulates in nucleus and cytoplasm of *Drosophila*. Part 1. Particulate area of nucleolus. Part 2. Area of the endoplasmic reticulum, from Fig. 13, part 2. Part 3. Large granules from RNA puff near end of chromosome 2 (cf. Fig 12, part 1). This material is not obviously particulate, as in the nucleolar substance shown in part 1.

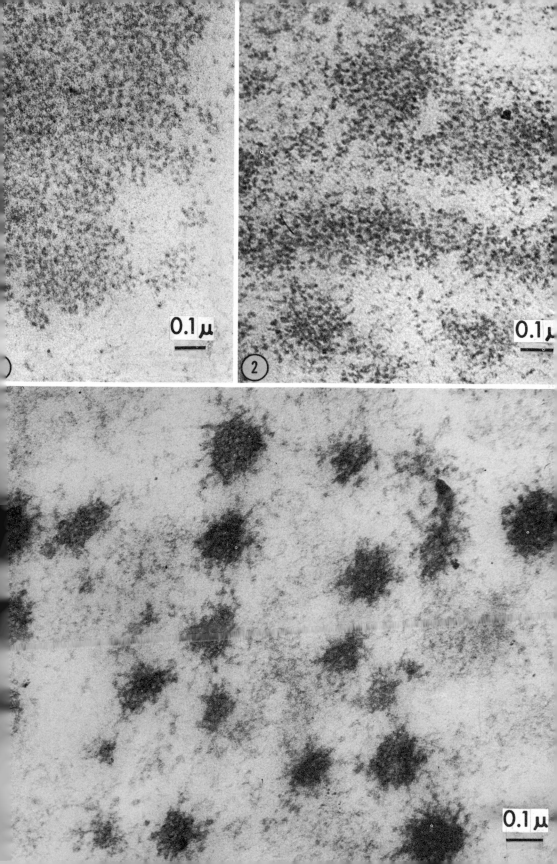

0.1μ

2

0.1μ

0.1μ

pands the chromosome, suggesting that ring material is made within chromosomal substance rather than merely aggregating from other sites in the nucleus. Radioautographic data have also suggested that labeled RNA forms first at the interface between chromosome and nucleolus, thus implicating the chromosome itself in the synthesis of nucleolar RNA (Pelling, 1959; Sirlin, 1960). If the amorphous (usually inner) portion of the nucleolus had a higher incorporation rate than the outer granular portion, then the region nearest the chromosome would label first, without necessarily indicating that the chromosome is necessary for nucleolar synthesis. Indeed, both in amphibian oocytes (Ficq, 1955) and in *Sciara* salivary glands, nucleolar fragments not in contact with chromosomes still show rapid precursor incorporation. The fact that nucleoli label, even when not directly in contact with chromosomal material, suggests either that nucleoli possess an autonomous synthetic mechanism, or that they are aggregation centers for RNA made elsewhere.

What is the indication that nucleolar RNA, at least in part, derives from the chromosomes? In *Drosophila*, but not necessarily in other forms, the chromosomal RNA fractions labeled much more slowly than the nucleolus. For the first two hours following the presentation of the precursor, the chromosomes were essentially unlabeled, while the nucleolus showed considerable incorporation after 30 minutes. This strongly suggests, as stressed by McMaster-Kaye (1960), that the nucleolus has its own synthetic system, independent of chromosomal RNA. It is still possible, however, that this rapidly labeled nucleolar RNA derives from the chromosomes as a highly motile fraction that leaves the chromosomes and aggregates in the nucleolus as soon as it is formed. Although the possibility of such a fraction cannot at present be ruled out, there is as yet no evidence at all for two different (motile and stationary) RNA-containing components of chromosomes. It is, of course, also possible that chromosomal RNA is transferred to the nucleolus, but that this is a relatively slow process, masked in radioautographs by the rapid turnover of the labile nucleolar fraction. In *Drosophila* salivary glands the abrupt and short-lived increase in puff activity just prior to pupation deserves more study. Radioautographs are needed on carefully staged larvae during this period.

FIG. 15. Part 1. Section of the salivary gland of *Sciara* prepupa, showing nucleolus (upper right), chromosomes, nuclear membrane, and a portion of the cytoplasm. Part 2 shows particulate (p) and amorphous (a) areas of the nucleolus, adjacent to a condensed chromatin area (c).

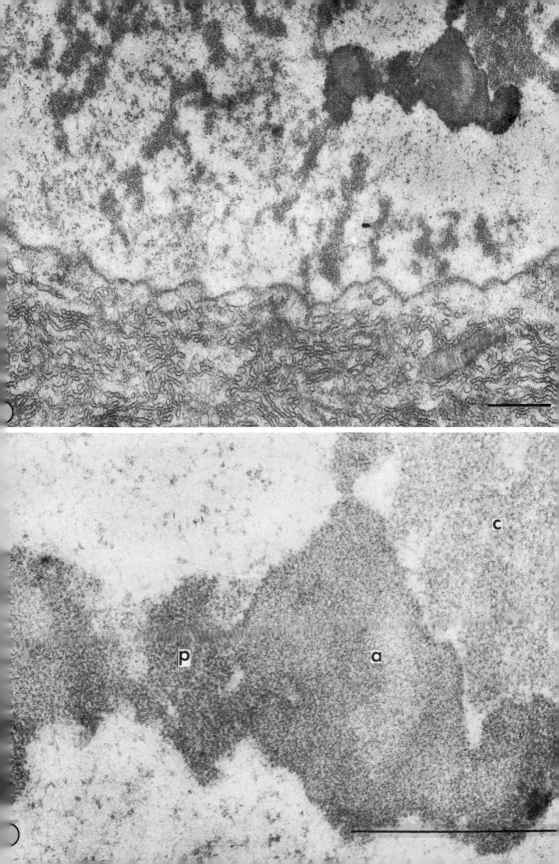

Although it is possible to imagine some nucleolar substance as derived from the chromosomes, by resorting to various schemes involving multiple fractions, we can certainly say that the bulk of the evidence points to nucleolar and chromosomal fractions as substantially independent.

About the possible relations between nuclear and cytoplasmic RNA we can say little. McMaster-Kaye (1960) has made the interesting observation that in *Drosophila* larvae fed with adenine-C^{14} for two hours, and then grown on unlabeled food, nucleolar RNA rises to a peak of incorporation, and then declines in activity before any label appears in the cytoplasm. This implies that at least some label is lost from the nucleolus through RNA breakdown rather than through transfer to the cytoplasm. Her conclusion that it demonstrates the complete independence of nucleolar and cytoplasmic RNA seems unwarranted, since this still could involve the slowly incorporating fraction. Several workers (for example, Gall, 1956a; Porter, 1960) have pointed out the resemblance between nucleolar particles and ribosomes. Although it is possible that ribosomes are manufactured in the nucleolus and emerge through the annular "pores" in the nuclear membrane to take their places on the endoplasmic reticulum, this seems as yet a somewhat fanciful concept without supporting evidence. In many tissues ribosomes are arranged in specific patterns on the cytoplasmic membranes, and their position within the complex of the endoplasmic reticulum is certainly not random.

RNA-containing fractions of the cell are both complex and various. It seems likely that RNA-puff formation is a concomitant of gene action, and ribonucleoproteins are quite possibly the materials which transfer genetic information from the chromosome to sites of protein synthesis in the cytoplasm. How this is accomplished, and the role of the nucleolus in this process is at present largely obscure. The universal occurrence of enlarged nucleoli in cells engaged in protein synthesis (Caspersson, 1950), the apparently rapid synthesis and breakdown of nucleolar RNA, and the usually unimpressive incorporation of amino acids into nucleolar proteins (Woodard et al., 1961), would possibly point to the nucleolus as synthetic center for a nonspecific, small-molecular-weight component required in protein synthesis, such as "soluble RNA."

CYTOPLASMIC PROTEIN SYNTHESIS

A major function of the *Drosophila* salivary gland is the secretion of mucoprotein cement substances, for the adherence of the pupa case to the substrate. Large cytoplasmic vesicles containing mucoprotein materials accumulate in the cytoplasm during the final stages of gland growth. These stain intensely for polysaccharides with the PAS reaction (Fig. 11, part 1).

Throughout the cytoplasm of the gland, areas of lamellar endoplasmic reticulum are evident, interspersed with small clusters of Golgi material (Fig. 13, part 2 and Fig. 16, parts 1 to 3). In some areas vesicles of the endoplasmic reticulum are distended with electron-dense material, apparently representing an early stage in formation of secretion deoplets. Occasionally these vesicles are seen to contain typical ribosome-bearing membranes on one surface, and smooth, Golgi-like membranes on another. Such areas may represent the transformation of secretion products from inside particle-lined membranes to smooth membranes (Fig. 16, part 3) (cf. Palade, 1959). Secretory droplets are apparent in a variety of sizes, from Golgi vesicles up to large secretory inclusions. Large droplets may coalesce in glands from prepupae, and enter the lumen of the gland between complex folds and microvilli of the apical cell membrane (Fig. 16, part 1). These cells contain many other morphological features of interest which must be discussed elsewhere.

CONCLUSIONS

There are several implications of the work discussed above that should be emphasized. Studies on DNA puffs suggest the existence of two kinds of DNA — one which follows the patterns of DNA constancy and comprises the greater part of the chromosomal material, another which is out of synchrony with these patterns, showing wide variation in particular cell types at particular stages in ontogeny.

There are at least four possibilities as to the nature of this variable fraction. These we can call (1) the theory that variability is a *basic property of all DNA;* (2) the theory of *DNA duality;* (3) extra DNA as *gene product,* and (4) extra DNA as an *episomal* component.

All DNA may undergo synthesis and breakdown to some extent during normal activity. These cases may merely represent this process in more marked and recognizable degree. This possibility, on the basis of much evidence for the metabolic stability of DNA, at present seems unlikely (for example, see Hotchkiss, 1955).

The genome may consist of two distinct types of genetic material. Synthesis of the variable fraction may be under different control processes, and may be associated with genetic activity of a different type. The concept of the "polygene" nature of heterochromatin (Mather, 1944) is no longer acceptable because of the number of good genetic characters now known to be associated with these areas. Nevertheless, heterochromatin certainly differs from euchromatin in genetic properties (for example, see Hannah, 1951; Baker, 1953). Heterochromatin is also often associated with fundamental cell components (nucleoli and centromeres). It is quite possible, for example, that nucleoli produce nonspecific components (e.g., soluble RNA) needed in the synthesis of specific ribonucleoproteins.

A DNA puff may represent the formation of a specific gene product at a specific chromosomal locus. It may differ from most other gene products in that it is a DNA-histone complex instead of a ribonucleoprotein. This would mean that "extra DNA" is constructed *upon* the chromosome (as presumably is RNA in RNA-puff formation) and is not a part of it. One would thus expect "extra" DNA to come off the chromosome after puff formation. This loss of DNA-puff material from the chromosome was described by Stich and Naylor (1958) in *Glyptotendipes*. It has not been observed in *Sciara*.

A number of genetic traits are carried by virus-like elements, that may occur attached to specific chromosomal loci, or as independent infective particles. These elements have been called episomes (Jacob and Wollman, 1958). Although best known from bacteria, certain other infective or variable traits may fall into the same category, such as CO_2 sensitivity (L'Heritier, 1958) and sex ratio (Malogowkin and Poulson, 1958) in *Drosophila*. Electron micrographs of DNA puffs in *Sciara* have so far shown no evidence for virus-like particles.

In the discussion of chromosome structure we pointed out the general agreement between tritiated thymidine labeling, X-ray breakage, and cytochemical studies on lampbrush and polytene chromosomes, all of which suggest the chromosome is functionally one- or two-stranded in anaphase and early interphase of somatic cells. The simplest concept of chromosome structure, and one which fits the cytochemical data discussed above, considers the chromosome before replication as only one or two much coiled or

---

FIG. 16. Parts 1-3. Possible steps in protein synthesis in *Drosophila* cytoplasm. Part 1. Apical portion of salivary gland cell from late third instar larva, showing the prominent brush border, with densely packed and occasionally branched microvilli. Golgi area (arrow) contains small vesicles which resemble the large secretory granules (*ag*) in density and in the nature of the surrounding membrane. Part 2. Area of enlarged vesicles of the endoplasmic reticulum (*er*) immediately adjacent to areas of Golgi material (*g*). Part 3. Higher magnification of a portion of Part 2, showing regions of the endoplasmic reticulum (arrows) apparently lacking ribosonal particles, similar to the membranes of the Golgi material.

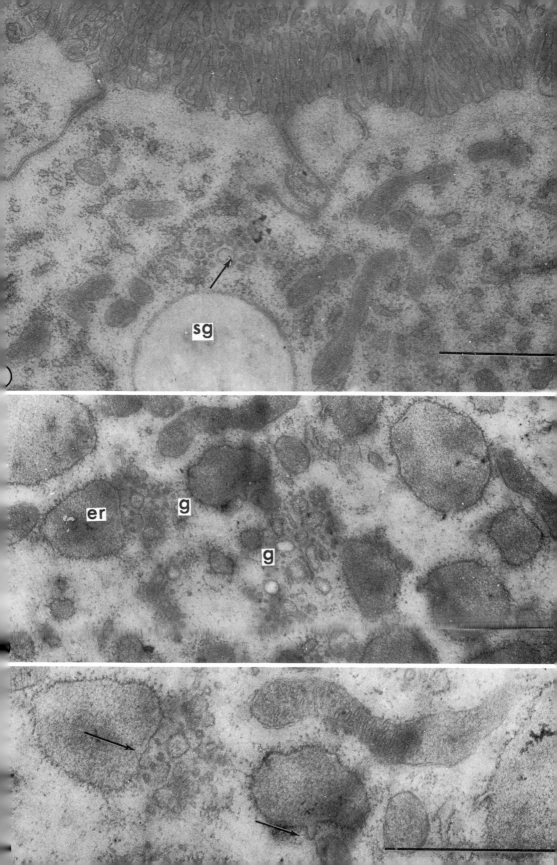

folded double helices of DNA, combined with histone, accumulating RNA and nonhistone proteins at genetically active loci.

Against this concept we have cited the frequent cytological observations of the doubleness of the anaphase chromosome, visible in the light microscope. It is interesting to note that many classical cytologists have considered this doubleness an optical illusion (for example, see Wilson, 1925). The electron microscope has also presented data on the multistrandedness of the chromosome, but in no case has the possibility that the apparent fiber bundle may be due to folding or looping of a single axis been adequately eliminated. It is also possible that chromosomes in different species or strains may have different degrees of strandedness, as suggested by some studies of differences in amounts of DNA between related species. But the presence of multiple-stranded chromosomes also entails the problem of how a multiple component can behave functionally as single or double, particularly in terms of such complex phenomena as mutation, crossing-over, and rejoining processes in chromosomal aberrations.

Studies on the RNA distribution of polytene chromosomes seem clearly to indicate a basic distinction between DNA puffs and RNA puffs. Whereas RNA puffs occur in many, and probably in all, species with polytene chromosomes, DNA puffs have so far been described from only three species. All puffs in *Drosophila* so far studied involve the accumulation of RNA and nonhistone protein, and amounts of DNA are unchanged during the puffing process. Though our present knowledge of chromosomal changes is certainly inadequate and incomplete, it seems probable that a fundamental difference exists between these two phenomena.

Radioautographic data, though inconclusive, suggest the nucleolus contains a rapid RNA metabolism of its own, and is not wholly dependent on the accumulation of chromosomal RNA for its existence. Nucleoli in some forms label first at the interface between nucleolus and chromosome. This would suggest nucleolar substance is synthesized by chromosomal material. However, fragmented nucleoli (as in *Sciara* and amphibian oocytes) not in contact with the chromosome also label rapidly. Either these fragments accumulate a very active fraction from the chromosomes (for which there is as yet no evidence) or they have a vigorous synthetic activity of their own. The latter possibility, which now seems most likely, would obviously involve RNA synthesis independent of the chromosomes. The nucleolus contains two morphologically distinct RNA-containing regions. These could represent either two distinct fractions (possibly the rapidly and slowly incorporating fractions found in other tissues), or probably less likely, two different functional states of a single fraction.

Lastly we have briefly outlined some of the cytoplasmic changes leading to the mucoprotein secretion product of the mature larval salivary gland. The electron microscope reveals a cytoplasm with abundant endoplasmic reticulum in both *Drosophila* and *Sciara*. In some areas of *Drosophila* salivaries, vesicles of the endoplasmic reticulum are enlarged and filled with electron-dense material, and occasionally they appear connected with membranes of the Golgi substance, suggesting transfer of material from one to the other component. Secretory granules of a variety of sizes are visible, from small Golgi-like vesicles to large, strongly PAS-positive inclusions. During the late larval secretion phase these inclusions pass out through the microvillar border of the cell apex, and enlarge the lumen of the gland.

ACKNOWLEDGMENTS

The invaluable technical assistance of Mr. Irvin Heilmann, who made many of the slides and took a number of the micrographs, is gratefully acknowledged. Many of the photometric measurements on *Sciara* were made by Dr. Ellen M. Rasch, and will appear elsewhere in greater detail. Initial work on cytochemistry and electron microscopy of *Drosophila* was undertaken in this laboratory by Dr. Miriam F. Schurin, and appears in her Ph.D. thesis (1957). The skilled assistance in electron microscopy of Mrs. Betty Jane Adams is also acknowledged with appreciation. The work was aided by grants from the U.S. Public Health Service, the National Science Foundation, and the Abbott Memorial Fund. Sciara stocks were kindly provided by Dr. Helen Crouse.

REFERENCES

Alfert, M. (1950), A cytochemical study of oogenesis and cleavage in the mouse. *J. Cell. Comp. Physiol.*, 36:381-409.
—— (1954), Composition and structure of giant chromosomes. *Intern. Rev. Cytol.*, 3:131-176.
—— and W. Balamuth (1957), Differential micronuclear polyteny in a population of the ciliate *Tetrahymena pyriformis*. *Chromosoma*, 8:371-379.
—— and I. Geschwind (1953), A selective staining method for the basic proteins of cell nuclei. *Proc. Nat. Acad. Sci. U.S.*, 39:991-999.
Atwood, K. C. (1960), Sequential deoxyribonucleic acid replication. *Science*, 132: 617-618.
Baker, W. K. (1953), V-type position effects of a gene in *Drosophila virilis* normally located in heterochromatin. *Genetics*, 38:328-344.

Bauer, H. (1935), Der Afbau der Chromosomen aus den Speicheldrüsen von *Chironomus thummi* Kiefer. *Z. Zellforsch.*, 23:280-313.

—— and T. Caspersson (1948), Cytochemical observations on nucleolus formation in *Chironomus. Proc. Intern. Congr. Genet. 8th Congr., Stockholm*, p. 533.

Bayreuther, K. (1952), Extrachromosomale Feulgen-positive Körper (Nukleinkörper) in der Oogenese der Tipuliden. *Naturwiss.*, 39:71.

—— (1956), Die Oogenese der Tipuliden. *Chromosoma*, 7:508-557.

Becker, H. J. (1959), Die Puffs der Speicheldrüsenchromosomen von *Drosophila melanogaster. Chromosoma*, 10:654-678.

Beermann, W. (1952), Chromosomenkonstanz und spezifiche Modifikationen der Chromosomenstruktur in der Entwicklung und Organdifferenzierung von *Chironomus tentans. Chromosoma*, 5:139-198.

—— (1957), Nuclear differentiation and functional morphology of chromosomes. *Cold Spring Harbor Symposia Quant. Biol.*, 21:217-232.

—— (1959), Chromosomal differentiation in insects, in *Developmental Cytology*, D. Rudnick, ed.,The Ronald Press Company, New York, pp. 83-103.

—— and G. Bahr (1954), The submicroscopic structure of the Balbiani-ring. *Exp. Cell Research*, 6:195-201.

Bendich, A., P. J. Russell, and G. B. Brown (1953), On the heterogeneity of the desoxyribonucleic acids. *J. Biol. Chem.*, 203:305-318.

Boss, J. M. N. (1959), The contribution of the chromosomes to the telophase nucleus in cultures of fibroblasts of the adult crested newt *Triturus cristatus carnifex. Exp. Cell Research*, 18:197-216.

Breuer, M. E., and C. Pavan (1955), Behavior of polytene chromosomes of *Rhynchosciara angelae* at different stages of larval development. *Chromosoma*, 7:371-386.

Buck, J. B., and R. D. Boche (1938), Some properties of living chromosomes. *The Collecting Net*, 13:201-203.

Callan, H. G. (1955), Recent work on the structure of cell nuclei. *Symposium on Fine Structure of Cells, Leiden, Intern. Union Biol. Sci.*, B 21:89-109.

—— and H. C. Macgregor (1958), Action of deoxyribonuclease on lampbrush chromosomes. *Nature*, 181: 1479-1480.

Caspersson, T. (1950), *Cell Growth and Cell Function*. W. W. Norton & Company, Inc., New York.

Cavalieri, L. F., B. H. Rosenberg, and J. F. Deutsch (1959), The subunit of desoxyribonucleic acid. *Biophys. Biochem. Research Commun.*, 1:124-128.

Clever, U., and P. Karlson (1960), Induktion von Puff-veränderungen in den Speicheldrüsenchromosomen von *Chironomus tentans* durch Ecdyson. *Exp. Cell Research*, 20:623-626.

Crampton, C. F., W. H. Stein, and S. Moore (1957), Comparative studies on chromatographically purified histones. *J. Biol. Chem.*, 225:363-386.

Crouse, H. (1943), Translocations in *Sciara;* their bearing on chromosome behavior and sex determination. *Missouri Agri. Exp. Sta. Res. Bull.*, 379:1-75.

—— (1954), X-ray breakage of lily chromosomes at first meiotic metaphase. *Science*, 119:485-487.

Daly, M. M., and A. E. Mirsky (1955), Histones with high lysine content. *J. Gen. Physiol.*, 38:405-413.

DeRobertis, E., W. Nowinski, and F. Saez (1960), *General Cytology*, W. B. Saunders Company, Philadelphia (3d ed.), p. 272.

Dobzhansky, T. (1944), Distribution of heterochromatin in the chromosomes of *Drosophila pallidipennis. Am. Naturalist*, 78:193-213.

Ephrussi, B., and G. W. Beadle (1936), A technique of transplantation for *Drosophila*. *Am. Naturalist*, 70:218-225.

Evans, W. L. (1956), The effects of cold treatment on the desoxyribonucleic acid (DNA) content in cells of selected plants and animals. *Cytologia*, 21:417-432.

Fabergé, A. C. (1958), Relation between chromatid-type and chromosome-type breakage-fusion-bridge cycles in maize endosperm. *Genetics*, 43:737-749.

Ficq, A. (1955), Etude autoradiographique du métabolisme des protéines et des acides nucléique au cours de l'oogenèse chez les Batraciens. *Exp. Cell Research*, 9:286-293.

—— and C. Pavan (1957), Autoradiography of polytene chromosomes of *Rhynchosciara angelae* at different stages of larval development. *Nature*, 180:983-984.

Flax, M., and M. Himes (1952), Microspectrophotometric analysis of metachromatic staining of nucleic acids. *Physiol. Zoöl.*, 25:297-311.

Freese, E. (1959), The arrangement of DNA in the chromosome. *Cold Spring Harbor Symposia Quant. Biol.*, 23:13-18.

Gall, J. G. (1956a), Small granules in the amphibian oocyte nucleus and their relationship to RNA. *J. Biophys. Biochem. Cytol.* Suppl. 2:393-396.

—— (1956b), On the submicroscopic structure of chromosomes. *Brookhaven Symposia in Biol.*, 8:17-32.

—— (1958), Chromosomal differentiation, in *Chemical Basis of Development*, McElroy and Glass, eds., Johns Hopkins Press, Baltimore, pp. 103-135.

—— and W. W. Johnson (1960), Is there "metabolic" DNA in the mouse seminal vesicle? *J. Biophys. Biochem. Cytol.*, 7:657-666.

Gay, H. (1955), Serial sections of smears for electron microscopy. *Stain Technol.* 30:239-242.

—— (1957), Nucleocytoplasmic relations in *Drosophila*. *Cold Spring Harbor Symposia Quant. Biol.*, 21:257-268.

Geitler, L. (1937), Die Analyse des Kernbaus und der Kernteilung der Wasserläufer *Gerris lateralis* und *Gerris lacustris* (Hemiptera, Heteroptera) und die Somadifferenzierung. *Z. Zellforsch*, 26:641-672.

Giardina, A. (1901), Origine dell'oocite e delle cellule nutrici nel *Dytiscus*. *Intern. Monatschr. Anat. Physiol.*, 18:1-68.

Guyénot, E., and M. Danon (1953), Chromosomes et ovocytes de Batraciens. *Rev. Suisse zool.*, 60:1-130.

Hall, C. E., and M. Litt (1959), Morphological features of DNA macromolecules as seen with the electron microscope. *J. Biophys. Biochem. Cytol.*, 4:1-4.

Hannah, A. (1951), Localization and function of heterochromatin in *Drosophila melanogaster*. *Advances in Genetics*, M. Demerec, ed., Academic Press, Inc., New York, vol. 4, pp. 87-127.

Heitz, E. (1931), Nukleolen und Chromosomen in der Gattung *Vicia*. *Planta*, 15: 495-505.

—— and H. Bauer (1933), Beweise für die Chromosomenstruktur der Kernschliefen in den Knäuelkernen von *Bibio hortulanus* L. (*Cytologische Untersuchungen an Dipteran*, I.) *Z. Zellforsch.*, 17:67-82.

Horn, E. C., and C. L. Ward (1957), The localization of basic proteins in the nuclei of larval *Drosophila* salivary glands. *Proc. Nat. Acad. Sci. U.S.*, 43:776-779.

Hotchkiss, R. D. (1955), The biological role of the deoxypentose nucleic acids, in *The Nucleic Acids*, E. Chargaff and J. N. Davidson, eds., Academic Press, Inc., New York, vol. 2, pp. 435-473.

Hughes-Schrader, S. (1940), The meiotic chromosomes of the male *Llaveiella tac-*

nechina Morrison (Coccidae) and the question of the tertiary split. *Biol. Bull.*, 78:312-337.

—— and F. Schrader (1957), The *Nezara* complex (Pentatomidae-Heteroptera) and its taxonomic and cytological status. *J. Morph.*, 101:1-24.

Huskins, C. L. (1947), The subdivision of the chromosomes and their multiplication in non-dividing tissues: Possible interpretations in terms of gene structure and gene action. *Am. Naturalist*, 81:401-434.

Jacob, F., and E. L. Wollmann (1958), Les episomes, éléments génétiques ajoutés. *Compt. Rend. Acad. Sci.*, 247:154-156.

Kaufmann, B. P. (1934), Somatic mitoses of *Drosophila melanogaster*. *J. Morph.* 56:125-155.

—— (1948), Chromosome structure in relation to the chromosome cycle. *Botan. Rev.*, 14:57-126.

—— and M. R. McDonald (1957), The organization of the chromosome. *Cold Spring Harbor Symposia Quant. Biol.*, 21:233-246.

——,H. Gay, and M. R. McDonald (1960), Organizational patterns within chromosomes. *Intern. Rev. Cytol.*, 9:77-127.

Kroeger, H. (1960), The induction of new puffing patterns by transplantation of salivary gland nuclei into egg cytoplasm of *Drosophila*. *Chromosoma*, 11:129-145.

Kuwada, Y. (1939), Chromosome structure. A critical review. *Cytologia*, 10:213-256.

LaFontaine, J. G., and H. Ris (1958), An electron microscope study of lampbrush chromosomes. *J. Biophys. Biochem. Cytol.*, 4:99-106.

LaCour, L. F., E. M. Deely, and J. Chayen (1956), Variations in the amount of Feulgen stain in nuclei of plants grown at different temperatures. *Nature*, 177:272-273.

Leuchtenberger, C., and F. Schrader (1952), Variation in the amount of desoxyribose nucleic acid (DNA) in cells of the same tissue and its correlation with secretory function. *Proc. Nat. Acad. Sci. U.S.*, 38:99-105.

L'Heritier, P. (1958), The heriditary viruses of *Drosophila*. *Advances in Virus Research*, K. M. Smith and M. A. Lauffer, eds., Academic Press, Inc., New York, vol. 5, pp. 195-245.

Lima-de-Faria, A. (1959), Differential uptake of tritiated thymidine into hetero- and euchromatin in *Melanoplus* and *Secale*. *J. Biophys. Biochem. Cytol.*, 6:457-466.

Lowman, F. G. (1956), Electron microscope studies of *Drosophila* salivary gland chromosomes. *Chromosoma*, 8:30-52.

McClintock, B. (1938), The production of homozygous deficient tissues with mutant characteristics by means of the aberrant mitotic behavior of ring-shaped chromosomes. *Genetics*, 26:542-571.

—— (1941), Spontaneous alterations in chromosome size and form in *Zea mays*. *Cold Spring Harbor Symposia Quant. Biol.*, 9:72-81.

McMaster-Kaye, R. (1960), The metabolic characteristics of nucleolar, chromosomal, and cytoplasmic ribonucleic acid of *Drosophila* salivary glands. *J. Biophys. Biochem. Cytol.*, 8:365-378.

Malogowkin, C., and D. F. Poulson (1958), Infective transfer of maternally inherited abnormal sex-ratio in *Drosophila willistoni*. *Science*, 126:32.

Manton, I. (1945), New evidence for the telophase split in *Todea barbara*. *Am. J. Botany*, 32:342-348.

Mather, K. (1944), The genetical activity of heterochromatin. *Proc. Roy. Soc.* (London), *B* 132:308-332.

Mechelke, F. (1953), Reversible Strukturmodifikationen der Speicheldrüsenchromosomen von *Acricotopus lucidus*. *Chromosoma*, 5:511-543.

Metz, C. W., M. S. Moses, and E. N. Hoppe (1926), Chromosome behavior and genetic
behavior in *Sciara*. I. Chromosome behavior in the spermatocyte divisions.
Z. Abstamm. Vererb., 42:237-270.

Mirsky, A. E., and H. Ris (1947), The chemical composition of isolated chromosomes. *J. Gen. Physiol.*, 31:1-18.

Mitra, S. (1958), Effects of X-rays on chromosomes of *Lilium longiflorum* during
meiosis. *Genetics*, 43:771-789.

Nebel, B. (1941), Structure of *Tradescantia* and *Trillium* chromosomes with particular emphasis on the number of chromonemata. *Cold Spring Harbor Symposia
Quant. Biol.*, 9:7-12.

Öestergren, G., and T. Wakonig (1954), True or apparent subchromatid breakage
and the induction of labile states in cytological chromosome loci. *Botan.
Notiser.*, 4:357-375.

Ohno, S., W. D. Kaplan, and R. Kinosita (1958), Demonstration of bipartite spiral
structure on spermatogonial anaphase chromosomes of *Mus musculus*. *Exp.
Cell Research*, 15:426-428.

Palade, G. E. (1959), Functional changes in the structure of cell components. In
Subcellular Particles, Hayashi, ed., The Ronald Press Company, New York,
pp. 64-83.

Palay, S. L., and A. Claude (1949), An electron microscope study of salivary
gland chromosomes by the replica method. *J. Exp. Med.*, 89:431-438.

Pavan, C. (1959), Morphological and physiological aspects of chromosomal activities. *Proc. Intern. Congr. Genetics, 10th Congr.*, pp. 321-336.

—— and M. E. Breuer (1955), Differences in nucleic acid content of the loci in
polytene chromosomes of *Rhynchosciara angelae* according to tissues and
larval stages. *Symposium on Cell Secretion, Belo Horizonte, Brazil*,
pp- 90-99.

Pelc, S. R. (1958), Nuclear uptake of labeled adenine in the seminal vesicle of the
mouse. *Exp. Cell Research*, 14:301-315.

—— and L. F. LaCour (1959), The incorporation of H^3-thymidine in newly differentiated nuclei of roots of *Vicia faba*. *Experimentia*, 15:131.

Pelling, C. (1959), Chromosomal synthesis of ribonucleic acid as shown by incorporation of uridine labeled with tritium. *Nature*, 184:655-656.

Porter, K. R. (1960), Problems in the study of nuclear fine structure. *Proc. Intern.
Conf. on Electron Microscopy, 4th Conf.*, Springer-Verlag, Berlin, vol. 2,
pp. 186-199.

Poulson, D. F., and C. W. Metz (1938), Studies on the structure of nucleolus-
forming regions and related structures in the giant salivary gland chromosomes
of Diptera. *J. Morph.*, 63:363-395.

Ris, H. (1957), Chromosome structure, in *Chemical Basis of Heredity*, McElroy and
Glass, eds., Johns Hopkins Press, Baltimore, pp. 23-62.

—— (1959), Discussion in *Brookhaven Symposium*, 12:118-120.

—— and H. Crouse (1945), Structure of the salivary gland chromosomes of Diptera.
Proc. Nat. Acad. Sci. U.S., 31:321-327.

—— and A. E. Mirsky (1949), Quantitative cytochemical determination of desoxyribonucleic acid with the Feulgen nucleal reaction. *J. Gen. Physiol.*, 33:125-145.

Rudkin, G. T., and S. L. Corlette (1957), Disproportionate synthesis of DNA in a
polytene chromosome region. *Proc. Nat. Acad. Sci. U.S.*, 43:964-968.

—— and P. Woods (1959), Incorporation of H^3 cytidine and H^3 thymidine into giant chromosomes of *Drosophila* during puff formation. *Proc. Nat. Acad. Sci. U.S.*, 45:997-1003.

Sax, K., and E. D. King (1955), An X-ray analysis of chromosome duplication. *Proc. Nat. Acad. Sci. U.S.*, 41:150-155.

Schultz, J. (1941), The evidence of the nucleoprotein nature of the gene. *Cold Spring Harbor Symposia Quant. Biol.*, 9:55-65.

—— (1957), The relation of the heterochromatic chromosome regions to the nucleic acids of the cell. *Cold Spring Harbor Symposia Quant. Biol.*, 21:307-328.

Schurin, M. (1957), Cytochemistry and electron microscopy of *Drosophila virilis* salivary chromosomes. Ph.D. thesis 3605, University of Chicago.

Schwartz, D. (1958), Deoxyribonucleic acid side-chain model of the chromosomes. *Nature*, 181:1149-1150.

Sirlin, J. L. (1960), Facts and speculation on the function of nuclear components, in *The Cell Nucleus*, J. S. Mitchell, ed., Academic Press, Inc., New York, pp. 35-48.

Sonnenblick, B. P. (1950), The early embryology of *Drosophila melanogaster*, in *The Biology of Drosophila*, M. Demerec, ed., John Wiley & Sons, Inc., New York, pp. 62-167.

Stedman, E., and E. Stedman (1950), Cell specificity of histones. *Nature*, 166:780-781.

Steffensen, D. (1959), A comparative view of the chromosome. *Brookhaven Symposium*, 12:103-118.

Stich, H. F., and J. M. Naylor (1958), Variation of desoxyribonucleic acid content of specific chromosome regions. *Exp. Cell Research*, 14:442-445.

Swanson, C. P. (1947), X-ray and ultraviolet studies on pollen tube chromosomes. II. The quadripartite structure of the prophase chromosomes of *Tradescantia*. *Proc. Nat. Acad. Sci. U.S.*, 33:229-232.

Swift, H. (1950a), The desoxyribose nucleic acid content of animal nuclei. *Physiol. Zoöl.*, 23:169-198.

—— (1950b), The constancy of desoxyribose nucleic acid in plant nuclei. *Proc. Nat. Acad. Sci. U.S.*, 36:643-654.

—— (1953), Quantitative aspects of nuclear nucleoproteins. *Intern. Rev. Cytol.*, 2:1-76.

—— (1958), Cytoplasmic particulates and basophilia, in *The Chemical Basis of Development*, McElroy and Glass, eds., Johns Hopkins Press, Baltimore, pp. 174-210.

—— (1959a), Studies on nucleolar function, in *A Symposium on Molecular Biology*, Zirkle, ed., University of Chicago Press, pp. 266-303.

—— (1959b), Studies on nuclear fine structure. *Brookhaven Symposium*, 12:134-151.

—— and R. G. Kleinfeld (1953), DNA in grasshopper spermatogenesis, oogenesis and cleavage. *Physiol. Zoöl.*, 26:301-311.

Taylor, J. H. (1957), The time and mode of duplication of chromosomes. *Am. Naturalist*, 91:209-221.

—— (1958), Sister chromatid exchanges in tritium-labeled chromosomes. *Genetics*, 43:515-529.

—— (1960), Asynchronous duplication of chromosomes in cultured cells of the Chinese hamster. *J. Biophys. Biochem. Cytol.*, 7:455-464.

——, P. S. Woods, and W. L. Hughes (1957), The organization and duplication of chromosomes as revealed by autoradiographic studies using tritium-labeled thymidine. *Proc. Nat. Acad. Sci. U.S.*, 43:122-128.

Tobias, P. V. (1956), *Chromosomes, Sex-cells and Evolution in a Mammal*. Percy Lund, Humphries, and Company, London.

Tomlin, S. G., and H. G. Callan (1951), Preliminary account of an electron microscope study of chromosomes from newt oocytes. *Quart. J. Microscop. Sci.*, 92:221-224.

Tschermak-Woess, E. (1960), Uber den Einbau von H^3-thymidin in die DNS und die Endomitosetätigkeit in der Wurzel von *Vicia faba*. *Chromosoma*, 11:25-28.

Vincent, W. S. (1957), Heterogeneity of nuclear ribonucleic acid. *Science*, 126:306-307.

Wilkins, M. H. F. (1957), Physical studies on the molecular structure of deoxyribose nucleic acid and nucleoprotein. *Cold Spring Harbor Symposia Quant. Biol.*, 21:75-90.

Wilson, E. B. (1925), *The Cell in Development and Heredity*. The Macmillan Company, New York (3d ed.), pp. 138-139.

Woodard, J., E. Rasch, and H. Swift (1961), Nucleic acid and protein metabolism during the mitotic cycle in *Vicia faba*. *J. Biophys. Biochem. Cytol.*, 9:445-462.

Yasuzumi, G., Z. Odate, and Y. Ota (1951), The fine structure of salivary chromosomes. *Cytologia*, 16:233-242.

Chapter Three

Nucleo-Cytoplasmic Relations in Normal and Malignant Cells

TORBJÖRN CASPERSSON

Institute for Cell Research, Karolinska Institutet, Stockholm, Sweden

In the study of the manner in which the nucleus influences the general cell processes two questions take precedence. One concerns the way the early chemical processes in gene activity take place within the cell nucleus and the other the manner in which they are reflected in the cytoplasm. Our knowledge in this field is still very limited despite attacks upon it with numerous different methods. Enzyme chemical investigations have shown that the nucleus performs functions in the cell metabolic activity both through induction of enzyme synthesis and through regulation of enzyme function. Metabolic studies with radioisotopes have revealed an intimate interaction between certain groups of substances in the nucleus and the cytoplasm, especially the ribose nucleotides. Numerous morphologic observations, some dating back many years, also show the occurrence of an intense exchange of substances between nucleus and cytoplasm in certain phases of the cell activity. That this exchange can assume imposing proportions is evident, especially from work with quantitative cytochemical methods. High-resolution ultramicrospectrography, microinterferometry, and also microradiography have their particularly favorable areas of application in this field and have contributed fundamentally to broadening our knowledge of it.

For work in this field elaborate biophysical tools are needed, and the rate of development in the field is conditioned by the technical problems. The evolution of suitable methods has accelerated during recent years, and in my opinion, we are now at the beginning of a period of rapid expansion on this front.

My aim is to discuss the particular individual types of problems in nucleo-cytoplasmic relations to which quantitative cytochemical methods have been applied and thereafter to present examples of the further working possibilities made accessible by technical developments during recent years.

STUDIES ON BIOLOGICAL MATERIALS

The early investigations with quantitative ultramicrospectrography in ultraviolet and visible regions (Caspersson, 1950) almost twenty years ago showed that the scale of the synthesizing processes taking place around the gene-bearing elements in the nucleus, and also around the nuclear membrane in connection with cell growth and cell function, is surprisingly great. Another early and somewhat unexpected observation was the very high concentrations of material present in certain nuclear elements — in the first-line mitotic chromosomes and certain types of nucleoli. Dry-substance values above 60 per cent are not unusual. These observations show that many nucleo-cytoplasmic interactions are reflected in changes in the composition of the individual cell components of sufficient magnitude to place them within easy reach of quantitative cytochemical methods. On the other hand, the presence of such high concentrations of substances introduces considerable technical difficulties. In the first place, it means there is an enormous degree of inhomogeneity, which complicates the work with optical methods and especially the measurements of total quantities of different substances in the cell parts. In the second place, conditions are such that the dry-substance concentrations are so high that special methods must be developed for the determination of the optical constants for different substance groups under the conditions encountered in the cell. The optical constants obtained on dilute solutions cannot be applied directly in the determination of concentrations on the basis of absorption or refraction-index data from the biological object.

In three types of biological object cytochemical study of the nucleo-cytoplasmic relations was started early. The first type concerned the substances appearing around the gene-bearing loci in connection with cytoplasmic metabolic processes — in this field of study the *salivary gland type of nuclei* from certain insects afforded particularly favorable working conditions. The second type was *rapidly growing tissues primarily from higher organisms* in which the cytoplasmic-RNA synthesis and the nucleolar development were studied. The third type comprised cells of the second type in which disturbances in the RNA metabolism and the nucleolar apparatus occur as a result of certain pathologic processes, principally *tumor development* and *virus infection.*

Among the special types of cell material that have been used to obtain more detailed information on primary processes of nucleo-cytoplasmic relationships, the *salivary gland type of nuclei* in certain insects have proved exceptionally well suited. As a result of the unique combination of endomitosis and somatic pairing after the last cell division, which takes place in the early larval stage, unusually large nuclei appear during the larval development in which the function corresponds to that of ordinary nuclei but in which the main features of the metaphase chromosome's structure are still present. They are especially well suited to cytochemical studies with ultramicrospectrographic methods and afford a unique opportunity for investigation of the relation between the chemical changes in the vicinity of individual gene loci and the cell function (Caspersson, 1941). Ultramicrospectrographic investigations show, for example in Drosophila, how, as the cell grows, and therewith the chromosome volume as well, interbands with high protein content appear between the individual, gene-bearing, DNA-rich bands. These were interpreted as primary effects of the activity of different genes — an accumulation of early gene products around the gene loci. In the same object, which has prominent heterochromatic chromocenters in the salivary glands, it was also possible to demonstrate intimate relations between its chemical composition and that of the principal nucleolus (Caspersson and Schultz, 1940; Caspersson, Schultz, and Aquilonius, 1940). This indicates that the substance of the latter is derived from this heterochromatin but has accumulated not only between the chromomeres but also, because of its large quantity, outside them. Similar phenomena were also evident in Chironomus, which in some cases affords better conditions for cytochemical studies because of the size of the chromosomes (Caspersson, 1956).

These observations are important for our understanding of nucleolar function. The conception — nucleolus — is still complex and relatively undefined; it includes structures of different compositions within the nucleus of the cell. When, in connection with the gene function, protein and RNA-containing masses occur about gene loci, it is to be expected that these would give rise in certain cases to nucleolar formations, especially when particularly active gene groups are involved. That there are two reasons for the accumulation to a greater extent of such substances further complicates the matter. It can be due either to an especially strong synthesis around specific gene groups or to the collection of substances from different parts of the genome on special "nucleolar organizers." Naturally it is often difficult to differentiate these two phenomena. In certain material, for example the large nucleolus in the salivary glands from Chironomus species, it seems highly probable that a localized, extremely intensive synthesis occurs (Caspersson, 1956; Vogt Köhne, 1960).

The cytochemical studies on *tissues in rapid growth* show that a special process, the synthesis of the principal mass of the cytoplasmic proteins, is accompanied by a particularly extensive synthesis of nucleolar substance. The cytochemical data supporting this hypothesis are obtained from the second type of material mentioned earlier — rapidly growing tissues from higher organisms. In such tissues one process is singularly striking: the occurrence of unusually large nucleoli at the same time that large RNA masses appear around the nuclear membrane and later farther out in the cytoplasm. This takes place concurrently with an increase in the cytoplasmic proteins. Figure 1 shows a diagram of this so-called principal nucleolus mechanism (Caspersson, 1941, 1950), which seems to be a universal cell mechanism active in the processes of cytoplasmic protein synthesis. More detailed analysis showed that, with the onset of a rapid growth process, nucleolar substances first appear within parts of the chromatin in rapidly increasing quantities so that this chromatin, which was termed "nucleolus-associated chromatin," appears to "explode." The nucleolus is very rich in proteins and can contain RNA up to several per cent of the dry weight. At the nuclear membrane and outside it, the RNA concentrations can attain the same order of magnitude in very rapid growth.

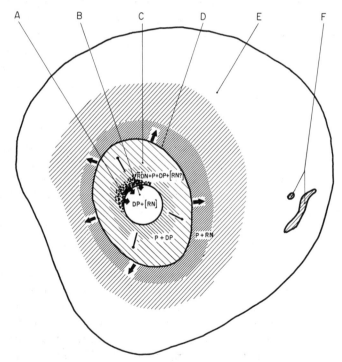

FIG. 1. Diagram of the function of the principal nucleolus system.
A. Nucleolus-associated chromatin. B. Principal nucleolus.
C. Nucleus. D. Nuclear membrane. E. Cytoplasm. F. RNA-containing systems in the cytoplasm. (*From Caspersson, Cell Growth and Cell Function, 1950.*)

This indicates clearly a transportation of substances from the nucleolus-associated chromatin and the nucleolus towards the nuclear membrane and cytoplasm where processes of the synthesis are carried on.

This *principal nucleolus system* has been demonstrated in a very large number of different tissues from different organisms. The degree of its development, measured by the quantity of nucleolar substances and the RNA concentration in the cytoplasm, is the more marked the more rapidly the cytoplasmic protein formation processes take place, irrespective of whether it is a question of true growth processes or of cell processes of another type that require rapid protein synthesis. The phenomenon is so constant that it has been possible to use it to determine whether or not cells are in the process of rapid cytoplasmic protein formation.

Cytophysiologically it is understandable that the protein formation in the cytoplasm, which is beyond all comparison the most comprehensive of all synthesizing processes that an average tissue cell has to perform, should require a special cytogenetic mechanism and that, when the processes are so extensive, the cytochemical expression becomes particularly prominent.

The nucleolus-associated chromatin in the Drosophila salivary gland cell is heterochromatic, as mentioned earlier. This is the best analyzed case thus far. Heterochromatic regions have been shown to exert a strong influence on both nucleotide and protein metabolism in the cell nucleus and cytoplasm (Caspersson and Schultz, 1940). This and certain other indirect evidence can be produced in support of the assumption that the nucleolus-associated chromatin corresponds in character to heterochromatin. It seems probable (Caspersson, 1941, 1950) that the heterochromatin contains reduplications of a small number of genes for the special purpose of meeting the tremendous demand for synthesizing activity that arises in conjunction particularly with the rapid protein synthesis during growth. During the past few years other support for this view has also been advanced (see, for example, Wright, 1959).

When we examine this system for the function of the principal nucleolus against the background of the general synthesizing activities that lead to the appearance of proteins around gene loci in connection with the gene function, it does not appear to be other than a final or extreme link in a chain of gene-function processes of varying scope, where the quantity of substances around the different gene groups roughly reflects the degree of activity.

This general picture seems to be rather well corroborated by different observations in other lines of research in this general field. An intimate interaction between certain chromosome regions and the nuclear membrane has been beautifully demonstrated electron-microscopically (Gay, 1956, 1960). Relations between the nuclear membrane, endoplasmatic reticulum and ergastoplasm have also been demonstrated by various groups. The assumption of transportation of RNA from the region of the principal nucleolus to the cytoplasm has also received support from radioautographic investigations by several research teams. In principle the cytochemical picture is in accordance with the assumption that the DNA information is transmitted to a newly synthesized RNA chain, which subsequently mediates the protein synthesis. However, in cytochemical work proteins are always encountered simultaneously with RNA or DNA. No metaphase chromosome examined so far has been found to contain proteins in quantities of a lesser order than the nucleotides. The proteins always greatly predominate in the nucleoli. Therefore, the material that is transported from the immediate vicinity of the gene-bearing elements to the cytoplasm appears to be RNA plus protein. Certain staining and absorption conditions indicate with some probability that relatively large quantities of hexone bases are present in the proteins occurring in conjunction with both DNA and RNA within the nucleus. Thus in the formation of the cytoplasmic proteins it is a question essentially of two protein-synthesizing processes which must be distinguished. On the one hand, protein synthesis takes place at the gene chain, presumably mediated by RNA. The other process is the actual cytoplasmic protein synthesis, which takes place in the presence of RNA at and outside the nuclear membrane.

The third type of material on which early cytochemical studies of the nucleo-cytoplasmic relations were started was *tumor cells* and *virus-infected cells.* In such tissues the cytoplasmic protein metabolism is often greatly disturbed, and extensive changes were also observed in the nucleolar system and the RNA metabolism in the cytoplasm. It was found that in rapidly growing, cytoplasm-rich tumors the principal nucleolus system is in extreme function. Conspicuous disturbances in the system were also observed. This led to the hypothesis that the occurrence of disturbances in the heterochromatin system is one of the factors required for the malignant type of growth. Subsequent observations have supported that assumption, but the technical difficulties in the cytochemical work were tremendous, and, notwithstanding that this field is one of the most intriguing in the cytochemistry of today, it has taken a long time to develop suitable techniques for the work.

The interaction of different virus types with the principal nucleolus system is a field of importance. It has been shown that a number of different virus types cause well-defined disturbances in the function of this system. The disturbances are highly characteristic for certain virus species. It is a common finding that the infection starts the function of the system and then interferes with its normal course (for references on the tumor and virus field see Caspersson, 1950). Little work has been done in this field lately in spite of the fact that suitable techniques are available.

PRESENT STATUS OF THE CYTOCHEMICAL TECHNIQUES SUITABLE FOR THE STUDY OF NUCLEO-CYTOPLASMIC RELATIONS

The data I have presented thus far show that the quantitative cytochemical approach gives access to the study of several fundamental aspects of the nucleo-cytoplasmic relations. They also show clearly how the advances in the field are closely tied to the progress of the measuring techniques. In the last few years there has been considerable progress on the technical side, which has as yet been exploited only in special cases for biological studies in the field under discussion.

The greatest difficulties in the study of the composition of the individual nuclear structures arise in part from the frequently exceedingly high concentrations of substances in these structures and in part from the fact that the work involved in determinations of total quantities in such inhomogeneous cell material is so extraordinarily time consuming.

The first of these obstacles has been largely eliminated by the development of intercoordinated measuring procedures applicable to the same object in both optical and roentgen regions and which also permit determinations of the optical constants needed for the data analysis with the aid of model systems.

The other difficulty — the time factor in the work — has led to the development of automatic measuring procedures, which have resulted in a tremendous time saving.

These procedures have been described in detail in the literature to which I refer you for particulars (for example, Caspersson and collaborators, *Experimental Cell Research*, Suppl. 4, 1957). Diagrams present a schematic picture of the most important procedures in the form best suited for work on the fields in question here. "UMSP" represents a scanning integrating ultramicrospectrograph working with a higher resolution than 1μ. It can be used for determination of absorption spectra of object elements in ultraviolet and visible regions as well as for total quantity determinations with the aid of scanning measurements in combination with arrangements for electronic data transformation. "Interfer UMP" designates a scanning data-computing microinterferometer working with high resolution, and "X-ray mass MSP" indicates a microradiographic mass

QUANTITATIVE HIGHRESOLUTION ULTRAMICROSPECTROPHOTOMETRY
(ARRANGEMENT SPEC. FOR PROTEIN, RNA AND DNA)

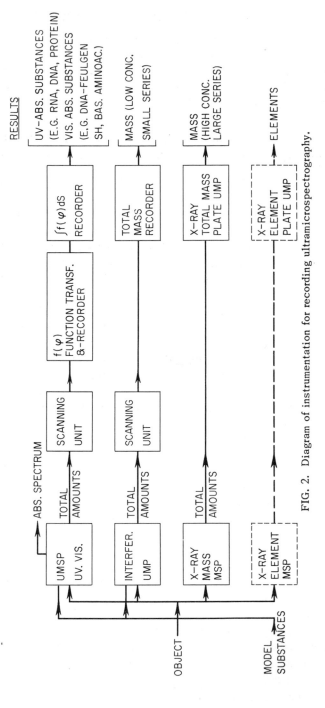

FIG. 2. Diagram of instrumentation for recording ultramicrospectrography.

134

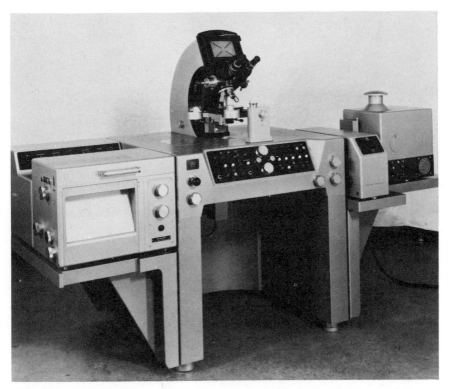

FIG. 3. A scanning high-resolution ultramicrospectrophotometer. (*At present manufactured by C. Zeiss in Western Germany.*)

determination unit especially suitable for high-resolution work in biological systems with low absorption.

The ultramicrospectrographic work and the interferometric work including scanning and data computation can be combined in a "Universal ultramicrospectrophotometer" (Caspersson, 1955), in which the work is rapid and so simple that the instrument is suitable for work in biological laboratories. Figure 3 shows a commercially available model of that instrument recently developed (Caspersson, Lomakka, and Trapp, in press).

Figures 4 and 5 show two examples of the working procedure with objects of the aforementioned types. They have been taken from a series of studies on the development and composition of the nucleolar system during the larval development of Chironomus (Vogt-Köhne, in press). Figure 4 shows absorption curves from spots with a diameter of 0.5 μ from different parts of the small fourth chromosome. Figure 5 illustrates the procedure in determinations of RNA and of total mass in different parts of the same system. As indicated in the

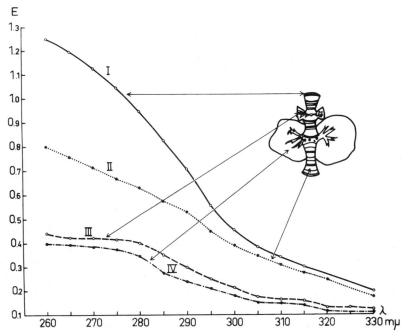

FIG. 4.   Absorption spectra recorded from different spots (smaller than 0.5 μ) in different parts of the fourth chromosome in *Chironomus thummi* larval salivary gland.

small inserted drawing of the chromosome, a series of scanning measurements is made across the chromosome with its nucleolus. All these measurements are recorded after electronic transforma-

FIG. 5.   Diagram of the procedure for determination of total amounts of absorbing and refracting substances in different parts of the same type of chromosomes as in Fig. 4. Above: extinction measurements in ultraviolet. Below: microinterferometric dry-mass determinations.

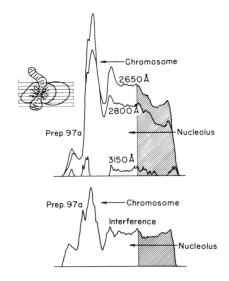

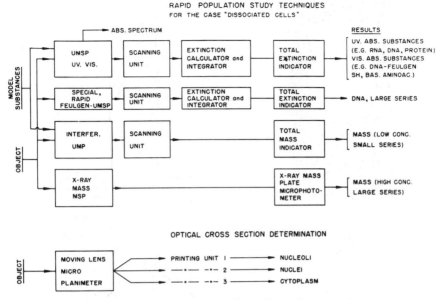

FIG. 6.   Diagram of procedures for cell-population studies.

tion of the transmission data into extinctions or, in the case of the interferometric measurements, into refractive increment. The figure gives only one of the sweeps over the object but demonstrates how it is possible to recognize very precisely the different parts of the object in the recording. The total amounts of substances can then be determined from these recordings. This work is considerably speeded up by the use of special equipment for the curve analysis (Lomakka, 1957).

There are very special technical requirements for the study of the nucleo-cytoplasmic relations in malignantly growing tumor cells. As shown by even the earliest cytochemical investigations, these cell populations, in comparison with normal tissues, are distinguished by exceptionally great variations between the individual cells. This makes it necessary to be able to analyze large cell populations as a rule of the order of several hundred cells. With the methods discussed earlier this is practically unfeasible because of the time factor, which is the principal reason that the DNA, RNA, and nucleolar relations in tumor cell populations have been so little studied cytochemically thus far.

During the past three years, however, especially rapid methods have been developed for this purpose within our institution. They have been designed especially for work on cell populations from which preparations with isolated cells can be produced. These

FIG. 7. A rapid ultramicrospectrophotometer.

methods are not recording but they do work from 10 to 100 times faster than the procedures described earlier.

Figure 6 shows a diagram of these methods in their present form, presented in a manner analogous to that used in Fig. 2. The bottom line represents an automatically recording microplanimeter, an instrument developed especially for the study of nucleolar volume in large cell series.

Figure 7 shows the appearance of the rapid optical ultramicrospectrograph (T. Caspersson, G. Lomakka, and O. Caspersson, 1959) and Fig. 8 the rapid microinterferometer (see Lomakka and Issler).

Figure 9a, b, and c, from a study by N. Ringertz, E. Klein, and the writer, demonstrates the type of data obtainable in an analysis of the growth in a tumor cell population. From such measurements it is possible to deduce directly the distribution of and the changes in the total mass per cell and the DNA and RNA content in cytoplasm, nucleus, and nucleolus, for example.

These procedures are now being used to an ever-increasing extent for studies of the nucleo-cytoplasmic relations in different tumor spe-

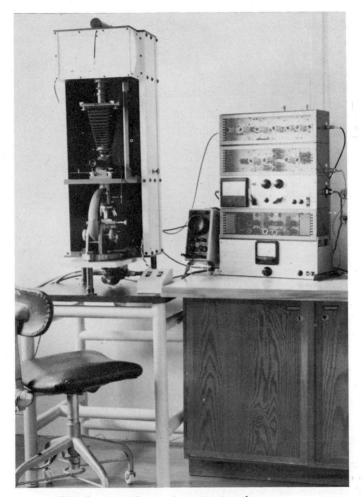

FIG. 8. A rapid-scanning microinterferometer.

cies and, for comparison, in certain normal tissues. They are exploited also in study of the early changes in the nucleolar-cytoplasmic
nucleotide apparatus during carcinogenesis.

The possibilities opened up by these methods for investigation of
the way in which external factors such as irradiation and chemical
substances affect the complex nucleo-cytoplasmic relations during
growth, and which are accessible cytochemically, are of particular
importance. In connection with the efforts to develop chemotherapeutic methods for the treatment of tumors it is necessary to collect
information on whether different groups of substances affect different
phases in the interaction between nucleus and cytoplasm. This can-

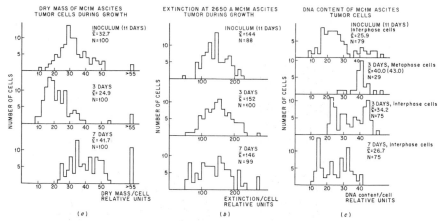

FIG. 9. Histograms of the distribution of dry mass, total extinction at 2,650 A and of Feulgen-positive substance in a population of a mouse ascites tumor at different stages of growth. N = number of cells measured. ε = mean.

not be accomplished without cytochemical methods of population analysis. Investigations during the past two years of the effects of different types of chemotherapeutic agents on the RNA and cytoplasmic protein metabolism, and of the development of tumor species resistant to certain substances have already shown that this should prove to be a fruitful field for cytochemical work and a field capable of development.

REFERENCES

Caspersson, T. (1940): Die Eiweissverteilung in den Strukturen des Zellkerns. *Chromosoma*, 1:562.

—— (1941): Studies über den Eiweissumsatz der Zelle. *Naturwiss.*, 29:33.

—— (1950): *Cell Growth and Cell Function.* W. W. Norton & Company, Inc., New York.

—— (1955): Quantitative cytochemical methods for the study of cell metabolism. *Experimentia*, 11:45.

—— (1956): Quantitative cytochemical determination on endonuclear structures. *Cold Spring Harbor Symposia Quant. Biol.*, 21.

—— and L. Santesson (1942): Studies on protein metabolism in the cells of epithelial tumours. *Acta Radiol.*, Suppl. 46.

—— and J. Schultz (1940): Ribonucleic acids in both nucleus and cytoplasm and the function of the nucleolus. *Proc. Natl. Acad. Sci. U.S.*, 26:507.

—— —— (1950): Cytochemical measurements in the study of the gene. *Genetics in the 20th century*, New York.

—— , —— , and L. Aquilonius (1940): The genetic control of nucleolar composition. *Proc. Natl. Acad. Sci. U.S.*, 26:515.

—— , T. Fredriksson, and K. G. Thorsson (1953): A microplanimeter for measurement of endonuclear structures. *Hereditas*, 39:201.

—— , E. Klein, and N. R. Ringertz: (under publication).

—— , O. Caspersson, and G. Lomakka (1960): A recording microplanimeter. *Acta Morph. Neerlando-Scandinavica*, 3:205-214. .

——, G. Lomakka, and O. Caspersson (1960): Quantitative cytochemical methods for the study of tumour cell populations. *Biochem. Pharmacology*, 4:113.

—— , —— , G. Svensson, and L. Carlson (1957): Several articles in *Exp. Cell Research*, Suppl. 4.

—— , ——, and L. Trapp: *Exp. Cell Research* (in press).

Gay, H. (1956): Nucleocytoplasmic relations in Drosophila. *Cold Spring Harbor Symposia Quant. Biol.*, 21.

—— (1960): Nuclear control of the cell. *Scientific American*, 1:126.

Lomakka, G. (1957): Computers for microphotometric data analysis. *Exp. Cell Research*, Suppl. 4, 54.

—— and P. Issler: (under publication).

Vogt-Köhne, L.: (under publication).

Wright, S. (1959): Genetics and the hierarchy of biological sciences. *Science*, 130:959-965.

Chapter Four

The Relation of Cell Structure to Metabolic Activity

PHILIP SIEKEVITZ

The Rockefeller Institute , New York

If one were to look at the span from a few decades ago to the present time, one could make out some distinct phases in the techniques
and hence in the ideas, or should I say, in the ideas and hence the
techniques, of biochemistry. First, we could describe what might
best be called a physiological phase; this involved essentially gross
measurements on what went into the organism, gross measurements
on what came out, and inferences on what happened in between. Sometimes the inferences were remarkably prescient; I need only mention
Knoop's wonderful work on beta-oxidation. Later, we can discern the
chemical phase of biochemistry; the isolation of biological and chemical agents, factors, cofactors and substrates, and the elucidation of
some of their chemical interactions. This phase came to pass firstly
because of the realization among biochemists that of necessity they
must learn more about the purely chemical reactions which might
take place in the cell before they could venture into physiological
speculations, and secondly because of the increase in the amount and
in the sensitivity of analytical tools which a biochemist uses. This
phase is still with us, but I think it is coming to an end. I do not think
that I am too far wrong when I say that we have already mapped out
the major features of the purely chemical metabolism of the cell, the
chemical conversion of one compound to another; and all this in just
a few decades! Of course there is still much to be done, but the main
outlines of metabolism, of intermediary metabolism to be exact, are
now known. Thus, the biochemist is ready, and indeed starting, to
go back to the cell from which he had extracted his enzymes and his
compounds. He is ready because he realizes that the remaining questions to be answered in metabolism, the why's and wherefore's of the
syntheses of large molecules, the direction of syntheses, the direction
of metabolic movement throughout the cell, are certainly inseparable
from questions about cell structure. We still need to know the mechanism of many of these synthetic reactions, but it is possible, and
probable, that these mechanisms are tied in with cell morphology,

143

and really cannot be understood unless we learn more about the over-
all physiology of the cell. This feeling on the part of the biochemist
would be only intuitive if he were still unacquainted with cell morphology. But let him look at the pictures of the cell, being shown
these days by the score by electron microscopists, and this intuition
will become a certainty. For, as Fig. 1 shows, gone is the idea of
chemical reactions in a one-phase, soluble environment, for where
is such an environment in the cell? With such a profusion of intracellular structures, of intracellular membranes, of changes in phase,
who can doubt that the enzymatic reactions which take place in such
a milieu might be quite different in scope and direction from the reactions which we assay in an aqueous, one-phase medium? And this

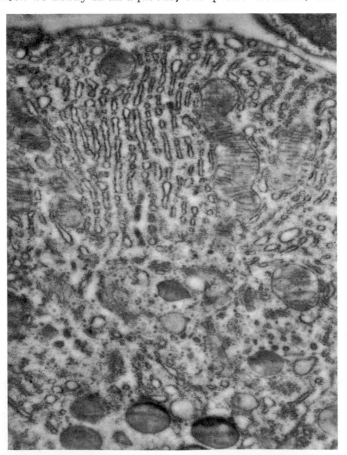

FIG. 1. Electron micrograph of guinea-pig pancreas. Region near
Golgi zone. Shown are endoplasmic reticulum membranes with and
without attached ribonucleoprotein particles. Mitochondria and
zymogen granules (at bottom) are also in the picture. Mag. 18,000 X.
(*Picture, courtesy of G. E. Palade.*)

particularly is what I would like to discuss here, the possible differences in the activity characteristics of enzymes because of their adherence to, indeed of their being a part of, the cellular structure.

As you are all aware, there has been much work done within the last ten years on the localization of components within, or being a part of, various intracellular entities. I am not going to mention anything more in this vein, but merely cite the best recent reviews on this subject (de Duve and Berthet; Hogeboom, Kuff and Schneider; Allfrey), reviews relating the results and also the pitfalls to be expected from using such approaches. Instead, what I am going to concentrate on is the idea, put forth by Schneider, that "physical factors, other than intracellular location, may play a role in metabolic regulation." There is only fragmentary data concerning this idea, but I will cite specific instances which tend to validate it, and cite cases where changes in enzyme activity are probably due to differences in the state of the enzyme, whether it is "soluble" or not or whether it is bound to some cellular structure or not. In doing so, I make no attempt to review the literature, but merely to cull out some experimental results representative enough to make clear certain of my points. However, since today such experiments are still relatively few, speculation on my part will be relatively large.

First, however, I would like to mention a remarkable case of cellular localization, that of the lysosomal hydrolases discovered by de Duve and his collaborators (cf. de Duve). These various hydrolytic enzymes, at least in liver, have one property in common, and that is that they exhibit little or no activity unless something is done to them, and this something is the rupturing of the veritable bag within which they lie enclosed in the cytoplasm. De Duve believes that the release of these enzymes, and hence their "activation," more precisely the rupture of the bags or lysosomes, is under metabolic control, and might be hormonely regulated. Here then is a good example of great differences in enzymatic activities between enzymes within cells and enzymes in "solution." This is a special case, however, in which it is pretty clear that the reason for this great difference in activity is due solely to the inaccessibility of substrate to enzyme, neither can get across the lysosomal membrane. As I go on, you will notice that certain of my examples from the literature could well fall into this class of "activation by accessibility," but there are others for which a more sophisticated reason must be found.

There is another way in which differences could arise between enzymes acting in a uniphasic medium and those acting in a diphasic medium, and that is due to the possible differences in pH between these two cases. Danielli in 1937 had suggested that enzymes located on the plasma membrane of the cell (now we would also add the in-

tracellular membranes) could well be acting in a milieu in which
there is as much as 2 pH units difference from that of the medium
outside these membranes. Enzymes having a sharp optimum curve
could well have differences of tenfold or more in activity over this
pH range. That this idea might be more than a happenstance is suggested by the results of various workers. For example, Huennekens
has found that mitochondrial malic oxidase has a pH optimum of pH
7.8, while the "solubilized" enzyme has one at pH 9.5. Dickman and
Speyer found that liver mitochondrial aconitase has pH optima at 5.8
and 7.3 while the enzyme "solubilized" from these mitochondria has
one at 7.3. Also, Esterman, Conn, and McLaren found that the aconitase in lupine mitochondria has a pH optimum of 5.8 while the enzyme
extracted out has one at 7.0. McLaren and Babcock have remarked
on the characteristics of enzymes acting at surfaces, particularly
stressing just this point of differences in pH between this surface
and the medium. It is best that we do not draw too rigid a conclusion
from these experiments, for these differences could be due to the pH
activity curve of the enzyme per se superimposed on the pH curve of
the permeability of substrate into mitochondria. But they do tell us
that we should be cautious in translating parameters obtained from
enzymes acting in solution to those acting within the cell.

Now, before I go any further, I think we should look into this term
"soluble." To me, this is a vague term. What are the criteria for
solubility? When are enzymes soluble? Certainly not when they re-
sist centrifugation in a specified gravitational field, for perhaps a
higher field will cause them to sediment. I think that we can only say
that a protein is soluble when it is completely surrounded by water
molecules. And in too many cases when proteins have been termed
"soluble" there is really no good reason to think this might be so.
Two or more proteins can be so tightly bound to each other that we
cannot separate them in aqueous media by our known physical techniques. We can have in hand what we think is a very purified protein solution, yet the enzymatic characteristics of this protein are
not solely that of one protein enzyme but that of the enzyme plus the
contaminants which have come along, whether these are other proteins, or are lipids or carbohydrates.

On the other hand, when we extract and really purify a protein,
and measure certain parameters, like pH optima, reaction rates,
equilibrium constants, substrate binding constants, we have no idea
whether this same protein does have these characteristics when it
is embedded within the cell. This is particularly true of proteins
which are known to exist within cells in chains, enzymes which because of their function can only exist so lined up, one next to the
other. A prime example is the electron transport chain in mitochon-

dria. Of these enzymes, Green and Järnefelt state that "the enzymatic activity of composite systems may not always be demonstrated as the sum of the activities of the individual enzymes contained therein." A classic example in this regard is the one uncovered in 1952 by Tsou, who found that the cytochrome c extracted from muscle is not the same as the cytochrome c which is part of the muscle, specifically the mitochondrial, structure. Its catalytic properties had been altered by the extraction while even the position of the absorption bands was changed. However, it can be mixed with the cytochrome c-less extract to give back all the characteristics of the endogenous form of cytochrome c, including the specific absorption spectrum. These findings have been further investigated and extended to "soluble" succinic dehydrogenase by Keilin and King. These authors found that the solubilized enzyme is unstable and does not react with cytochrome c. When soluble cytochrome c, soluble succinic dehydrogenase, and a deficient heart muscle preparation were mixed, both succinic dehydrogenase and cytochrome c were found to have regained those properties which they had lost upon extraction. Thus the extraction procedures did not cause any permanent change in the properties of the proteins, for upon reincorporation into their matrix, these enzymes regained these properties. Evidently the soluble enzymes are the same as the insoluble ones, but the expression of their intrinsic properties is different depending upon the milieu in which each is situated.

Ever since the extraction of the succinic oxidase complex by Keilin and Hartree in 1940, many workers have struggled toward the elucidation of the electron transport system, with the people in Green's laboratory (cf. Green) playing probably the most important part. I need not go into the detailed findings of this group, but it is clear that what we had been formerly isolating as constituent enzymes of this complex are not exactly the same catalytic proteins as those which exist in the cell (cf. Green and Järnefelt). Especially in line with what I have said, is the finding of the group that some, perhaps all, of the proteins and flavoproteins exist in the cell as tight lipid complexes, as, for example, diaphorase (Ringler, Green, and Doeg) and cytochrome c (Green, Järnefelt, and Tisdale). Ball (Ball and Cooper), Stotz (Marinetti, Kochen, Erbland, and Stotz), and Nason (Donaldson and Nason) and their collaborators have reached the same conclusions about many of those enzymes constituting the electron transport chain. The reactivity of these enzymes is quite different when they are attached to their lipids than when they are free, and of course this attachment might explain the findings of Tsou and of Keilin and Hartree. For example, Mackler and Green found that the DPNH oxidase activity of a heart muscle preparation has different catalytic

properties as regards the electron acceptors for DPNH whether or
not the preparation is broken open by a detergent, deoxycholate (DOC),
which presumably strips off the lipid from the enzyme protein. In the
cases where it has been examined, it has been found that there were
no intrinsic changes in the enzyme itself during these stripping procedures; but the purified enzyme is not the same as it is in the cell.
We can thus say that purification produces an artifact; we can indeed
go too far. However, I do not wish to be misunderstood, for we must
first know all the possible enzymatic activities and characteristics
of the protein before we can know anything of its probable activity in
the cell, and for this, protein purification is a necessity.

The interaction of lipid with protein makes one think of membranes,
and indeed, long ago, when it was difficult to purify the succinic dehydrogenase complex from muscle, it was thought that this enzyme
complex was lipid bound, and perhaps membrane bound also. We now
know that this is so. Figure 2 shows an electron micrograph of a
liver mitochondria, and Fig. 3 shows the membrane fractions which
can be obtained from these mitochondria by the detergent, DOC (Watson and Siekevitz). Table 1 gives some biochemical data on the suc-

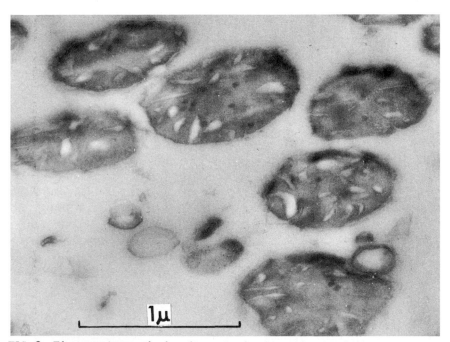

FIG. 2. Electron micrograph of rat-liver mitochondria isolated in 0.44 M sucrose.
The cristae are more distorted and the contents of the matrix are more dense than
seen in *in situ* mitochondria. Mag. 43,000 X. (*Taken from M. L. Watson and P. Siekevitz.*)

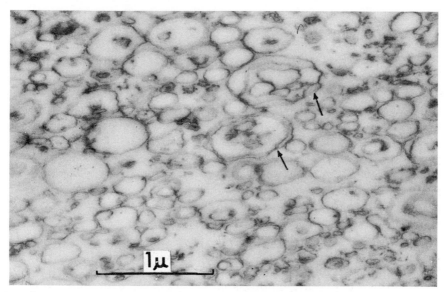

FIG. 3. Electron micrograph of membrane fraction of rat-liver mitochondria obtained by centrifugation at 105,000g for 60 minutes. Shown are single- and multiple-membraned elements. Mag. 30,000 X. (*Taken from M. L. Watson and P. Siekevitz.*)

TABLE 1

Recovery of Mitochondrial Membranes and Succinoxidase Activity

Fraction	Succinoxidase	
	Activity (μl O_2/60 min)	Specific Activity (act./mg protein-N)
1. Mitochondria	1,320	868
2. Mitochondria in deoxycholate	590	388
3. Mitochondrial subfraction 1	15	1,500
4. Mitochondrial subfraction 2	229	1,206
5. Mitochondrial membrane fraction	498	5,550
6. Supernatant from (5)	70	56
Recovery	812	–
7. Mitochondrial membrane fraction from (6)	420	4,900

Data taken from Siekevitz and Watson.

cinic oxidase activity of these membranes (Siekevitz and Watson).
This membrane fraction contains a good deal of phospholipid, in fact,
for every mg protein there are 0.6 to 0.8 mg phospholipid. It was
found that the whole succinoxidase and cytochrome oxidase complexes
of mitochondria are a part of these membranes. Even though we could
not find DPNH oxidase activity here, it is thought, from other work,
that this enzyme system is also a membrane-bound complex. From
Table 1, you can see that we can initially spin down about one-half of
the succinoxidase from a DOC-treated, "solubilized" mitochondria
preparation. The supernatant from this membrane fraction contains
a little activity, but when we further spin this supernatant, we get
another membrane fraction, with a much greater activity than apparently existed in the supernatant. In other words, the enzyme was inactivated by DOC, but reversibly, and when we got rid of the detergent, by spinning it out, the enzymatic activity reappeared. This
reversible inactivation by detergents seems to be a property of membrane, or lipoprotein, enzymes. What happens is uncertain. One can
postulate that the detergent opens up the complex to available substrate, thus making it more active. In some cases one does obtain an
activation this way (cf. below); in other cases, as the above, one only
sees an inhibition. Thus one must further postulate that the detergent
in some cases can deposit on the lipoprotein complex, thus blocking
enzymatic activity toward substrate. Washing out the detergent then
restores the activity.

These effects I have mentioned above are not peculiar to mitochondrial enzymes, for microsomal membrane enzymes behave in
similar ways. Figure 4 shows an electron micrograph of a typical
microsome preparation, in this case from pancreas, and Fig. 5 shows
the membranes which can be isolated from a liver microsome preparation, again by means of DOC (Ernster, Siekevitz, and Palade).
These membranes contain the microsomal electron transport system,
which contains the enzymes oxidizing DPNH by cytochrome c (cyto-
chrome-c reductase) or by a suitable dye (diaphorase). This is shown
in Table 2. In both mitochondria and microsomes there is another
system, that which oxidizes TPNH, and in both cases this enzyme
system is easily "solubilized" away from the membrane preparations. As will be seen below, the microsomal TPNH (nonmembrane)
enzyme complex behaves quite differently from the microsomal
DPNH (membrane) enzyme. Now, the microsomal DPNH enzyme
complex has many peculiar properties, of which I would like to mention some, for I think these properties are indicative of the membranous character of the preparation. For example, this membrane
complex is apparently only stable in the presence of the detergent.
As Fig. 6 shows, once we begin diluting the membrane preparation

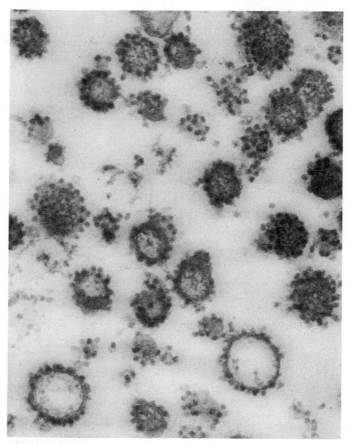

FIG. 4. Electron micrograph of guinea-pig pancreas microsomes.
Nearly all of the membrane elements contain bound ribonucleoprotein particles. In some cases a tangential slice of the membrane-
bound vesicles was made, thus obscuring the membrane. Liver
microsome preparations are very similar to this pancreas preparation. Mag. 100,000 X. (*Picture, courtesy of G. E. Palade.*)

with water, as indeed we must do in order to measure it, the activity
very rapidly declines. This does not happen with the nonmembrane
enzyme, the TPNH-cytochrome-c reductase. When we went back to
the whole microsome preparation, we found that the enzyme behaved
similarly, as Tables 3, 4, and 5 indicate. The microsomal DPNH-
cytochrome-c reductase can be activated by standing in sucrose, more
so by standing in DOC; later the effect of DOC is slowly to inactivate
the enzyme. Sometimes the microsomal activity is high to start with,
presumably because the enzyme has become activated during the
processing of the tissue; DOC then lowers this activity. But interest-
ingly enough, the microsomal TPNH-cytochrome-c-reductase activity

TABLE 2

Localization of DPNH-Cytochrome-*c* Reductase and Diaphorase in Microsomes

| Fraction | Cyt.-*c*.-Red. Activity | | | | Diaphorase Activity | | | |
| | DPNH | | TPNH | | DPNH | | TPNH | |
	Act.	Act./mg	Act.	Act./mg	Act.	Act./mg	Act.	Act./mg
Microsomes	121	3.8	9.0	0.28				
RNP	1	0.2	0.0	0.00				
Mem. fraction	290	50.2	2.8	0.42				
Recovery	322	8.5	11.1					
Microsomes	241	13.5	5.3	0.30	37.5	2.10	4.1	0.23
Mem. fraction	134	49.8	0.9	0.33	19.3	7.18	0.6	0.24
Recovery	157	10.0	5.1	0.33	25.5	1.62	3.9	0.25

Data taken from Ernster, Siekevitz, and Palade.

TABLE 3

Effects of Standing, Dilution, and DOC Treatment on Microsomal
Cytochrome-*c*-Reductase Activities

| Procedure | Cyt.-*c*-Reductase Act. | |
	With DPNH	With TPNH
1. Mi* in sucrose, fresh	292	
2. Mi in sucrose, after 6 hrs at 0°C	550	
3. Mi in 0.026% DOC, after 6 hrs at 0°C	711	
4. Mi in 0.26% DOC, after 0.5 hrs at 0°C	780	
5. Mi in 0.26% DOC, after 3.3 hrs at 0°C	588	
6. Mi in 0.26% DOC, after 6 hrs at 0°C	453	
1. Mi in sucrose, fresh	558	8.0
2. Mi in sucrose, after 8 hrs	266	9.2
3. Mi in 0.26% DOC, diluted 5 times, tested after 6 hrs	148	8.6

Data taken from Ernster, Siekevitz, and Palade.
*Microsomes.

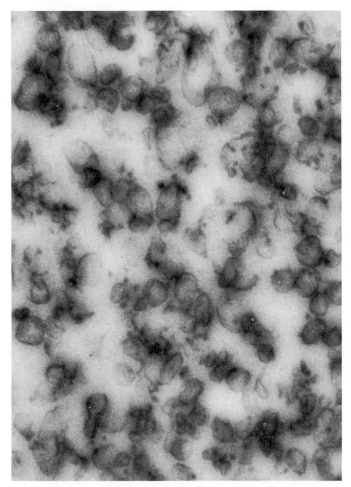

FIG. 5. Electron micrograph of membrane fraction prepared from rat-liver microsomes by DOC treatment and subsequent centrifugation. Visible are membranous elements of the endoplasmic reticulum, but with very few particles. Mag. 113,000 X. (*Taken from L. Ernster, P. Siekevitz, and G. E. Palade.*)

remains rather constant under all these conditions. Also, as in the case with the mitochondrial membrane succinoxidase, the microsomal membrane DPNH-cytochrome-c-reductase is reversibly inactivated by DOC. Figure 7 shows that microsomes assayed in the presence of DOC are completely inactive with respect to this enzyme, but as soon as the detergent is diluted out, and more microsomes added to counter the dilution of enzyme, the activity comes back, apparently unimpaired. And again, like the isolated membrane preparation, the microsomal enzyme loses activity when diluted, but

TABLE 4

Effects of Standing, Dilution, and DOC Treatment on Microsomal
Cytochrome-*c*-Reductase Activities

Procedure	Cyt.-*c*-Reductase Act.
	With DPNH
1. Mi in 0.26% DOC, diluted 50 times, tested immediately	473
2. Mi in 0.26% DOC, diluted 50 times, tested after 12 min	270
3. Mi in 0.26% DOC, diluted 50 times, tested after 18 min	132
4. Mi in 0.26% DOC, diluted 50 times, tested after 33 min	113
5. Mi in 0.26% DOC, undiluted, tested after 50 min	430

Data taken from Ernster, Siekevitz, and Palade.

if kept undiluted, even in the presence of DOC, no loss occurs. Similar results have been described by Ernster (1958) with the mitochondrial and microsomal DPNH- and TPNH-cytochrome-*c* reductases.
It is difficult to give precise reasons for these effects, but it would
seem that these would have to do, not with changes in the intrinsic
catalytic properties of the enzyme, but with the fact that the enzymes
in question are à part of a structure, a membrane, and it is this
whole structure which responds to the effects produced by dilution

TABLE 5

Effects of Standing, Dilution, and DOC Treatment on Microsomal
Cytochrome-*c*-Reductase Activities

Procedure	Cyt.-*c*-Reductase Act.
	With DPNH
1. Mi in sucrose, diluted 50 times, tested immediately	684
2. Mi in sucrose, diluted 50 times, tested after 12 min	298
3. Mi in sucrose, diluted 50 times, tested after 18 min	254
4. Mi in sucrose, diluted 50 times, tested after 30 min	207
5. Mi in sucrose, undiluted, tested after 40 min	478

Data taken from Ernster, Siekevitz, and Palade.

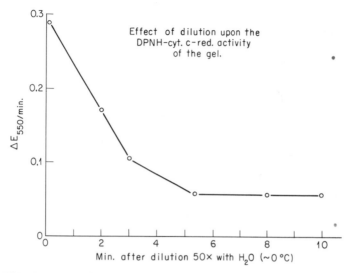

FIG. 6.   Effect of dilution of the microsomal membrane preparation (Fig. 5) on the DPNH-cytochrome-*c*-reductase activity of the preparation. (*Data from L. Ernster, P. Siekevitz, and G. E. Palade.*)

or by the detergent. All that we can say at present is that nonmembrane enzymes do not appear to react in the same way.

Let us look now at this concept of membrane-bound enzymes. It is rather easy to see that anything which primarily affects the lipid portion of the membrane will secondarily affect the protein part, and if this protein be an enzyme, we will see differences in rates of activity. And if this protein is purified away from the lipid, its activity will not necessarily be the same, indeed it will probably be different from its activity when that enzyme is part of the lipoprotein. But another result of having an enzyme bound to a membrane is that here is provided a surface for bringing together enzyme and substrate in a more concentrated configuration than would be the case for enzymes and substrate in solution. Thus we can postulate that enzymes in solution might be less active than those bound to a surface, all other conditions being equal. That this might be the case is shown by the data in Table 6 (Siekevitz and Potter). When a suspension of liver mitochondria is mixed with a yeast hexokinase solution, and then centrifuged, some of the enzymes come down with the recentrifuged mitochondria. When we measured the initial, added, soluble enzyme activity and the amount of activity remaining in the supernatant after spinning down the mitochondria, we should have got, by difference, the amount of activity which was brought down with the mitochondria. What we did get were values of from two to ten times this amount, depending on

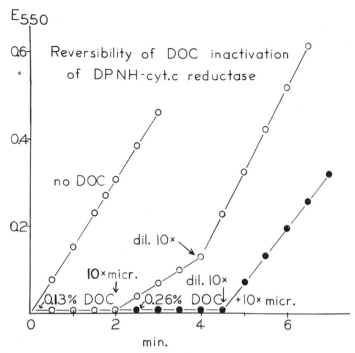

FIG. 7. Reversibility of DOC inactivation of the DPNH-cytochrome
c-reductase activity of liver microsomes. DOC in the concentration
noted was added to the assay tubes. At the time noted the concentration of DOC was lowered tenfold by adding H_2O, and the concentration of enzyme was maintained by adding ten times more microsomes. (*Data taken from L. Ernster, P. Siekevitz, and G. E. Palade.*)

TABLE 6

Activation of Yeast Hexokinase Activity Bound to Mitochondria

ml Hexokinase Added	Hexokinase Activity			
	Added (1)	In Medium (2)	On Mito. (3)	(1) Minus (2)
0.1	1.6	1.2	0.9	0.4
0.3	4.2	3.6	2.1	0.6
0.6	7.8	7.0	8.5	0.8

Data taken from Siekevitz and Potter.

the amount of hexokinase initially added. In other words we obtained much higher enzymatic activities than we started with, and the increase in the amount is almost certainly due to the increase in activity of that hexokinase which was bound to the mitochondria. We do not know the reason for "activation," but two possible reasons are immediately apparent. The hexokinase could have been initially somewhat inhibited by having an inhibitor bound to it; when this complex reached the mitochondrial membrane, the inhibition was released. The other reason is that the membrane provided an active surface for the close configurations of ATP, glucose, and enzyme, the reactants in the reaction. Lynn, Brown, and Mullins also found that when lactic or malic dehydrogenase was added to a washed preparation of testicular microsomes and these microsomes then resedimented, the microsomes were found not only to have adsorbed some of the enzyme, but also to have caused apparent 100 per cent increase in the activities of these enzymes.

Another effect of surface is provided by the finding of Gaudette and Brodie that the rate of oxidation of various drugs by liver microsomes is proportional to the solubility of these drugs in chloroform, as if those drugs which can be attacked by the microsomal enzymes are those which first have to be anchored in the lipoidal part of the microsomal lipoprotein membranes. In this respect, it has been found by Ryan and Mavrides that glucuronidase activity is increased by the addition of chloroform to an aqueous mixture of substrate and enzyme. Since the enzyme is believed to be a lipoprotein, it could well be that the interface produced by chloroform addition provides a suitable milieu for maximum enzymatic activity. It should be added that there are many enzymatic reactions known in which the product inhibits the reaction. It could well be that in some cases of membrane-bound enzymes, any differences in water or lipid solubility between substrate (for example, a large molecular-weight ester) and product (the acid produced) would tend to get the product away from the site of the reaction and thus speed up the reaction rate.

Now we come to the increasing literature of the presence of low-activity, or even inactive, enzymes, which, when something is done to the enzyme extract, can be "activated." Ribonuclease (RNase) has been found to be in a low-activity state in liver (Roth), in mouse pancreas (Dickman and Morrill), and in E. coli (Elson). In the case of the liver, there is an RNase inhibitor present which combines with the enzyme (Roth). In the case of E. coli (Elson), and also liver (Tashiro) some of the enzyme is found attached to the ribonucleoprotein (RNP) particles of the cell. In all cases, once the enzyme is removed from the structure it becomes more active. The reason that the RNase does not degrade the RNA of the RNP particles is prob-

TABLE 7

Some Enzymatic Activities of Pancreatic RNP Particles

Treatment	Amylase (activity/gm)			RNase (activity/gm)			TAPase (activity/gm)		
	Pellet	Supernatant	Additive total	Pellet	Supernatant	Additive total	Pellet	Supernatant	Additive total
1. No incubation	–	–	66.8*	–	–	26.8*	–	–	62.7*
2. Incubated in water	83.0	20.8	103.8	16.2	5.4	21.6	43.3	9.2	52.5
3. Incubated in 0.5 mM inorganic phosphate	16.3	83.6	99.9	1.0	21.8	22.8	14.3	41.0	55.3
4. Incubated in 0.5 mM ATP	13.3	89.0	102.3	0.9	21.8	22.7	13.1	45.0	58.1

Data from Siekevitz and Palade, 1960.

Particle aliquots equivalent to 0.5 gm tissue were incubated in 2 ml 0.44 M sucrose with the additions listed in the table. After incubation, the aliquots were combined two by two in samples equivalent to 1 gm tissue which were centrifuged for 90 minutes at 105,000g to separate the particles (pellet) from the incubating medium (supernatant). Enzymatic assays were carried through on both. One gram tissue equivalent of RNP particles (line 1) was not incubated, but kept at $\sim 0°C$ until the end of the incubation and centrifugation of the treated particles (~ 2 hours).

*These figures were obtained experimentally as described above.

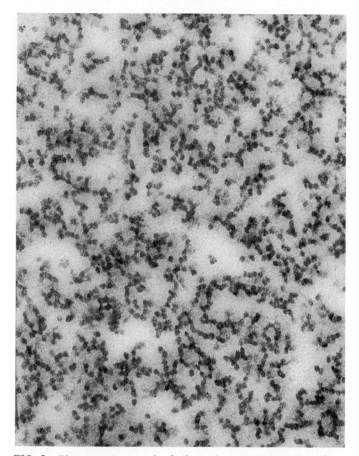

FIG. 8. Electron micrograph of ribonucleoprotein particles of pancreas microsomes, obtained by treating the microsome with DOC.
Some particles remain single but most are in stringed clusters. The
average diameter of the particles is 150 A. Mag. 100,000 X. (*P. Siekevitz and G. E. Palade.*)

ably because the RNA is protected by a protein coat of the particles.
For in the case of liver (Taghiro) and pancreas (Siekovitz and Palade)
there is RNase activity coming down with these particles; this activity does not appear to be latent, and yet there is no evidence of
the breakdown of the RNA in these particles. Figure 8 shows the
RNP particles of the pancreas, obtained from pancreatic microsomes by "solubilizing" the microsomes with DOC. Table 7 shows
that these isolated particles contain RNase, amylase, and trypsin-
activatable proteolytic (TAPase) activities. All these enzymes seem
to be fully active when the particles are isolated, except for amylase. This latter activity can be increased by merely washing and

resedimenting the particles. The partial latency of amylase has been noticed before (Douglas and Munro), but at present we do not know what could occur to activate this enzyme. All these enzymes can be stripped off the particles, or could be made active if they are completely inactive (Elson), by procedures which disrupt the particles, like urea (Elson), or in our case by Mg^{++}-complexing agents such as ATP, pyrophosphate, or versene (Siekevitz and Palade). It is of interest that antibody has been found to be associated with microsomes of lymph nodes (Kern, Helmreich, and Eisen), for it is known and has been beautifully shown recently (Garvey and Campbell) that there is a reservoir of antibody within the tissues which is not in equilibrium with circulating antibody. This tissue antibody seems to be masked and unaccessible, and might be called "inhibited" antibody. This "latent" antibody could be mobilized by a further injecjection of antigen (Garvey and Campbell).

There are also many mitochondrial enzymes which exhibit a property of "latency," that is, showing low or no activity until something is done to the mitochondria, usually by swelling these particulates with water or with certain detergents . Among these enzymes may be cited cytochrome oxidase (Simon), glutamate dehydrogenase (Ernster and Navazio, 1956a), isocitric dehydrogenase (Ernster and Navazio, 1956b), TPNH diaphorase and TPNH-cytochrome-c reductase (Ernster, 1958), aconitase (Dickman and Speyer), acetyl coenzyme A deacylase (Szekely), and rhodanese (Greville and Chappell). In fact, for a while it was thought that liver mitochondria lacked isocitric dehydrogenase and aconitase, because these enzymes could not be demonstrated in intact mitochondria (Schneider and Hogeboom). However, when the mitochondria were treated, it was found that there were sufficient activities of these enzymes to account for an active Krebs cycle (Ernster, 1959). It is not known whether these enzymes were inhibited within the mitochondria, or whether upon altering the mitochondrial structure, the substrates were accessible to the enzymes. However, in one case, that of yeast catalase (Kaplan and Paik), there is good evidence that this enzyme is present within the yeast cell in an adsorbed, inhibited state.

There have been numerous cases in which tissue extracts have been found to show inhibitory effects towards enzymes, hexokinase being a good example (cf. Stern). That most of these effects are inhibitory in nature and not due to an inactivation of the enzyme has been shown by washing experiments and by the additions of other proteins, in which case an activation occurs. In these latter cases, it is thought that the addition of the activator involves the competition of specific proteins for an inhibitor associated with the enzyme in question. A curious case was discovered by Swartz, Kaplan, and Frech.

These workers found that only by boiling an extract for a few minutes could they show any DPN pyrophosphatase activity in this extract. They eventually found that this effect was due to the binding of a heat-labile inhibitor by a heat-stable enzyme. These authors also give other instances of the inhibition of enzymes in the natural state within the cell, and they suggest that in many cases the inhibited state of the enzyme is the normal one, and that this state thus lends itself easily to metabolic control.

Finally, I would like to mention hormones. The question, simply put, is this: do hormones act upon individual enzymatic reactions, to change the rate or equilibrium of a reaction, or do they act upon a higher order of the cell, upon the framework in which the enzymes are enmeshed? It has been shown that certain estrogenic hormones can mediate the transfer of electrons between DPN and TPN (Talalay and Williams-Ashman) and can enhance the activities of other types of dehydrogenase reactions (Williams-Ashman, Cassman, and Klavins; Klebanoff; Lee, Takemori, and Lardy), while certain steroid hormones inhibit DPNH-cytochrome-c reductase (Yielding and Tomkins). Also, diethylstilbesterol can inhibit succinoxidase, and progesterone or testosterone can reverse this inhibition (Wight); this mirrors the effects of these hormones on growth rates. However, it has long been thought that hormones must have something to do with over-all cell function, and recently Peters has postulated a "modification of the cytoskeleton of the cell." Paradoxically enough, one of the main arguments for this latter point of view is that hormonal effects in many cases seem to be organ specific; if every organ has more or less the same enzymes and enzyme capacity, then the effects of hormones must not be on enzymes per se, but on the substratum on which the enzymes are embedded. The thought is not that hormones do not have an effect on enzymatic rate, but that they have this effect only secondarily. In the gist of what I have already mentioned, one can postulate many places where hormones can act in this respect, such as by releasing inhibitors from enzymes to activate them, by releasing an inactive enzyme from its membrane binding and thus activate it, by binding an enzyme to a membrane and either inhibiting or activating it; by extending structures, such as mitochondria, so that substrate can have better access to enzyme; by altering the intracellular localization of an enzyme through increased or decreased membrane binding, and so on. In this connection, it has been shown (Friis and Ottolenghi) that during adaptation by yeast cells to sucrose splitting, there is a change in the localization of the cellular invertase from an intracellular to a cell-wall location. Adaptation to various compounds in microorganisms might be analogous to hormone action in the multicellular organism, and might have the same underlying mechanism. In the studies mentioned above with mitochondria and hexokinase, we could not find any effect of insulin added in vitro on the binding of hexokinase by the mitochondria. If these general views are correct it should be possible to show an effect by hormones on cell structure, but as yet there has been very little work done on this. I would cite only the effect of the continued injection of dl-thyroxine on the mitochondria of rat liver; these are greatly extended and swollen and might even have lost some of their matrix (Schultz, Löw, Ernster, and Sjöstrand). Barnett and Ball have indicated that insulin produces extensive vesiculation of the plasma membrane in the fat body, while Deane and Porter (personal communication) have evidence that testosterone produces an increase in the ergastoplasm in epithelial cells of the seminal vesicle. But there are no indications whether these are primary or secondary effects.

A cytochemical effect of hormones has also been found with hydrocortisone (Gallagher), and particularly with thyroxine (Lehninger, Ray, and Schneider; Lehninger). It has been shown that mitochondria can bind thyroxine (Klemperer; Tapley and Basso), and that thyroxine causes a swelling of the mitochondria (Lehninger) as does hydrocortisone (Gallagher). There are many biochemical lesions of mitochondrial metabolism produced by the in vitro addition of thyroxine, the best known being an uncoupling of oxidative phosphorylation (cf. Lehninger, Ray, and Schneider), and possibly an inhibition of the DPN dehydrogenases of the mitochondria (Wolff and Wolff, 1957). All the effects produced seem to center around the availability of DPN within the mitochondria (cf. Lehninger, Ray, and Schneider). But whether the action of thyroxine is primarily on oxidative phosphorylation, which defect then leads to swelling, or whether it is primarily on the structure, causing distortions of the mitochondrial membranes, which effect then leads to biochemical changes, is not known. Lehninger believes the action of this hormone to be primarily on a mitochondrial contraction system, and not on oxidative phosphorylation. For a potent uncoupler of oxidative phosphorylation, like DNP, does not lead to swelling, or to many of the other changes which thyroxine produces. Thus it is extremely difficult to determine which is the initial effect in many hormonal-influenced physiological mechanisms, for the cytochemical interdependence of the cell is great. We must use inferences, as, for example, when mitochondria are placed in water and become swollen, we know their enzyme systems react as if more cytochrome c or DPN were available to them; and likewise, when thyroxine produces the same swelling phenomenon, and somewhat the same biochemical effects, we conclude that possibly the primary action of the hormone, like the primary action of water, is upon the structure of the mitochondria.

However, I would like to emphasize that the terms "structure" and "function" are not only inseparable physiologically, but are also inseparable in a biochemical sense, though we do not certainly know this to be true. A cellular enzyme, I think, should be looked upon as part of a structure; a structure has enzymatic activity. I need only cite muscle actinomyosin and ATPase. Thus, what we mean when we say that a hormone might have a primary effect on the structure, is that it has no effect on the activity center of the enzyme, but on the structure of which this enzyme is a part. It could well have a secondary effect on the substrate-binding site of the enzyme, if this is also where the protein enzyme is bound to a nonprotein structure. There are many possibilities, and it is probable that all hormones which might be shown to have an effect on enzymatic activity through an effect on the enzyme-structure complex, will have these effects at different points of this enzyme-structure relationship. Thus the organ specificity of many hormones might be due, not to differences among the enzymes in the different organs, but to differences among the enzyme-structure relationship among these organs. For example, insulin is bound to diaphragm, as initially found by Stadie (Stadie, Haugaard, Marsh, and Hills); it is concentrated by liver and even by certain intracellular structures in the liver cell (Lee and Williams). An enzyme might be loosely bound to some structure in one tissue, and be fully active; the same enzyme might be tightly bound to structure in another tissue and be inactive; the hormone might only cause an effect in the latter case, for it may well release the enzyme from the binding site and hence "activate" it. Many hormones are steroids, and the possible differential solubility of these in membranes within various cells would lead to what we observe as organ specificity. The possibilities are many, and each will have to be checked for every hormone. As Ernster (1959) has put it, "To map the relationship between structural alteration and the pattern in which cellular enzymes react and interact may come to be, I believe, one of the most important achievements of future biochemistry."

In summary, I believe we are entering a new phase of biochemistry in which extracted, purified enzymes are going to be added back to the cell structures from which they were initially obtained. We shall find, I think, great differences in rates, in equilibria, perhaps in all those enzyme parameters which are studied on purified enzymes. We shall have to check many assumptions which we now take for granted. Can we be sure that the added substrate has ready access to the enzyme? Is the pH of the medium the pH at the site of enzymatic reaction? For those enzymes which act in chains, can we know which reactions are rate-limiting by measuring the various rates and equilibria of the isolated enzymes separately? Can we be sure that enzymes which are extracted and found to be very active are not in an inhibited state in the cell? Does the fact of product inhibition, which has been found for many enzymatic reactions, make any sense in a cell where the enzyme-substrate complex might be in one phase and the product in another? Do the lipoprotein membranes of the cell interior alter enzymatic activities out of all proportion to what can be observed in the test tube? All these questions are begging for answers, and some experimental work has already been done to try to answer them (Dickens, Glock, and McLean; Racker and Wu). We have made a start with the cell-fractionation techniques, and with looking at individual reactions in whole cells, whole mitochondria, or whole organs, as Chance, Holzer, Lynen (Lynen, Hartmann, Netler, and Schuegraf), and Bücher (Hohorst, Kreutz, and Bücher), Racker (Racker and Wu), Pardee, and Magasanik and their collaborators have done. But these are the easiest parts of the problem. Now we have to apply the chemistry we learned concerning biochemistry to the biology which we are just beginning to learn with regard to biochemistry. Unfortunately, we have much more quantitative data on the isolated chemical reactions of the cell than we have on its biological reactions. This then is the gist of it — to invent new techniques, to come up with new ideas, in order to make valid measurements on the biological, or should I say, cytochemical, variables of biochemistry. This will be no easy task.

REFERENCES

Allfrey, V. (1959), in *The Cell*, vol. I, J. Brachet and A. E. Mirsky, eds., Academic Press, Inc., New York, p. 193.

Ball, E. G., and O. Cooper (1949), *J. Biol. Chem.*, 180:113.

Barnet, R., and E. G. Ball (1960), *J. Biophys. Biochem. Cytol.*, 8:83.

Chance, B. (1959), in *Ciba Symposium on Regulation of Cell Metabolism*, London.

Danielli, J. F. (1937), *Proc. Roy. Soc.* (London), B122:155.

Deane, H. W., and K. R. Porter (1960), *Z. Zellforsch.*, 52:697.

de Duve, C. (1959), *Exp. Cell Res.*, Suppl. 7:169.

—— and J. Berthet (1954), *Intern. Rev. Cytology*, 3:225.

Dickens, F., G. E. Glock, and P. McLean (1959), in *Ciba Symposium on Regulation of Cell Metabolism*, London.

Dickman, S. R., and G. A. Morrill (1959), *Ann. N.Y. Acad. Sci.*, 81:585.

—— and J. F. Speyer (1954), *J. Biol. Chem.*, 206:67.

Donaldson, K. O., and A. Nason (1957), *Proc. Natl. Acad. Sci. U.S.*, 43:364.

Douglas, T. A., and H. N. Munro (1959), *Exp. Cell Res.*, 16:148.

Elson, D. (1959), *Biochim. Biophys. Acta*, 27:216.

Ernster, L. (1958), *Acta Chem. Scand.*, 12:600.

—— (1959), *Biochem. Soc. Symposia (Cambridge, Engl.)*, 16:54.

—— and F. Navazio (1956a), *Acta Chem. Scand.*, 10:1038.

—— and —— (1956b), *Exp. Cell Res.*, 11:483.

——, P. Siekevitz, and G. E. Palade, unpublished observations.

Esterman, E. F., E. E. Conn, and A. D. McLaren (1959), *Arch. Biochem. Biophys.*, 85:103.

Friis, J., and P. Ottolenghi (1959), *Compt. Rend. Lab. Carlsberg*, 31:259.

Gallagher, C. H. (1958), *Nature*, 182:1315.

Garvey, J. S., and D. H. Campbell (1959), *J. Exp. Med.*, 110:355.

Gaudette, L. E., and B. B. Brodie (1959), *Biochem. Pharmacol.*, 2:89.

Green, D. E. (1959), in *Subcellular Particles*, T. Hayashi, ed., The Ronald Press Company, New York, p. 84.

—— and J. Järnefelt (1959), *Perspectives Biol. Med.*, 2:163.

——, ——, and H. D. Tisdale (1959), *Biochim. Biophys. Acta*, 31:34.

Greville, G. D., and J. B. Chappell (1959), *Biochim. Biophys. Acta*, 33:267.

Hogeboom, G. H., E. L. Kuff, and W. C. Schneider (1957), *Intern. Rev. Cytol.*, 6:425.

Hohorst, H. J., F. H. Kreutz, and T. Bücher (1959), *Biochem. Z.*, 332:18.

Holzer, H. (1959), *Ciba Symposium on Regulation of Cell Metabolism*, London, p. 277.

Huennekens, F. M. (1951), *Exp. Cell. Res.*, 2:115.

Kaplan, J. G., and W. K. Paik (1956), *J. Gen. Physiol.*, 40:147.

Keilin, D., and E. F. Hartree (1940), *Proc. Roy. Soc.*, (London), B129:277.

—— and T. E. King (1958), *Nature*, 181:1520.

Kern, M., E. Helmreich, and H. N. Eisen (1959), *Proc. Natl. Acad. Sci. U.S.*, 45:862.

Klebanoff, S. (1959), *J. Biol. Chem.*, 234:2437, 2480.

Klemperer, H. G. (1953), *Biochem. J.*, 60:128.

Lee, N. D., and R. H. Williams (1954), *Endocrinology*, 54:5.

Lee, Y.-P., A. E.Takemori, and H. A. Lardy (1959), *J. Biol. Chem.*, 234:3051.

Lehninger, A. L. (1959), *J. Biol. Chem.*, 234:2187.

——, B. L. Ray, and M. Schneider (1959), *J. Biophys. Biochem. Cytol.*, 5:97.

Lynen, F., G. Hartmann, K. F. Netler, and A. Schuegraf (1959), *Ciba Symposium on Regulation of Cell Metabolism*, London, p. 256.

Lynn, E. S., Jr., R. H. Brown, and J. Mullins (1958), *J. Biol. Chem.*, 232:995.

Mackler, B., and D. E. Green (1956), *Biochim. Biophys. Acta*, 21:1.

McLaren, A. D., and K. C. Babcock (1959), in *Subcellular Particles*, T. Hayashi, ed., The Ronald Press Company, New York, p. 23.

Magasanik, B., A. K. Magasanik, and F. C. Neidhardt (1959), in *Ciba Symposium on Regulation of Cell Metabolism*, London, p. 334.

Marintetti, G. V., J. Kochen, J. Erbland, and E. Stotz (1958), *J. Biol. Chem.*, 229:1027.

Pardee, V. R. (1959), in *Ciba Symposium on Regulation of Cell Metabolism*, London, p. 295.

Peters, R. A. (1956), *Nature*, 177:426.

Potter, V. R., and H. Niemeyer (1959), in *Ciba Symposium on Regulation of Cell Metabolism*, London, p. 230.

Racker, E., and R. Wu (1959), in *Ciba Symposium on Regulation of Cell Metabolism*, London, p. 205.

Roth, J. S. (1958), *J. Biol. Chem.*, 231:1097.

Ryan, M. T., and C. A. Mavrides (1960), *Science*, 131:101.

Schneider, W. C. (1955), *Proc. Intern. Congr. Biochem.*, *3rd Congr.*, *Brussels*, p. 305.

—— and G. H. Hogeboom (1956), *Ann. Rev. Biochem.*, 25:201.

Schultz, H., H. Löw, L. Ernster, and F. Sjöstrand (1957), *Proc. Conf. Electron Microscopy, Stockholm*, Academic Press, Inc., New York, p. 134.

Siekevitz, P., and M. L. Watson (1956), *J. Biophys. Biochem. Cytol.*, 2:653.

—— and G. E. Palade (1960), *J. Biophys. Biochem. Cytol.*, 7:619, 631.

—— and V. R. Potter (1953) (unpublished observations).

Simon, E. W. (1958), *Biochem. J.*, 69:67.
Stadie, W. C., N. Haugaard, J. B. Marsh, and A. G. Hills (1949), *Am. J. Med.*, 218:265.
Stern, J. (1954), *Biochem. J.*, 58:536.
Swartz, M. N., N. O. Kaplan, and M. E. Frech (1956), *Science*, 123:50.
Szekely, M. (1955), *Acta Physiol. Acad. Sci. Hung.*, 8:291.
Talalay, P., and H. G. Williams-Ashman (1958), *Proc. Natl. Acad. Sci. U.S.*, 44:15.
Tapley, D. F., and N. Basso (1959), *Biochim. Biophys. Acta*, 36:486.
Tashiro, Y. (1958), *J. Biochem.*, Japan, 45:937.
Tsou, C. L. (1952), *Biochem. J.*, 50:493.
Watson, M. L., and P. Siekevitz (1956), *J. Biophys. Biochem. Cytol.*, 2:639.
Wight, K. H. (1957), *Biochim. Biophys. Acta*, 23:139.
Williams-Ashman, H. G., M. Cassman, and M. Klavins (1959), *Nature*, 184:427.
Wolff, J., and E. C. Wolff (1957), *Biochim. Biophys. Acta*, 26:389.
Yielding, C. L., and G. M. Tomkins (1959), *Proc. Natl. Acad. Sci. U.S.*, 45:1730.
Ziegler, D. M., D. E. Green, and K. A. Doeg (1959), *J. Biol. Chem.*, 234:1916.

Chapter Five

The Fine Structure of the Gene*

M. DEMEREC†

Carnegie Institution of Washington, Department of Genetics, Cold Spring Harbor, New York

In the early days of genetics the picture of a gene, or a "factor" as it was then called, was vague. "In Mendelian heredity the word 'factor' is used for something which segregates in the germ cells, and which is somehow connected with particular effects on the organism that contains it" (Morgan et al., 1915). Thus, a gene was visualized as "something" in the germ cells that "somehow" performs a certain function. Through the brilliant work with Drosophila carried on by Morgan and his associates, particularly C. B. Bridges, H. J. Muller, and A. H. Sturtevant, our concepts of the gene and of the mechanism of heredity became clearer and better defined. This work provided evidence that the genes are located on chromosomes and are, moreover, arranged there in a linear order. A chromosome was compared to a string of beads, the genes being the beads.

The Mendelian theory postulated that a gene exists in either of two forms, representing two contrasting characteristics (for example, in peas, yellow or green, smooth or wrinkled). Genetical research soon revealed, however, that a gene may exist in more than two forms. A classic example, detected early in the work with Drosophila, is the "white eye color" gene; it occurs in at least a dozen phenotypically distinguishable forms, which determine shades of eye color ranging from white to the normal wild-type red (e.g., pearl, ivory, buff, honey, cherry, eosin, apricot, blood, coral).

Various forms of the same gene are called "alleles." In the terminology we employ, the expression "gene locus" or, in briefly, "locus," designates the region of chromosome occupied by a certain gene in any of its forms. The word "gene" we use in a more specific sense to refer to a particular form (allele) occupying the locus. For example, by "*tryD* locus" we mean the region that may be occupied by any of the *tryD* alleles, either wild type (*tryD*$^+$) or mutant (e.g., *tryD*-10).

*Aided by a grant from the American Cancer Society.
†Present address: Department of Biology, Brookhaven National Laboratory, Upton, N. Y.

Ever since the early days of genetics, evidence has been accumulating to show that basically the same genetic mechanism operates in all living organisms. Within the past decade a significant confirmation of this conclusion has emerged from research with the smallest known form of life, the bacterial viruses, or phages (Hershey and Chase, 1951; Visconti and Delbrück, 1953). Not only have genes been identified in these viruses, but it has been established that they are linearly arranged in a "gene string" and segregate according to Mendelian expectation. The evidence shows, moreover, that in bacterial viruses DNA is the carrier of genetic information.

Our knowledge about the biological structure of genetic mechanisms has been derived primarily by observing the frequencies of appearance of various classes of offspring from parents that differ in two or more genes. The principle is very simple. Whereas two genes located in different chromosomes will segregate freely, two genes located in the same chromosome (i.e., linked genes) will assort in such a way that the classes representing the parental types are larger than the recombinant classes. Recombination involving two linked genes is accomplished through a process known as crossing over, which is responsible for interchange of homologous regions between two members of a pair of chromosomes. Since frequency of crossing over is a function of the distance between the genes involved, it forms the basis for construction of "linkage maps," delineating the genetic structure of chromosomes.

The same principle — that is, the relation between frequency of recombination and the positions of the genetic markers involved — is now being applied to investigate the fine structure of the gene itself. A new element has been introduced with the development of very sensitive techniques for detecting recombination in microorganisms. Our laboratory is participating in this kind of study, using *Salmonella typhimurium* as a research material; and I shall devote the major part of my discussion to a review of our results.

There are two prerequisites for a biological study of the structure of genetic material: first, the availability of a sufficient number of genetic markers (mutant genes) in the region to be analyzed; and, second, the existence of a technique capable of detecting recombinations of these markers if they should occur. Both requirements are satisfied in our work with strains of S. *typhimurium*.

Mutants representing changes at various gene loci, as well as changes within the same locus, can be easily accumulated. It seems a reasonable guess that between 1,000 and 3,000 different gene loci are present in a bacterium. We may also assume that mutations at all these loci occur spontaneously with a low frequency, and can be recognized if one examines a large enough number of individuals.

Now, a Salmonella culture grown in 10 ml of broth contains about 2×10^{10} cells. During the development of such a large population of cells, it is fairly certain that each different bacterial locus will undergo mutation in some cell or cells, and that a mutant gene at every locus will be present somewhere in the population.

The problem facing a bacterial geneticist, then, is not how to produce mutants but how to recognize them, and how to isolate an individual carrying a particular mutant gene from among a large population of cells. Techniques are available for isolating certain kinds of mutants. For example, if a large population of a phage-sensitive strain of bacteria is plated together with a large number of phage particles, only phage-resistant individuals will survive and form colonies. Thus, mutants that are resistant to various phages can be isolated. A similar technique is applied in isolating mutants that have acquired resistance to antibiotics or to certain other chemical compounds. Mutations at a large number of loci controlling different steps of the biochemical reactions occurring in bacterial cells can be identified by the "penicillin technique" (Lederberg and Zinder, 1948; Davis, 1948), and mutations at loci concerned with fermentation processes are detected by plating cells on medium that differentiates between mutant colonies.

Our studies have made extensive use of a group of mutants, known as auxotrophs, which are defective with respect to various steps in the synthesis of amino acids, purines, pyrimidines, and vitamins. In this group, variants from the mutant forms can be readily detected. I shall briefly describe the principle of the technique. Strains LT-2 and LT-7 of *S. typhimurium* can synthesize all the essential organic compounds, and thus are able to grow on a synthetic medium lacking all the amino acids. But a cell originates by mutation, and from it a mutant strain can be established, that cannot synthesize a certain amino acid, say tryptophan (or methionine, histidine, proline, etc.). Cells of such a tryptophan-defective strain can grow on synthetic medium only if tryptophan is added to it. When plated on a synthetic agar medium that does not contain tryptophan, they undergo only a few divisions and then stop dividing. If, however, the cells on the plate include any variants that do not require tryptophan, those cells will continue to divide and will form colonies. The presence of an extremely small proportion of variants (1×10^{-11}) can be detected in this way, and their number accurately determined. The variants may have originated through another mutational change —either a reversion in the mutant gene or a suppressor mutation in some other gene — or they may be the result of recombination involving two mutant genes.

As was mentioned earlier, the two prerequisites for a study of the

genetic structure of chromosomes and gene loci are availability of
mutants and availability of a technique for detecting recombinants.
It is evident from the above discussion that our material affords an
abundant supply of detectable mutants. The technique of transduction
(Zinder and Lederberg, 1952) has proved extremely sensitive for the
study of recombination processes in Salmonella (Demerec, 1956). A
bacterial cell is usually haploid, that is, its gene string is single
rather than double; and in order to obtain recombinants it is essential to have a pair of gene strings, contributed by different bacteria
and differing from each other in certain genes. Some phages are
capable of carrying small segments of gene string from the bacteria
in which they develop to the bacteria they infect. Bacteria that receive such small segments are thus diploid for a short region of the
gene string, and recombination can occur between the genetic markers
that happen to be located within that region. This process is called
"transduction."

We have accumulated in our laboratory a collection of more than
3,000 mutant lines of *S. typhimurium* strains LT-2 and LT-7. The mutants originated independently, most of them by spontaneous mutation,
but some after treatment with certain mutagenic agents. They include
77 mutants defective in the synthesis of tryptophan (*try* mutants).
Studies by several biochemists have revealed that the biosynthesis of
tryptophan in bacteria proceeds as shown below:

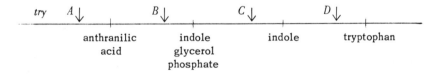

anthranilic acid	indole glycerol phosphate	indole	tryptophan

Our mutants fall into four groups: *tryA* (13 mutants), *B* (40), *C* (6),
and *D* (18), each blocked in the biosynthetic reaction at the point indicated in the diagram. The available evidence leads to the conclusion
that each of the groups represents changes at one gene locus, that is,
that the members of each group are allelic. Transduction experiments
in which one allele (*tryD*-1) was present in the recipient bacteria, and
another (*tryD*-10) in the transducing fragments, produced wild-type
recombinants, indicating that these two alleles are due to mutations
in different parts (sites) of the same locus. Similar results have been
obtained in experiments between a great majority of the other tryptophan alleles. Three-point recombination tests (Demerec and Hartman, 1956) have shown that the sites are linearly arranged. Thus it
has been learned that a locus occupies a linear section of gene string
(chromosome), and that changes occurring at different sites give rise
to different alleles.

In our collection of over 3,000 mutants, we have identified about
60 gene loci on the basis of two criteria, namely, linkage relations
and phenotypic expression. In 56 cases in which two or more alleles
were available for study, either all the alleles or a large percentage
of them were found to be nonidentical: recombination took place between them. This finding justifies the conclusion that nonidentical
allelism (complex structure of loci) is not a special feature of certain gene loci but a general property of all, at least in Salmonella.
A similar situation has been observed in work with other microorganisms, particularly phages (Benzer, 1955; Streisinger and Franklin,
1956), Neurospora (Giles, 1951; Bonner, 1951), Aspergillus (Roper,
1953; Pontecorvo, 1952), and yeasts (Leupold, 1956; Roman and Jacob,
1958), as well as in maize (Nelson, 1959). It seems probable that the
phenomenon in Drosophila known as pseudoallelism belongs in the
same class.

PROPERTIES OF GENE LOCI

Thus the results of biological experiments indicate that a locus
comprises smaller sections (sites), separable from one another by
recombination. A site, then, is a subunit of a locus, at which mutation may occur but within which recombination has not been observed
and presumably does not occur. It is evident that the identification of
a site depends on the sensitivity of the method available for detecting
recombinants. It is believed that the methods developed for work with
certain loci in bacterial viruses (Benzer, 1955) and bacteria (Demerec,
1956) are sensitive enough to detect recombination between two markers if there is a possibility of its occurring.

Two kinds of mutations within loci have been recognized: those
that are limited to a single site, and those that involve two or more
adjacent sites, or even extend to an adjoining locus (multisite mutations). Auxotrophs produced by multisite mutations, in addition to
failing to recombine with a number of closely linked markers, do not
revert to prototrophy. In several respects multisite mutations resemble the chromosomal alterations observed in higher organisms.
It is generally assumed that they are deletions. As a rule they are
less frequent than single-site mutations.

Number of sites. According to the available evidence, the number
of sites per gene locus is large. More than 50 different sites have
already been identified in the *leu* locus of Salmonella (Glanville and
Demerec, 1960), close to 100 in the *cysC* locus of the same organism
(unpublished), and more than 200 in the *rII* locus of phage T4 (Benzer,
unpublished); and there is no indication that a saturation point has
been approached. The total number may well be in the thousands, as

is to be expected if a site corresponds to one nucleotide pair of the Watson-Crick (1953) model of the DNA molecule.

Differentiation among alleles. Alleles in microorganisms, like those in higher organisms, differ considerably from one another. One class of differences, observed in fungi, bacteria, and bacterial viruses, concerns mutation pattern — the degree of spontaneous and induced mutability. As a rule, different mutant alleles of the same gene locus differ both in frequency of occurrence of spontaneous reversion and in frequency of induction of reversion by treatment with different mutagens. These differences are illustrated by an analysis of eighteen alleles of the *tryD* locus of *S. typhimurium* made by Dr. E. Balbinder (Demerec et al., 1960). Figure 1 demonstrates the results obtained with four of the alleles, *tryD*-1, -42, -10, and -55. The upper part of the figure shows the order of these alleles on a linkage map of the *tryD* locus. Beneath are photographs of sixteen Petri dishes on which bacteria of the four allelic strains were grown on enriched minimal medium, which cannot support their full growth. Each vertical row represents four plates of the allelic strain indicated above on the linkage map, and each horizontal row contains characteristic samples of untreated bacteria (control) and bacteria treated with the chemical listed in the left-hand column. Every plate was spread with 0.1 ml of culture suspension, containing about 2×10^8 bacteria. Under the conditions of the experiments, these bacteria multiplied to about 4×10^9 cells during 48 hours of incubation, and then stopped dividing. At the time of plating,

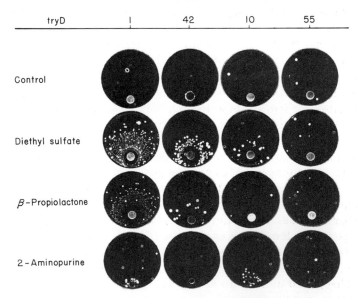

FIG. 1. Induction of reversions in four *tryD* alleles by three mutagens. Description in text. (*From Demerec et al.*, 1960.)

a drop of a solution of the chemical (a drop of sterile water for control plates) was placed either on a filter-paper disk or in a hole made in the medium with a cork borer (the last horizontal set of plates). Colonies on the control plates developed from bacteria in which the *tryD* gene had undergone reverse mutation, and the number of colonies on each plate indicates the frequency of spontaneous mutation per 2×10^9 cells. On the treated plates, colonies in excess of the numbers appearing on the control plates represent mutations induced by the treatment. Thus the differences between four of the *tryD* alleles with regard to mutability pattern are made evident. Spontaneous mutability in some of the alleles is too low to be demonstrated on a single plate. The spontaneous frequencies are about 6×10^{-10} in *tryD*-1, 1.5×10^{-10} in *tryD*-42, 3×10^{-10} in *tryD*-10, and 17×10^{-10} in *tryD*-55. As the figure shows, all three chemicals induced mutations in *tryD*-1; in *tryD*-42, diethyl sulfate and β-propiolactone were effective and 2-aminopurine was not; in *tryD*-10, β-propiolactone was not effective whereas the other two were; and in *tryD*-55 none of the compounds induced mutations. Strain *tryD*-55 displays what has been called "mutagen stability" (Demerec and Cahn, 1953); that is, it possesses the capacity to mutate spontaneously, but the rate of its mutability is not increased by any mutagen with which it has been tested.

Allelic mutants may also differ in ability to grow at different temperatures, in ability to grow on minimal medium or medium partially enriched with the compound for which they are deficient, in ability to grow on medium containing a compound other than the one characterizing the deficiency of the locus, in their reaction to suppressor mutations, in their accumulation of certain compounds, and in their complementation relations. Even mutations at the same site, it has been found, may give rise to several phenotypically different alleles; therefore the site is not the ultimate unit of mutation.

There are several methods of determining the order of sites and constructing a genetic map of a locus. The most reliable is the well-known three-point test, which has been extensively employed in linkage studies in higher organisms. Studies have revealed a nonrandom distribution of sites associated with similar properties (Demerec, 1957). A particularly strong tendency toward grouping of functionally related sites is shown by the sites of complementary alleles (Hartman, Loper, and Serman, 1960).

Limits of the locus. The studies with S. *typhimurium* have revealed that genes controlling related reactions are frequently located next to one another, and moreover, that they are arranged in the same order as the series of biosynthetic reactions they control. This assembly-line arrangement of functionally related genes has been established for four tryptophan loci (Demerec and Demerec, 1956), eight histidine loci (Hartman, Hartman, and Šerman, 1960; Hartman, Loper, and Šerman, 1960), four threonine loci (Glanville and Demerec, 1960), and five isoleucine and isoleucine-valine loci (Glanville and Demerec, 1960). It has been demonstrated with four tryptophan loci in *Escherichia coli* strain B (Skaar, 1957) and four in strain K-12 (Yanofsky and Lennox, 1959). Since this kind of arrangement has not been observed in fungi and other higher organisms, it probably occurs only in bacteria. It allows us to determine, with a reasonable degree of certainty, when two loci are adjacent to each other, and to analyze the areas near their boundary line. Good material for such analysis has been provided by the adjacent *hisB* and *hisC* loci, two of the series of eight loci studied by Hartman, 1957, Hartman, Hartman, and Šerman, 1960. His findings — that all of 34 alleles identified with 31 sites of the *hisB* locus control the enzyme imidazoleglycerol phosphate ester dehydrase, and that 35 alleles identified with 33 sites of the *hisC* locus control imidazoleacetol phosphate ester transaminase — indicate a sharp dividing line between the *B* and *C* loci (Demerec and Hartman, 1959).

Composition of the gene string. Recent studies of a region of the Salmonella genome which includes three proline loci have contributed some evidence bearing on the question whether the gene string is composed entirely of genetically active material or contains both active and inactive portions (Miyake and Demerec, 1960). Following is a brief summary of the evidence.

Ozeki's (1959) data indicate that the transducing fragments carried by particles of phage P-22 are, as regards any one region of chromosome, approximately identical. It may reasonably be assumed that frequency of recombination is generally a function of the length of the region within which it occurs. Therefore, in transduction experiments in which the recipient carries a mutant marker and the donor carries its wild-type allele, the frequency of replacement of the mutant marker by the wild-type gene reflects the distances between the mutant site and the two ends of the transducing fragment.

In the fragment concerned here, three *pro* loci have been identified: *proA* and *B*, adjacent to each other, and *proC* some distance away. Judging by frequencies of transduction with the wild-type donor the three loci are in the central part of the transducing fragment, with sections of considerable length on either side of them (1 and 3 below).

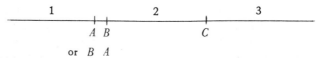

Out of eight mutants resulting from multisite mutations (deletions) in the region of chromosome represented by this fragment, two gave rise to very few recombinants in transduction experiments. Analysis showed that the mutations covered all the known sites of loci *proA* and *proB*, and extended through section 1 nearly to the end of the transducing fragment. The fact that the phenotypes of these two mutants do not differ from those of single-site *proA* or *proB* mutants suggests that the deleted portion outside *proA* and *B* either carries genes that produce no detectable effects or carries no genes at all (is genetically inert). Judging by the observed frequencies of recombination in section 1, the deleted portion must be of considerable length, which makes more probable the second of the two possibilities mentioned above, and indicates that a chromosome consists of genetically active and genetically inert areas. The inert areas may correspond to the heterochromatic regions detected in many higher organisms. Studies of the salivary-gland chromosomes of Drosophila suggest that these are distributed throughout the chromosomes (Hannah, 1951). In terms of the Watson-Crick model of DNA, the inert areas would be noncoded parts of the molecule, called by Crick "nonsense regions."

CONCLUSIONS

A gene locus comprises a finite section of a chromosome (or gene string) and contains the information necessary to control a particular chemical reaction or class of reactions. Within the gene locus, smaller units (sites) can be identified by means of recombination experiments. A site represents the smallest portion of genetic material that is not divisible by recombination. A change (mutation) occurring at any one of its many sites affects the expression of a whole gene locus.

Mutants resulting from mutations at different sites of the same gene locus, or even at the same site, may differ from one another in several respects (stability, reaction to mutagens, temperature sensitivity, nutritional requirements, complementary relations). As a rule, however, such mutants have one feature in common: they are changed with regard to a specific function, controlled by that particular gene locus. In some or perhaps most cases, control of the function is effected through an enzyme, whose structure, and consequently in a large measure character and specificity, are determined by the gene.

The findings about the structure of loci are in accordance with the view that DNA is the carrier of genetic information in phages and bacteria, and with the model of DNA structure proposed by Watson and Crick (1953). Observations concerning the nature of sites can be accounted for by assuming that a site is represented in the DNA molecule by either one or a few nucleotide pairs. It is estimated that phage T2 has two DNA molecules (Hershey et al., 1960) and about one hundred genes. Thus, many gene loci are contained in one molecule.

It should be stressed that the ideas discussed here have developed as logical steps in a chain of discoveries begun almost half a century ago. The basic principle guiding current studies of the genetic structure of genomes was formulated by Morgan and his coworkers, in their statistical analyses of patterns of segregation of genetic markers. Nor is the idea of complex structure of the gene a new concept. It was proposed in the late 1920s by a group of Russian geneticists (Dubinin, 1932; Serebrovsky, 1930) to explain their results in studies of the scute-achaete locus in *Drosophila melanogaster* (see Demerec and Hartman, 1959). They visualized that locus as containing separate, regularly spaced, and linearly arranged functional units. In fact, their picture of a gene locus (Dubinin, 1932) is almost identical with that currently being worked out by Giles and his coworkers in complementation studies with Neurospora (Giles, 1959).

REFERENCES

Benzer, S. (1955), Fine structure of a genetic region in bacteriophage. *Proc. Natl. Acad. Sci. U.S.*, 41:344-354.

Bonner, D. M. (1951), Gene-enzyme relationships in Neurospora. *Cold Spring Harbor Symposia Quant. Biol.*, 16:143-157.

Davis, B. D. (1948), Isolation of biochemically deficient mutants of bacteria by penicillin. *J. Am. Chem. Soc.*, 70:4267.

Demerec, M. (1956), A comparative study of certain gene loci in Salmonella. *Cold Spring Harbor Symposia Quant. Biol.*, 21:113-120.

—— (1957), Structure and arrangement of gene loci. *Proc. Intern. Genet. Symposia*, Tokyo, 1956 (suppl. *Cytologia*, 1957):20-31.

—— and E. Cahn (1953), Studies of mutability in nutritionally deficient strains of *Escherichia coli*. I. Genetic analysis of five auxotrophic strains. *J. Bacteriol.*, 65:27-36.

—— and Z. E. Demerec (1956), Analysis of linkage relationships in Salmonella by transduction techniques. *Brookhaven Symposia Biol.*, 8:75-84.

—— and P. E. Hartman (1959), Complex loci in microorganisms. *Ann. Rev. Microbiol.*, 13:377-406.

—— and Z. Hartman (1956), Tryptophan mutants in *Salmonella typhimurium*, in *Genetic Studies with Bacteria*, Carnegie Institution, Publ. 612, Washington, D.C., pp. 5-33.

——, E. L. Lahr, E. Balbinder, T. Miyake, J. Ishidsu, K. Mizobuchi, and Brigitte Mahler (1960), Bacterial genetics. *Carnegie Inst. Wash. Yr. Bk.* 59:426-441.

Dubinin, N. P. (1932), Step-allelomorphism and the theory of centres of the gene, achaete-scute. *J. Genet.*, 26:37-58.

Giles, N. H. (1951), Studies on the mechanism of reversion in biochemical mutants of *Neurospora crassa*. *Cold Spring Harbor Symposia Quant. Biol.*, 14:283-313.

—— (1959), Mutations in specific loci in Neurospora. *Proc. Intern. Congr. Genet.*, 10th Congr., Montreal, 1:261-279.

Glanville, E. V., and M. Demerec (1960), Threonine, isoleucine, and isoleucine-valine mutants of *Salmonella typhimurium*. *Genetics*, 45:1359-1374.

Hannah, Aloha (1951), Localization and function of heterochromatin in *Drosophila melanogaster*. *Advances in Genet.*, 4:87-125.

Hartman, P. E., Z. Hartman, and D. Šerman (1960), Genetic control of histidine synthesis in bacteria. II. Complementation mapping by abortive transduction of histidine-requiring Salmonella mutants. *J. Gen. Microbiol.*, 22:354-368.

—— J. C. Loper, and D. Šerman (1960), Genetic control of histidine synthesis in bacteria. I. Fine structure mapping by complete transduction between histidine-requiring Salmonella mutants. *J. Gen. Microbiol.*, 22:323-353.

Hershey, A. D., E. Burgi, C. Cocito, L. Ingraham, E. H. Simon, and T. Minigawa (1960), Growth and inheritance in bacteriophage. *Carnegie Inst. Wash. Yr. Bk.* 59:421-424.

—— and M. Chase (1951), Genetic recombination and heterozygosis in bacteriophage. *Cold Spring Harbor Symposia Quant. Biol.*, 16:471-479.

Lederberg, J., and N. Zinder (1948), Concentration of biochemical mutants of bacteria with penicillin. *J. Am. Chem. Soc.*, 70:4267.

Leupold, U. (1958), Studies on recombination in *Schizosaccharomyces pombe*. *Cold Spring Harbor Symposia Quant. Biol.*, 23:161-170.

Miyake, T., and M. Demerec (1960), Proline mutants of *Salmonella typhimurium*. *Genetics*, 45:755-762.

Morgan, T. H., A. H. Sturtevant, H. J. Muller, and C. B. Bridges (1915), *The Mechanism of Mendelian Heredity*. Holt, Rinehart and Winston, Inc., New York.

Nelson, Oliver E. (1959), Intracistron recombination in the *Wx-wx* region in maize. *Science*, 130:794-795.

Ozeki, H. (1959), Chromosome fragments participating in transduction in *Salmonella typhimurium*. *Genetics*, 44 (part 2):457-470.

Pontecorvo, G. (1952), Genetic formulation of gene structure and gene action. *Advances in Enzymol.*, 13:121-149.

Roman, H., and F. Jacob (1958), A comparison of spontaneous and ultraviolet-induced allelic recombination with reference to the recombination of outside markers. *Cold Spring Harbor Symposia Quant. Biol.*, 23:155-160.

Roper, J. A. (1953), Pseudo-allelism. *Advances in Genet.*, 5:208-215.

Serebrovsky, A. S. (1930), Untersuchungen über Treppenallelomorphismus. IV. Transgenation scute-6 und ein Fall des "Nicht-allelomorphismus" von Gliedern einer Allelomorphenreihe bei *Drosophila melanogaster*. Wilhelm Roux' *Arch. Entwicklungsmech. Org.*, 122:88-104.

Skaar, P. D. (1957), Genetics of *Escherichia coli*. *Ann. Rept. Biol. Lab.*, Cold Spring Harbor, 1956-1957, pp. 30-34.

Streisinger, G., and N. C. Franklin (1956), Mutation and recombination at the host range genetic region of phage T2. *Cold Spring Harbor Symposia Quant. Biol.*, 21:103-111.

Visconti, N., and M. Delbrück (1953), The mechanism of genetic recombination in phage. *Genetics*, 38:5-33.

Watson, J. D., and F. H. C. Crick (1953), The structure of DNA. *Cold Spring Harbor Symposia Quant. Biol.*, 18:123-131.

Yanofsky, C., and E. S. Lennox (1959), Transduction and recombination study of linkage relationships among the genes controlling tryptophan synthesis in *Escherichia coli*. *Virology*, 8:425-447.

Zinder, N. D., and J. Lederberg (1952), Genetic exchange in Salmonella. *J. Bacteriol.*, 64:679-699.

Chapter Six

The Genetic Control of Protein Specificity[*]

VERNON M. INGRAM

*Division of Biochemistry, Department of Biology
Massachusetts Institute of Technology, Cambridge,
Massachusetts.*

Recently the study of the chemistry and the three-dimensional structure of hemoglobin has exploded into life through the efforts of many workers throughout the world (1). In particular, intensive chemical investigations have been concerned with the genetically controlled alterations in the human hemoglobins (2). The X-ray work of Kendrew (3) and Perutz (4) has provided us with a structural model. As a result, a considerable amount is known about the kind of control exercised by the gene over the structure of the protein hemoglobin. In this article we shall examine some current hypotheses concerning this control. It is our belief that what we may deduce for hemoglobin will also be applicable to other proteins. The hemoglobin system has the advantage that we can now or will soon test the hypotheses experimentally.

Postulates

1. A protein is a single molecular species with a unique amino acid sequence. The concept is based on the work of Sanger (5) with insulin, of Hirs, Moore, and Stein with ribonuclease (6) and on our own experiences with human hemoglobin (2). This postulate is not invalidated by the fact that a protein as first isolated may be a mixture of several molecular species, since each component obeys the above assumption. The important distinction is that we do not find a continuum of different molecules.

2. It is sufficient to determine the primary structure of a protein, i.e., the amino acid sequence of its polypeptide chain or chains. It is believed that the coiling and supercoiling of such a chain (secondary and tertiary structure), as observed in myoglobin or hemoglobin, is a necessary consequence of the amino acid sequence. In time even the quaternary structure is already determined, by which is meant the

*This work has been supported in part by grants from the National Institutes of Health and the National Science Foundation.

fitting together of the four subunits of hemoglobin, for example (4). In its strictest sense, this postulate seems to apply to a small molecule such as insulin, where the very few amino acid alterations in insulin from different species are confined to a small extraneous loop (8). The statement is probably largely true for small globular proteins such as hemoglobin or myoglobin, but it may have to be modified for large proteins such as antibodies. Here it is conceivable that a particular amino acid sequence can give rise to a *number* of somewhat different configurations, each energetically similar. The actual folding may then depend on environmental factors.

3. The original "one gene-one enzyme" hypothesis of Beadle and Tatum (9) has been most helpful in guiding our thinking about possible mechanisms for controlling the structure of proteins. It has more recently been refined by Benzer (10) to state that the structure of a polypeptide chain is determined by a single gene. Since there are two different polypeptide chains in a hemoglobin, we would postulate that two different genes are concerned in the production of the protein portion of hemoglobin (see also refs. 11 and 12). More explicitly, we would postulate that by virtue of the linear structure of its DNA the gene determines the linear amino acid sequence of a particular hemoglobin polypeptide chain, its first protein product (7). Two different genes would be concerned, since two different peptide chains occur in a particular hemoglobin.

As yet there is no proof for such a hypothesis. It will have to come from a simultaneous study (12, 13) of the chemistry of a microbiological protein and its mutated forms and the fine-structure genetics of the relevant portion of the genome. The direct chemical investigation of the DNA concerned is at present beyond our horizon. In the meantime we can study in the human hemoglobins and in other systems the kind of chemical variation induced as a result of the mutation of a gene. The findings to be discussed in this article support the hypothesis of genetic control.

4. We can list the types of mutational alteration in a protein which could be caused by gene mutations.

Point mutations, the smallest conceivable alterations in a DNA molecule, cause only a single amino acid to be substituted by another. This is the kind of effect observed in the human hemoglobins. Alternatively, such a point mutation could lead to an amino acid being missing. The consequent gap in the peptide chain might well have the effect of stopping synthesis of the affected chain altogether. In a homozygote, this would probably be classed as a lethal mutation if the protein is vitally important.

Segment mutations are next in size. Provided the segment of DNA which alters is within the length of DNA which corresponds to a single amino acid, the observed effect on the protein will be as above. Conceivably, they might be differentiated in a microbiological system through an examination of back mutations. Should the segment of mutating DNA be longer, then a correspondingly larger number of amino acids will be altered or missing. Such changes are likely to affect the functioning of the protein more drastically. They have not been observed in the hemoglobins. Exchange of portions of a gene will fall into this category also.

Inversions of segments are well known genetically, though not within a gene. The inversion of segments of the amino acid sequence has not been observed between alleles. Present methods of analysis of hemoglobin by examination of tryptic peptides would only detect those inversions which happen to span the positions where trypsin leaves the chain. Detailed sequence analysis of each peptide will be required.

Normal Hemoglobin

What constitutes a "normal" protein? The detailed chemical examination of samples of hemoglobin from normal individuals will in due course provide evidence whether or not the amino acid sequence even in relatively unimportant parts of the molecule is always the same. In other words, we are looking for an answer to the question, what is the background variability of a normal protein in a human population? Those portions of the hemoglobin molecule where a particular sequence of amino acids is essential to the folding and functioning of the molecule would be expected to be free of random variability. An alteration would be eliminated by selection. On the other hand, we know already of several other regions in the molecule where amino acid substitutions can occur (2) (Table 1) without seriously affecting the functioning of the hemoglobin Hb $G_{San\ Jose}$, Hb I, Hb $G_{Philadelphia}$. In these latter regions, there would seem to be no compelling reason in the phenotype for maintaining a unique amino acid sequence. Preliminary results indicate that variability in some of these regions occurs rarely, if at all. We are forced to look for an explanation in the high intrinsic stability of the genes which control these peptide chains.

Abnormal Hemoglobins

Many of the known abnormal hemoglobins were discovered because they are found in the hereditary hemoglobinopathies (1). Indeed, it is the presence of such abnormal hemoglobin molecules in sufficient preponderance which causes the disease. For them, Pauling (14) has coined the phrase "molecular disease." It is more than likely that in the future other hereditary diseases will be shown to be due to a genetically determined abnormality in some important protein. Here

TABLE 1

Some of the Known Abnormalities in Human Hemoglobin

	Alpha Chain						
Position	1 2 16	30	57 58	68			141
	Val.Leu....Lys.	.......Glu........	Gly.His.	...Asp.NH$_2$		....	Arg
Hb Variant							
Hb I	.Asp.						
Hb G Honolulu		.Glu.NH$_2$.					
Hb Norfolk			.Asp.				
Hb M Boston			.Tyr.				
Hb G Philadelphia				.Lys.			

	Beta Chain								
Position	1 2 3	6	7	26	63	67	125	150
	Val.His.Leu....	Glu.	Glu....	Glu....	His....	Val.........	Glu.........	His
Hb Variant								
Hb S		.Val.						
Hb C		.Lys.						
Hb G San José			.Gly.					
Hb E				.Lys.				
Hb M Saskatoon					.Tyr.			
Hb M Milwaukee						.Glu.		
Hb Dβ Punjab (=Dγ)							Glu.NH$_2$	

A summary of the established amino acid substitutions in human hemoglobin variants. The complete amino acid sequence of the two chains is largely known through the efforts of the following: G. Braunitzer, N. Hilschmann, K. Hilse, B. Liebold and, R. Müller (1960a), Die Konstitution der β-Kette der Hauptkomponente des normalen adulten Humanhaemoglobins, Z. physicl. Chem. 322:96-100; G. Braunitzer, V. Rudloff, K. Hilse, B. Liebold, and R. Müller (1960b), Eine Partialformel der α-Kette der Hauptkomponents des adulten menschlichen Haemoglobins, Z. physiol. Chem., 320:283-288; R. J. Hill and W. Konigsberg (1061), The partial structural formula of the α-chain of human hemoglobins, J. Biol. Chem., 236:PC7-8. References for the amino acid substitutions are as follows: Hb's S, C, and E(2); Hb G San Jose, (16); Hb G Philadelphia; C. Baglioni and V. M. Ingram (1961), Four adult haemoglobin types in one person, Nature, 189:465-467; Hb I, Murayama (1960); The chemical difference between normal human hemoglobin and hemoglobin I, Federation Proc., 19:78; Hb Norfolk, C. Baglioni (1961), Chemistry of hemoglobin Norfolk, a rare variant of human hemoglobin, Federation Proc., 20:254; Hb Dβ Punjab, C. Baglioni (unpublished); Hb's M Boston, M Sakatoon, and M Milwaukee, Park Gerald (unpublished); Hb G Honolulu, R. T. Swenson and R. L. Hill (unpublished). The writer wishes to thank those authors who gave permission to use their unpublished results, and Dr. H. Eldon Sutton, to whom we owe this table.

again the hemoglobins provide examples which are readily accessible for study, but which illustrate a much more general situation.

Given that altered hemoglobins are likely to be relatively rare, as discussed in a previous section, we would expect to find a spectrum of abnormalities. They would range from those having no noticeable effect through some of intermediate severity to alterations which produce molecules carrying severe diseases, or maybe no molecules at all. The first and last group have not yet been observed for obvious reasons. In the middle range, we find such examples as are given in Table 1. Our knowledge of the structure of the molecule is not yet sufficiently far advanced to explain why the alteration (15) of Glu → Val in hemoglobin S produces the severe sickle-cell disease and why the neighboring Glu → Gly alteration (16) in hemoglobin G produces a molecule which appears to function normally (Table 2). All we know is that it is so. This situation shows the fine control exercised by the gene over the amino acid sequence of the peptide chain. It reinforces the idea that these may be point mutations.

It is worth noting that abnormal human hemoglobins carrying amino acid substitutions are produced at rates below that for normal hemoglobin A, with the possible exception of hemoglobin J. If the current view is correct that hemoglobin, like other proteins, is produced inside the so-called ribosomes, (17) the rate of production might well be controlled by the rate at which the finished chains leave the ribo-

TABLE 2

Amino Acid Sequences in Abnormal Hemoglobins

Tryptic Peptide 4

Hb A	Val.His$^+$.Leu.Thr.Pro.Glū.Glū.Lys$^+$ ↑ ...
Hb S	Val.His$^+$.Leu.Thr.Pro.Val.Glū.Lys$^+$ ↑ ...
Hb C	Val.His$^+$.Leu.Thr.Pro.Lys$^+$ Glū.Lys$^+$ ↑ ...
Hb G	Val.His$^+$.Leu.Thr.Pro.Glū.Gly.Lys$^+$ ↑

Tryptic Peptide 26

| Hb A | ... ↑ Val.Asp.Val.Asp̄.Glū.Val.Gly.Gly.Glū.Ala.Leu.Gly.Arg$^+$ ↑ ... |
| Hb E | ... ↑ Val.Asp.Val.Asp̄.Glū.Val.Gly.Gly.Lys$^+$ ↑ Ala.Leu.Gly.Arg$^+$ ↑ ... |

Notes: Tryptic peptide 4 is the beginning of the β peptide chain of hemoglobin, peptide 26 is third in that chain. The arrows indicate the points of trypsin splitting. The numbers are arbitrary. The first aspartic acid of peptide 26 is probably present in the form of aspargine Hb G = Hb G Philadelphia.

somes, coiling up as they leave. One of the controlling factors would then be the ease with which the chain could coil to form the final globular protein or protein subunit. An alteration in amino acid sequence might well reduce the ease of coiling and thus slow the whole process of hemoglobin manufacture. The idea that an amino acid substitution could reduce the rate of hemoglobin synthesis is the basis for our current thinking about the causes of thalassemia.

It has been said earlier that abnormal hemoglobins with amino acid substitutions are likely to occur only rarely. This is true for the majority of these hemoglobins, which are scattered thinly throughout the world. On the other hand, Table 1 contains several abnormal hemoglobins, each of which occurs with very high frequency in certain areas (hemoglobins S, C, E, and some forms of D). In addition, these hemoglobins produce the most serious diseases. To deal with this paradox it has been postulated (18) by Haldane that these "high-frequency" hemoglobins confer a selective advantage on their bearers which more than outweighs the loss of the genes through the disease. However, only in the case of sickle-cell hemoglobin are we in a position to substantiate this idea of "balanced polymorphism." It was first postulated by Allison (19) that individuals heterozygous for the hemoglobins S and A might have considerable advantage toward tertian malaria. After some controversy, this has been proved (20) to be the case for children under 2 years of age, the period when malaria is most threatening. The reason for the effect might lie in the considerably reduced lifespan of red cells containing hemoglobin S, since this would interfere with the life cycle of the parasite. Malaria has also been invoked to explain the high frequency of the forms of thalassemia found in Southern Italy and Southeast Asia, but without experimental evidence so far. In addition, Lehmann suggests (21) that hemoglobin E occurs frequently in Southeast Asia, because its presence prevents the occurrence of the linked homozygous form of thalassemia found there. It seems that the eventual importance of a particular hemoglobin mutation depends not only on its chemical effect on the molecule, but also on the interaction of the mutation with the environment.

Nonelectrophoretic Mutants of Hemoglobin

Up to now, we have discussed only those amino acid substitutions which involve an alteration in the charged groups of a protein molecule. Naturally, these are the easiest and hence the first ones to be detected, and also they are likely to have a more profound effect on the physiological performance of the altered hemoglobin. More frequently, because they are more numerous, we would expect to come across mutations leading to amino acid substitutions in the hemoglobin molecule which *do not* involve charged groups (e.g., glycine to leucine). Many such substitutions are theoretically possible. None have been detected so far, largely because they have not yet been deliberately searched for and partly because of the great technical difficulties involved. However, we postulate that such nonelectrophoretic alterations in hemoglobin are the basis of many forms of thalassemia (1, 22).

The outstanding characteristic of thalassemia is the low level of hemoglobin found in individual cells. This reflects, it is thought, an impairment in the rate of hemoglobin synthesis. On the other hand, such hemoglobin A as is made appears normal electrophoretically. It will be remembered that amino acid substitutions are known to lead to reduction in the rate of synthesis of hemoglobin. Combining these two arguments, we postulate that a nonelectrophoretic amino acid substitution might lead to reduced hemoglobin synthesis and could cause therefore the symptoms of thalassemia.

Drastic reduction in hemoglobin, such as would occur in a homozygous thalassemia, would call forth as a compensating mechanism the production of fetal hemoglobin (Hb F). Up to now we have discussed mutations of the two peptide chains (23) of adult hemoglobin (α = Val.Leu...., β = Val.His.Leu....), but there is no reason to suppose that fetal hemoglobin is immune. This form of hemoglobin shares the α chains of the adult form, (24) but has γ chains (23) (Gly.His.Phe....) instead of β chains.

$$\text{Hb A} = \alpha_2 \beta_2 \qquad\qquad \text{Hb F} = \alpha_2 \gamma_2$$

It is known (1) that in homozygous sickle-cell anemia where $\alpha_2^A \beta_2^S$ is produced, fetal hemoglobin is often found in amounts up to 40 per cent. This compensation is possible because in sickle-cell anemia the α chains remain normal. Normal hemoglobin F is made which does not use the β chains anyway. Of course, if the homozygous abnormality had been on the α chain, such compensation would not have been possible. This situation has not yet been observed, since the gene frequencies of all the known α-chain mutants of hemoglobin are very low.

If a homozygous thalassemia allows the compensatory production of fetal hemoglobin, that thalassemia is likely to be on the β chain. In the homozygous case where the thalassemia mutation is on the α chain, compensation would be impossible, Hb F formation would be depressed in the fetus, and the condition probably lethal.

It is a perplexing feature of thalassemia in its heterozygous or homozygous condition that it occurs in many diverse forms. There are many thalassemias differing to a greater or lesser extent in severity and in the details of the clinical picture. We can now see that thalassemias are classifiable into α- and β-chain thalassemias (22). Within each group, a variety of amino acid substitutions will be found differing in severity according to the particular amino acid substitution; some may not be made at all. The substitutions would form two allelomorphic series, within each of which they would correspond to Muller's "hypomorphs," producing less product than normal — or "amorphs," producing no peptide chains at all (25). It must be added that in some thalassemias, the impairment may be in one of the many enzymes involved in heme synthesis. The situation would be analogous, but the hemoglobin protein would be quite normal though reduced in amount. Compensation by fetal hemoglobin would be impossible. It is believed that not many instances of thalassemia belong to this class. Certainly not the so-called "interacting" thalassemias. A double heterozygote for a thalassemia and, for example, hemoglobin C, may or may not produce any hemoglobin A at all. If a person makes no hemoglobin A, it is an "interacting" thalassemia, which is of the β allelic series. if both β-chain genes are abnormal (β^C and β^X), he makes only hemoglobin C, but he can make fetal hemoglobin ($\alpha_2 \gamma_2$) as compensation. If he does make hemoglobin A, it is a "noninteracting" thalassemia, which belongs to the α-chain series. Such a person has still one normal α-chain gene (α^X/α^A) and one normal β-chain gene (β^A/β^C). Since the genes produce their products independently, both hemoglobin A and C are made. There is no need for compensation with F. In addition, electrophoretically indistinguishable thalassemic forms of the two hemoglobins may be made in small amount if at all ($\alpha_2^X \beta_2^A$ and $\alpha_2^X \beta_2^C$).

It should be added that in some thalassemias the normal minor (2.5 per cent) component, hemoglobin A_2, is doubled in amount (26). In other cases the level of this hemoglobin remains the same. There is now reason to believe that this is a third form of hemoglobin of general structure $\alpha_2 \delta_2$. Thus, again the same α chains are used, controlled by the same α-chain genes. In a β-chain thalassemia the amount of hemoglobin A_2 increases in compensation, in an α-chain thalassemia it cannot do so.

CONCLUSION

The human hemoglobins present a particularly well-studied example of a globular protein composed of subunits. Different types of hemoglobins are built up using the same unit — α chains — for part of the molecule in each case. These α chains not only appear to be common in the various human hemoglobins, but may be closely related to corresponding "α" chains in other vertebrate hemoglobins (27). When more is known about the chemistry of lower vertebrate hemoglobins, perhaps we shall be able to see how the separate parts of a protein of such universal importance have evolved.

In the meantime, the study of the abnormal human hemoglobins illustrates the effect of some kinds of gene mutation on the protein produced by the gene. The findings are thought to apply to proteins in general. The one gene-one peptide chain hypothesis and the idea of a structural relationship between gene and peptide chain are strongly supported. Possible effects of gene mutations on protein structure are discussed in general terms and in relation to the hemoglobinopathies. It is very much to be hoped that soon other cases of abnormal proteins will be investigated, especially in a microbiological system where so much more can be learned about gene structure.

NOTES AND REFERENCES

1. National Academy of Science, *Conference on Hemoglobin*, 1958; *Abnormal Haemoglobins*, Jonxis and Delafresnaye, eds., Basil Blackwell & Mott, Ltd., Oxford, 1959.
2. Hunt, J. A., and V. M. Ingram (1959), The genetical control of protein structure: the abnormal human hemoglobins, in *Ciba Symposium on Human Genetics*, J. & A. Churchill, Ltd., London.
   Ingram, V. M. (1961), *Hemoglobin and Its Abnormalities*, Charles C. Thomas, Publisher, Springfield, Ill.
3. Kendrew, J. C., G. Bodo, H. M. Dintzis, R. G. Parrish, and H. Wyckoff (1958), A three-dimensional model of the myoglobin molecule obtained by X-ray analysis. *Nature*, 181:662.
   —— et al. (1960), *Nature* (in press).
4. Perutz, M. F., M. G. Rossman, Ann F. Culles, H. Muirhead, and G. Will (1960), A three-dimensional Fourier at 5.5°A resolution, obtained by X-ray analysis. *Nature*, (in press).
5. Sanger, F., and L. F. Smith (1957), *Endeavour*, 16:48.
6. Moore, S., and W. H. Stein (1958), Determination of the structure of proteins: Studies on ribonuclease, in *Harvey Lectures, 1956-1957*. Academic Press, Inc., New York.
7. Crick, F. H. C. (1958), On protein synthesis. *Symposia Soc. Exp. Biol.*, 12:138.
8. Harris, J. I., F. Sanger, and M. A. Naughton (1956), Species differences in insulin. *Arch. Biochem. Biophys.*, 65:1.
   Brown, H., F. Sanger, and R. Kital (1955), The structure of pig and sheep insulin. *Biochem. J.*, 60:556.
9. Beadle, G. W., and E. L. Tatum (1941), Genetic control of biochemical reactions in Neurospora. *Proc. Natl. Acad. Sci. U.S.*, 27:499.
10. Benzer, S. (1957), Elementary units of heredity, in *The Chemical Basis of Heredity*, W. D. McElroy and B. Glass, eds., Johns Hopkins Press, Baltimore, p. 70.
11. Neel, J. V. (1959), Genetic aspects of abnormal hemoglobins, in *Abnormal Haemoglobins*, Jonxis and Delafresnaye, eds., Basil Blackwell and Mott, Ltd., Oxford, p. 162.
    Smith, E., and J. V. Torbert (1958), Study of two abnormal hemoglobins with evidence for a new genetic locus for hemoglobin formation. *Bull. Johns Hopkins Hosp.*, 101:38.

12. Brenner, S. (1959), Gene structure and protein structure, in *Structure and Function of Genetic Elements. Brookhaven Natl. Lab. Symposium* 12.
13. Levinthal, C. (1959), Genetic and chemical studies with alkaline phosphatase of *E. coli*, in *Structure and Function of Genetic Elements. Brookhaven Natl. Lab. Symposium* 12.
14. Pauling, L., H. A. Itano, S. J. Singer, and I. C. Wells (1949), Sickle cell anemia, a molecular disease. *Science*, 110:543.
15. Ingram, V.M. (1957), Gene mutations in human haemoglobin: The chemical difference between normal and sickle cell haemoglobin. *Nature*, 180:326.
    —— (1959), Abnormal human haemoglobins. III. The chemical difference between normal and sickle cell haemoglobins. *Biochim. Biophys. Acta*, 36.
16. Hill, R. L., and H. C. Schwartz (1959), A chemical abnormality in hemoglobin G. *Nature*, 184:642.
17. Hoagland, M. B. (1959), The present status of the adapter hypothesis, in *Structure and Function of Genetic Elements. Brookhaven Natl. Lab. Symposium* 12.
18. Haldane, J. B. S. (1949), Disease and evolution. *Ricerca Sci.*, 19, Suppl. 68.
19. Allison, A. C. (1954), Protection afforded by sickle-cell trait against subtertian malarial infection. *Brit. J. Med.*, 1:290.
20. Raper, A. B. (1956), Sickling in relation to morbidity from malaria and other diseases. *Brit. Med. J.*, 1:965.
21. Lehmann, H. (1959), Distribution of variation in haemoglobin synthesis; Maintenance of the haemoglobinopathies at high frequency, in *Abnormal Haemoglobins*, Jonxis and Delafresnaye, eds., Basil Blackwell & Mott, Ltd., Oxford.
22. Ingram, V. M., and A. O. W. Stretton (1959), The genetic basis of the thalassemia diseases. *Nature*, 184:1903.
23. Schroeder, W. A. (1959), The chemical structure of the normal human hemoglobins. *Fortschr. Chem. Naturstoffe*, vol. XVII.
24. Hunt, J. A. (1959), Identity of the chains of adult and foetal human haemoglobins. *Nature*, 183:1373.
25. Muller, H. J. (1932), Further studies on the nature and causes of gene mutations. *Proc. Intern. Congr. Genet., 6th Congr.*, 213.
26. Gerald, P. S., and L. K. Diamond (1958), The diagnosis of thalassemia trait by starch block electrophoresis of the hemoglobin. *Blood*, 13:61.
27. Anfinsen, C. B. (1959), *The Molecular Basis of Evolution*, John Wiley & Sons, Inc., New York, p. 161.

Chapter Seven

The Activity of Isolated Viral Deoxyribonucleic Acid in the Genesis of Proteins within Bacterial Cells

DAVID S. HOGNESS

*Department of Biochemistry, Stanford University
School of Medicine, Palo Alto, California*

INTRODUCTION

The argument that the linear sequence of the four bases in deoxyribonucleic acid (DNA) determines in some simple manner the linear sequence of amino acids in a given polypeptide chain forms the basic postulate of gene function in the synthesis of proteins. Accepting this postulate as a working hypothesis, we are interested in (1) the determination of the code for the translation from the four-symbol language of the DNA to the twenty-symbol language of the protein, and (2) the mechanism by which the cell performs this translation. These are significantly different problems in that it is, a priori, possible to discover the code without knowing the cellular mechanism involved, just as it is possible to discover many facets of the mechanism of translation without knowing the precise relationship between the two languages.

In considering the mechanism by which cells translate from the DNA to the protein language, the focal point of experimentation can be either the protein or the DNA. The emphasis of most of the experimental work concerning this mechanism has been placed on the former of these two foci of attention. This is owing to the fact that subcellular systems have been developed in which the synthesis of at least part of the polypeptide chain of a specific protein can be demonstrated (Hoagland, 1960), whereas no subcellular system has been developed in which the activity of DNA in controlling such synthesis can be observed.

The desirability of developing this latter type of system is evident. Indeed, if one were to indulge in a Walter Mitty-type dream state, the ideal experimental system one would tend to visualize would contain the following components: (1) A solution of DNA molecules, each of which was identical and contained only that amount of base sequence necessary for the specification of the amino acid sequence of a single protein (i.e., that amount of DNA corresponding to one gene, or more precisely, one cistron); and (2) a resolvable subcellular system in which the continued synthesis of this protein was dependent upon the presence of the above DNA molecules. One would expect such an experimental system to allow the determination of the basic steps in the translation process — i.e., through what chemical structures the information contained in the base sequence of DNA passes before being contained in the amino acid sequence of the protein. It could also offer a system for comparison of base sequence to amino acid sequence (i.e., determination of the code), should nucleic acid chemistry become sophisticated enough for the direct chemical determination of the base sequence of the DNA molecules in such a homogeneous solution.

Although this is the stuff of dreams, in the present state of our working hypothesis, attempts to approximate this ideal should be useful. It is the purpose of this article to define some recent developments with bacterial viruses which pertain to the approximation of this ideal.

The Choice of System

The first of the systems in which DNA molecules in solution could be demonstrated to have activity in controlling the synthesis of specific proteins was, of course, the genetic transformation of pneumococci. As early as 1944 the work of Avery, MacLeod, and McCarty (1944) allowed this transformation to be defined as the hereditarily stable change of cells in one phenotypic state, a, to an alternate state, b, by exposure of a-type cells to DNA isolated from b-type cells, the a and b cell types being related by mutation. By 1955, Hotchkiss and Marmur (1955) had demonstrated that such a and b states could be the incapacity and capacity, respectively, to synthesize a specific protein, mannitol phosphate dehydrogenase. This type of genetic transformation, in which both the recipient cells and the source of DNA are bacterial, has been extended to other bacteria, notably *Hemophilus influenzae* (Zamenhof, 1957) and more recently, *Bacillus subtilis* (Spizizen, 1959).

However, in the past few years another type of system showing DNA activity has been developed, which appears to offer several advantages over the above in approximating the previously visualized ideal. In these systems the source of the active DNA is a virus, more specifically, a bacterial virus or phage. The advantage of this source of DNA lies in the smaller genome of phage as compared with bacteria.

Thus the comparison of the amount of DNA per reproducing unit (cell or phage particle) given in Table 1 indicates that while bacteria (e.g., *E. coli*) are considerably simpler than mammalian cells in that they contain several orders of magnitude less DNA, the phages represent again another order of simplicity. If one assumes an upper limit to the size of DNA molecules that can presently be obtained in aqueous solution of about 2×10^5 bases per molecule (ca. 6×10^7 molecular weight, Thomas and Berns, 1961) then an *E. coli* nucleus would yield about 60 such molecules, whereas the phage T2 would yield only two and the phage λ only one. Supposing that all of the DNA in each organism is included in its genome, then the 60 molecules obtained from each *E. coli* nucleus would be presumed to contain different base sequences. With phage, on the other hand, it should be possible to better approximate homogeneity, since the DNA per particle is from two times (T2) to one-fortieth (ϕX174) the amount in a molecule containing 2×10^5 bases.

Another factor which favors the phage systems, and is also related to their smaller genome, is that the purity of a single functional unit, or cistron, should be higher in phage DNA solutions. Thus if one makes the reasonable assumption that the number of bases necessary to specify an amino acid sequence of given size is the same for phage as for bacteria, then that fraction of the total DNA representing a single protein would be from one to three orders of magnitude more for the phages given in Table 1 than for *E. coli*. This conclusion is consistent with the observation that individual bacteria appear to synthesize many more different types of protein than are synthesized as a result of phage infection of such bacteria.

TABLE 1

The DNA Content per Reproducing Unit from Various Sources

Source and unit	Deoxyribonucleotides per unit	Reference
Mammalian haploid cell (cattle)	$60,000 \times 10^5$	Vendrely, 1955
Escherichia coli haploid nucleus	120×10^5	Fuerst and Stent, 1956
Phage T2	4×10^5	Hershey and Melechen, 1957; Stent and Fuerst, 1955
Phage λ	2×10^5	Kaiser and Hogness, 1960; Smith and Siminovitch, 1953
Phage ϕX174	0.05×10^5	Sinsheimer, 1959a, b

Finally, it should be mentioned that the available systems of active DNA isolated from bacteria have not allowed a method of genetic analysis independent of transformation. As a consequence, extensive genetic maps of the chromosome(s) of these bacteria have not been constructed. On the other hand, extensive and detailed genetic maps of the chromosome of phages have been constructed, phage T2 and λ being in this class. Such a knowledge of the genetic structure of the organism providing the active DNA is, of course, essential for a comparison of map position, and position in the DNA. While perhaps not essential, it should also be very useful in the interpretation of experiments designed to obtain, or approximate, the ideal of a DNA solution containing only one cistron.

It is because of these potential advantages in approximating the visualized ideal that the emphasis of this article is placed on the phage systems. This viewpoint has resulted from concentrating on the nature of the active DNA solution, almost to the exclusion of considering that part of these systems which allows the expression of the DNA, namely the recipient bacteria. Consequently, certain present advantages of the all-bacterial systems, such as the greater efficiency in the assay of DNA activity (i.e., the number of altered cells per DNA added) have not been considered. It is hoped that such advantages are temporary and, indeed, that eventually the recipient cells can be replaced with subcellular components in the detection of DNA activity.

The Activity of DNA Isolated from Bacteriophage λ

General Properties of λ.[1] Bacteriophage λ is a particle of molecular weight about 1×10^8 consisting of approximately equal parts of DNA and protein (Kaiser and Hogness, 1960). It is tadpole-shaped, having a roughly spherical head 60 mμ in diameter, attached to a cylindrical tail 140 mμ long and 13 mμ in diameter (Arber and Kellenberger, 1958). This phage particle infects *E. coli* cells by first attaching the tip of its tail to the cell surface and then injecting the DNA that is contained within its protein-coated head into the host cell. No direct evidence exists concerning the amount of phage DNA and protein which enter the host cell. However, in analogy with evidence concerning T2 phage infection, obtained from the classical experiments of Hershey and Chase (1952) and their extensions (Hershey, 1955; Hershey and Burgi, 1956), it is generally assumed that all of the λ DNA and very little, if any, of its protein enters the host cell. In any case, experiments to be described here leave no doubt that the genetic specificity of λ resides in its DNA.

[1]Unless otherwise specified, the general properties of λ referred to in this section may be found in three review articles (Lwoff, 1953; Jacob and Wollman, 1957; and Bertani, 1958).

After injection of the λ DNA one of two results may follow. With a probability that is normally about 0.8 (but is dependent upon the phage genotype and environmental conditions) the infected cell will commence synthesis of the protein and DNA phage components so as to yield mature phage particles. A concomitant increase in a lysozyme activity results in lysis of the host cell and the release of the mature phage (Jacob and Fuerst, 1958). Infected bacteria which do not follow this lytic pathway survive and multiply as lysogenic bacteria. In these lysogenic bacteria the phage chromosome has become closely and persistently associated with the bacterial chromosome. Only temperate phage, such as λ, have both the lytic and lysogenic pathways available to them. Virulent phage, such as T2, are obliged to follow the lytic pathway.

Lysogenic bacteria possess two properties which distinguish them from nonlysogenic bacteria and indicate that there exists a stable association of phage and bacterial chromosomes within them. The first property is that they retain the capacity to produce the mature phage for which they are lysogenic, and the second is that they exhibit a specific immunity toward this phage.

Bacteria lysogenic for λ are normally quite stable, lysis and release of phage occurring at a frequency of about 10^{-4} per cell generation. However, if these bacteria are exposed to ultraviolet light, this frequency can be raised to about one. Thus it would appear that the λ chromosome is contained within the lysogenic bacterium as a stable associate of the bacterial chromosome such that both are replicated at the same rate. Ultraviolet irradiation leads to a destruction of this association and a consequent activation of the phage chromosome.

A second consequence of lysogeny is that, while bacteria lysogenic for λ can adsorb this phage and apparently allow the injection of its DNA, the probability that these events will lead to synthesis and a release of new phage is essentially zero. This immunity to infection by λ is specific. Thus a number of temperate phages have been isolated from *E. coli* which are sufficiently related to λ to undergo genetic recombination, but to which bacteria lysogenic for λ are not immune. Furthermore, each of these phages creates lysogenic bacteria which are immune to the given phage but not to other members of the group (Jacob and Wollman, 1956). The existence of the related phages with different immune specificities has made possible the determination of the region on the phage chromosome map that is responsible for immunity. It turns out that this immunity region is localized near the center of the λ chromosome and is contained within the so-called "*c* region"(Kaiser and Jacob, 1957) which occupies about one-tenth of the λ chromosome map (Fig. 1). This *c* region of λ contains at least three distinct functional units, or cistrons (C_I, C_{II}, and C_{III}), all of which play an important role in lysogenization (Kaiser, 1957). Thus, mutations in the C_I cistron destroy the capacity for lysogenization (frequency of lysogenization $< 10^{-5}$) and mutations in the C_{II} and C_{III} cistrons drastically decrease, but do not destroy, this capacity. The λ-immunity region includes the C_I cistron but does not include either the C_{II} or C_{III} cistrons (Kaiser and Jacob, 1957). It therefore appears that the C_I cistron controls not only a reaction necessary for the lysogenization process, but also the immunity pattern of the product of this process, the lysogenic bacterium.

Finally, since these properties of lysogenic bacteria are specific and hereditary, one can attempt to localize the responsible region on the chromosome map of the bacteria, much as one would determine the position of a bacterial mutation on that map. Such attempts (Jacob and Wollman, 1957, 1958b; Kaiser and Jacob, 1957) have led to the conclusion that specific sites exist on the chromosome map of *E. coli* for each of the lysogenic states that exhibit a different immunity pattern (Fig. 2). Since the immunity pattern is determined by an immunity region in the phage chromosome, this one-to-one correspondence between immunity pattern and lysogenic site on the

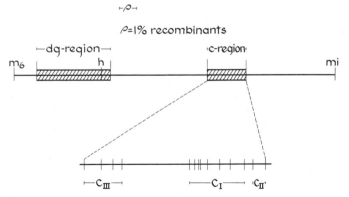

FIG. 1. Chromosome map of λ showing genes and regions referred to in the text. The limits of the known map are defined by m_6 and *mi* (plaque morphology mutants). The *dg* region is defined as that part of the λ chromosome which is not recoverable in active phage when λ*dg* is crossed to normal λ (Arber, 1958). The *c* region contains mutations which cause the production of clear plaques and decrease the frequency of lysogenization. It consists of at least three cistrons: C_I, C_{II}, and C_{III} (Kaiser, 1957). The *h* gene which lies within the *dg* region (and hence is not expressed in λ*dg*) controls the host range of λ.

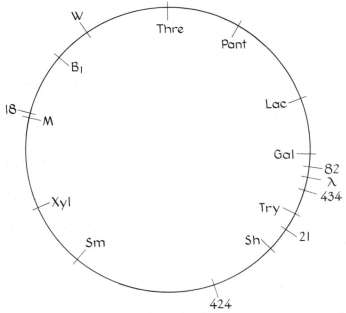

FIG. 2. Chromosome map of *E. coli* K12. This map represents only
the sequence of characters, not the distance between them. The
temperate phages 82, λ, 434, 21, and 424 form lysogenic bacteria
which are inducible with ultraviolet light. The temperate phages 18
and *w* form lysogenic bacteria which are not inducible. Each of
these temperate phages has a different immunity pattern. The symbols inside the circle refer to *E. coli* mutations which: (1) destroy
the capacity to synthesize vitamin B1, methionine (M), pantothenate
(Pant), shikimic acid (Sh), threonine (Thre), tryptophan (Try);
(2) destroy the ability to metabolize galactose (Gal), lactose (Lac),
xylose (Xyl); or (3) affect the sensitivity to streptomycin (Sm).
This map is adapted from that of Jacob and Wollman (1958a) and
indicates only a few of the known markers.

bacterial chromosome indicates that for each type of phage immunity
region there exists a complementary region on the bacterial chromosome at which the lysogenic association of phage and bacterial
chromosomes occurs. Specifically, since the C_I cistron in λ controls
the λ immunity pattern, it can be supposed that in the lysogenic state,
the C_I region of the λ chromosome forms a stable complex with a
unique, complementary region of the bacterial chromosome, the λ
lysogenic site (Kaiser and Jacob, 1957).

The λ*dg* **Variant of Bacteriophage** λ. While phages offer an almost
ideal system for genetic fine-structure analysis, the value of these
systems for the determination of protein-gene relationships has
suffered from the lack of mutations known to affect the synthesis of
easily separable proteins whose function defines a simple assay.

Although mutations affecting the synthesis of certain of the structural proteins of phages T2 and T4 apparently have been identified (Brenner, 1959; Brenner and Barnett, 1959), it is only recently that these proteins have been sufficiently separated to allow a positive identification of their individual functions, and the assay for such proteins remains relatively complex (Brenner et al., 1959). Consequently, it has been obvious for some time that the discovery of soluble enzymes, whose synthesis was specified by a phage genome, would be a great boon.

Two phage systems offer significant promise in this direction. One of these is the λ*dg* phage which is a variant of λ that contains the genetic determinants for those enzymes necessary for galactose metabolism in *E. coli*. The second is the T-even group of phages (T2, T4, T6) which will be discussed later.

Galactose is directed into the glucose metabolism of *E. coli* via the following three enzyme-catalyzed reactions (Kalckar et al., 1959):[2]

(1) Gal + ATP $\rightarrow$ Gal-1-P + ADP; galactokinase

(2) Gal-1-P + UDPG $\rightleftarrows$ UDP Gal + G-1-P; galactose-1 -phosphate uridyl transferase

(3) UDP Gal $\rightleftarrows$ UDPG; uridine diphosphogalactose 4-epimerase

The stoichiometry of the sum of these three reactions is the conversion of one molecule each of galactose and ATP to one molecule each of glucose-1-phosphate and ADP. If these three reactions are obligatory for the utilization of galactose as a carbon and energy source by *E. coli*, then the loss of any one of the three enzyme activities would yield a galactose-negative (gal$^-$) cell, i.e., a cell unable to grow in a medium containing galactose as the sole carbon source. Consequently, at least three types of gal$^-$ cells should arise from single mutations: (1) those lacking in the kinase activity (gal^-_k); (2) those lacking in the transferase activity (gal^-_t); and (3) those lacking in the epimerase activity (gal^-_e). Such mutants have been obtained and preliminary genetic analysis (Lederberg, E., 1958, 1960; Kalckar et al., 1959; Soffer, 1960) places them in a single cluster (*gal* region) very near the λ lysogenic site on the chromosome map of *E. coli* K12 (Fig. 2).

The proximity of the λ locus to the *gal* region evidently allows recombination to take place between the λ chromosome and a part of the bacterial chromosome which contains the *gal* region. Ultraviolet irradiation of galactose-positive *E. coli* lysogenic for λ initiates synthesis and release of phage particles. Most of these phages are ordinary λ. However, approximately one in 10^6 of the new

[2]Gal = galactose; Gal-1-P = α-D-galactose-1-phosphate; G-1-P = α-D-glucose-1-phosphate; UDPG = uridine diphosphoglucose; UDPGal = uridine diphosphogalactose; ATP = adenosine triphosphate; ADP = adenosine diphosphate.

phage particles is λdg. The λdg phage contains the gal region normally associated with the bacterial chromosome.

The presence of the gal region in the λdg phage can be detected
in two ways. When gal⁻ bacteria are infected with λdg, that fraction
of infected cells which become lysogenic for this phage also become
gal⁺. Thus λdg transduces galactose genes from the bacterium in
which it was produced to the bacterium it infects (Morse et al.,
1956a, b).

However, the resulting gal⁺ bacteria differ from the normal wild-
type gal⁺ in that they are much less stable, gal⁻ cells segregating
out at a frequency of about 10^{-3} per cell generation. This relative
instability can be accounted for by the observation that practically
all of the gal⁻ segregants have lost their immunity to λ; that is, they
are no longer lysogenic for the λdg phage (Campbell, 1957, Arber,
1958). This indicates that the inserted gal⁺ genes are linked to the
immunity region of the phage and hence form an integral part of the
λdg phage chromosome. Evidently the association between the λdg
chromosome and the bacterial chromosome is less stable than for
ordinary λ. Loss of the λdg chromosome results in loss of the incorporated gal⁺ genes. Thus the gal⁺ bacteria resulting from λdg
transduction can be regarded as containing two gal regions: (1) that
present in the recipient bacterial chromosome and containing the
gal⁻ mutation; and (2) that present in the associated λdg chromosome
and containing the gal⁺ allele. A cell thus situated has been termed
a heterogenote for the gal region (Morse et al., 1956b).

A second method for demonstrating the existence of the gal region
in λdg phage results from a more direct observation of the expression of the genes in this region. Consider the situation in which a
gal^-_k cell is infected with a λdg phage. If the λdg phage contains an
unblemished gal^+_k gene, it will be injected into a cell that has lost
its capacity to synthesize galactokinase as a result of mutational
damage to this gene. A determination of the galactokinase activity
of this culture from the time of infection should allow the observ-
ance of the expression of the injected gal^+_k gene in regard to synthesis of this enzyme. This type of experiment differs from the
preceding transduction experiments in that there is no a priori reason to suppose that such expression requires stable association between the injected gene and the recipient chromosome, whereas a
successful transduction depends upon such an association in order
to develop the observed gal⁺ clone.

When such an experiment is performed, the following results
ensue (Starlinger, 1959; Buttin et al., 1960). At the time of infection
there is, of course, no activity in the culture, since λdg phage con-

tains no galactokinase and the recipient bacteria is gal⁻$_k$. About ten minutes after the infection, however, galactokinase activity can be detected and this activity continues to increase with time in an essentially linear manner. This result indicates that a gal⁺$_k$ gene has been introduced into the recipient bacterium via λdg infection and consequently this gene must be contained in the phage.

Although these results bear a remarkable similarity to those obtained from inducible enzyme systems upon the introduction of small-molecular-weight inducer molecules (Hogness, 1959), they are distinct in two regards:

First, in wild-type gal⁺$_k$ E. *coli*, the synthesis of galactokinase is inducible by either of two sugars, D-galactose or D-fucose (Kalckar et al., 1959; Buttin et al., 1960). Thus, while the enzyme is synthesized at a detectable rate in the absence of either inducer, this rate can be increased many-fold by their addition. Mutation to gal⁻$_k$ renders the cell incapable of synthesis of galactokinase in an absolute sense, since this enzyme is not produced in the presence or absence of those sugars (Kalckar et al., 1959; Starlinger, 1959; Buttin et al., 1960), although it would appear that inducer molecules can enter such cells (Horecker et al., 1960). Consequently, the appearance of galactokinase activity after λdg infection cannot easily be explained by enzyme induction resulting from inducer molecules which might be present in the material injected by the phage, or alternatively, which might be formed in the cell as a result of infection.

Second, a further result of λdg infection is the creation of a clone of cells capable of galactokinase synthesis. Such a hereditary event is not observed as a result of introduction of inducer molecules into a cell. Results of a similar nature have been obtained with other enzyme systems and other means of gene injection. Thus β-galactosidase synthesis is observed in the E. *coli* zygote within one or two minutes after a male cell (Hfr) has injected the necessary unblemished gene into a female cell (F⁻) containing a damaged form of that gene (Riley et al., 1960). Similarly, Lacks and Hotchkiss (1960) have found that mutant strains of pneumococci, unable to form amylomaltase, will exhibit this enzyme activity within six minutes after exposure to DNA isolated from wild-type strains. Reference will be made later to the synthesis of a group of new enzymes in cells infected with T-even phages. In both the amylomaltase and β-galactosidase cases, there is a concomitant formation of clones of cells capable of synthesis of the given enzyme. Cells infected with T-even phages lyse and cannot form cell clones. Experiments of this nature constitute what is perhaps the most direct evidence available that DNA is the primary determinant in the synthesis of specific proteins.

Finally, it should be mentioned that the incorporation of the galactose genes into the λdg chromosome is accompanied by the loss of a part of the genetic activity present in ordinary λ; a loss which renders the λdg phage defective (Arber, 1958). The region of the λ chromosome which is inactive or absent in λdg is indicated on the chromosome map of λ given in Fig. 1. As a loss in this region always accompanies the gain of galactose genes from the bacterium, it is supposed that the galactose genes in λdg reside in this defective dg region of the phage chromosome (Campbell, 1959).

The defectiveness resulting from this loss of genetic activity is expressed in two ways. Whereas about 20 per cent of bacteria infected with ordinary λ become lysogenic under standard conditions, only 1 per cent become lysogenic when infected with λdg under the same conditions. However, if bacteria are simultaneously infected with λdg and λ, 20 per cent become lysogenic for both λdg and λ (Arber, 1958). Ordinary λ thus acts as a "helper" for the lysogenization of λdg, presumably by supplying a normal dg region.

The second way in which the defectiveness of λdg is expressed is that if bacteria lysogenic for λdg are exposed to ultraviolet light, they lyse, but do not produce any phage particles (Arber, 1958). However, doubly lysogenic bacteria, carrying both λdg and λ chromosomes, lyse and produce both λdg and λ when induced with ultraviolet light. Thus the presence of the normal dg region, supplied by λ, is necessary for the formation of mature phage particles. Consequently, all lysates containing the λdg phage will necessarily contain phage with a normal dg region.

Fortunately, the λdg phage can be separated from normal λ by virtue of a small difference in the buoyant density of these phages (Weigle et al., 1959). Thus when a density gradient is created by a centrifugal force acting on a cesium chloride solution, phage particles within that solution will, under the influence of that centrifugal force, form a band at that region of the gradient having a density equivalent to the buoyant density of the particles. Centrifugation of a mixture of λ and λdg in a cesium chloride density yields two bands as shown in Fig. 3. For the case of the λdg phage we have been using, the band at the lower density (1.49 g cm^{-3}) consists of λdg and the band at the higher density (1.51 g cm^{-3}) consists of ordinary λ (Kaiser and Hogness, 1960). If such centrifugations are carried out in a preparative nitrocellulose centrifuge tube, the two types of phage can be obtained in separate fractions by piercing a hole in the bottom of the centrifuge tube and collecting fractions as the liquid exits from the tube. By such techniques we have obtained λdg suspensions that are essentially free of normal λ particles ($<$ one λ per 10^3 λdg).

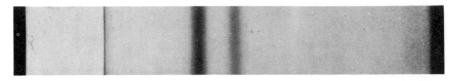

FIG. 3. The separation of λ*dg* and λ phage in a cesium chloride gradient after eight hours' centrifugation at 34,410 rpm. This photograph was taken using the ultraviolet absorption optics of the Spinco Model E ultracentrifuge. The more concentrated band of ultraviolet-absorbing material nearest the meniscus is λ*dg*, the other band being ordinary λ.

The activity of DNA isolated from λ*dg* (Kaiser and Hogness, 1960). The isolated λ*dg* phage affords a good example of the increased purity of phage DNA over bacterial DNA with respect to a single gene. Thus each λ*dg* particle contains one gal$^+{}_k$ gene within its DNA complement of 2×10^5 nucleotides, whereas the wild-type *E. coli* gal$^+$ cell contains one gal$^+{}_k$ gene within the haploid nucleus DNA complement of about 1.2×10^7 nucleotides. Consequently the gal$^+{}_k$ gene to DNA ratio is about sixtyfold greater for λ*dg* phage than for *E. coli*. The phage, by the specific incorporation of the bacterial *gal* region into its chromosome, has therefore effected a sixtyfold purification of the genes contained in this region. Moreover, during the isolation of this DNA, the protein coat of the λ*dg* phage protects the DNA from destruction by enzymes which hydrolyze nucleic acids (nucleases). A more satisfactory purification procedure would be hard to imagine.

Because of such advantages, Dr. Kaiser and I thought λ*dg* phage would be a good potential souce of genetically active DNA. We therefore sought to develop a system whereby DNA isolated from these phages could be demonstrated to have such activity. These attempts have been successful.

The preparation of the active DNA from the phage demands stripping the protein coat from the phage and isolating the internal DNA by techniques which are gentle in relation to the maintenance of DNA structure. Phenol extraction of λ*dg* suspensions has these desired properties; the DNA remains in the aqueous phase, while the phage protein is found at the phenol–water interface and in the phenol phase. Solutions of λ*dg* DNA obtained by this technique have about 0.1 per cent of the sulfur content of whole λ*dg* particles, and thus contain very little of the phage protein. They are highly viscous and have the typical ultraviolet absorption spectrum of DNA solutions. Furthermore, successive treatment with two nucleases (pancreatic DNase followed by venom phosphodiesterase) results in breakdown of all the DNA in the solution to mononucleotides. The aqueous phase resulting from phenol extraction of λ*dg* suspensions has, therefore, the chemical and physical properties of free DNA molecules in aqueous solution.

Such solutions of λ*dg* DNA are active in transforming gal⁻ *E. coli* cells to the gal⁺ state. This transformation is in many respects identical to the transduction reaction carried out by whole λ*dg* phage. It differs, however, in some important aspects. When gal⁻ *E. coli* cells are infected with λ*dg* phage particles, about 1 per cent of such cells become gal⁺, due to the low efficiency of lysogenization by the defective λ*dg* phage. When the gal⁻ cells are simultaneously infected with λ*dg* and ordinary λ, about 20 per cent of the infected cells become gal⁺, due to the "helper" effect of ordinary λ in the lysogenization process (Arber, 1958). If the λ*dg* DNA is substituted for the whole λ*dg* phage in such experiments, it is found that gal⁺ cells are obtained only if the recipient gal⁻ cells have been infected with a helper phage, e.g., ordinary λ. Thus the ratio between gal⁺ cells obtained in the absence to that in the presence of helper phage is less than 10^{-4} in the case of λ*dg* DNA, whereas it is 0.05 in the case of the whole phage. This difference in the effect of the helper phage on the two systems implies that, in the case of the DNA transformations, the helper phage supplies an additional function, present in the λ*dg* phage particles but absent in the DNA derived from these particles. This function could involve the adsorption of the DNA to the cell surface, the penetration of that surface, or the several reactions leading to the association of the *gal* region with the recipient bacterial chromosome. Which of these various possible functions of helper phage is operative has not yet been determined.

In any case, it is quite clear that the necessary gene components for this transformation reside in the λ*dg* DNA solution. Not only is the number of gal⁺ transformants obtained directly proportional to the amount of λ*dg* DNA used, but substitution of the λ*dg* DNA by DNA isolated from ordinary λ, or by λ*dg* DNA pretreated with pancreatic DNase (10^{-3} μg DNase per ml at 28° C for thirty minutes) yields no transformed gal⁺ cells. However, the efficiency of the transformation reaction with λ*dg* DNA is quite low (1×10^6 gal⁺ per μg DNA) when compared with the efficiency of the transduction reaction with λ*dg* phage (2×10^9 gal⁺ per μg DNA). This decrease in efficiency by a factor of 5×10^{-4} allows for the possibility that the gal⁺ transforming activity residing in the λ*dg* DNA solution is due to a small number of phages which have escaped damage during the phenol extraction.

The sensitivity of the transforming activity of the λ*dg* DNA solution to pancreatic DNase indicates that this activity is not due to complete λ*dg* particles, since these are completely insensitive to the

action of this enzyme. We should like, however, to be able to conclude that the transforming activity is contained in DNA molecules
that are essentially free of the phage protein. The sensitivity to
pancreatic DNase merely indicates that the active DNA is exposed
to the enzyme molecules. This exposure could result, for example,
from the loss, or change in topography, of only a small fraction of
the phage protein coat.

To characterize better the chemical nature of the active material
in the λdg DNA preparations, we resorted to the density-gradient
technique that has been referred to in the isolation of the λdg phage.
The λdg phage has a buoyant density in cesium chloride solutions of
1.49 g cm^{-3}. This density is consistent with the 1.0 value for the
protein to DNA mass ratio of the phage, since λdg DNA has a buoyant
density of 1.71 g cm^{-3} in cesium chloride solutions, and a density of
about 1.3 g cm^{-3} may be assigned to the phage proteins. One would
therefore expect that any product of the phenol degradation of λdg
phage would exhibit a density determined by its protein to DNA mass
ratio. Provided the active material in the λdg DNA preparations is
large enough to form a band in cesium chloride density gradient, the
density at the band position should yield a measure of the protein to
DNA mass ratio of the active unit.

The λdg DNA was therefore centrifuged in a cesium chloride density gradient, and the transforming activity as well as the DNA content determined in the fractions collected from the centrifuge tube.
The activity and the DNA formed coincident band distributions, each
with a mean density of 1.71 g cm^{-3}. This indicates that the protein
to DNA mass ratio of the active material is equal to, or less than,
that of the initial λdg DNA preparation, namely 0.001 on the basis of
protein sulfur content. Recent experiments carried out by Dr. John
Simmons in our laboratory indicate that the protein to DNA mass
ratio is even less than this value. Using λdg DNA isolated from
phage whose protein was labeled with radioactive S^{35}, Dr. Simmons
repeatedly centrifuged the isolated DNA-activity band until all the
sulfur in the preparation banded with the DNA and the activity. When
this point is reached, there is 3×10^{-5} as much sulfur per DNA as
there is in the whole phage. Thus, if this sulfur is an accurate measure of phage protein, the protein to DNA mass ratio of the active
material is equal to, or less than, 3×10^{-5}. We can conclude, therefore, that the active unit is a DNA molecule essentially free of phage
protein. This interpretation of the structure of the active units is
consistent with the fact that they (1) are insensitive to anti-λ serum
which inactivates whole λdg phage; and (2) exhibit a heat stability
equivalent to that of free DNA molecules in solution, a stability which
is much greater than that of whole λdg phage.

Having demonstrated that the active unit which brings the gal⁺ genes into the gal⁻ recipient cell is a molecule of DNA, we can now ask how much of the λdg chromosome is contained within such molecules. To answer this question we must inquire as to the state of the transformed gal⁺ bacteria. Such bacteria turn out to be heterogenotes. That is, they regularly segregate out gal⁻ bacteria and, if exposed to ultraviolet light, lyse, yielding dg-type phage and nondefective phage in approximately equivalent amounts. Evidently then, the gal⁺ genes in the transformed bacteria are contained within a phage chromosome that is in lysogenic association with the recipient bacterial chromosome. While this is consistent with the supposition that the active λdg DNA contains the entire λdg chromosome, it is conceivable that only the segments bearing the galactose gene(s) came from the λdg DNA, and the rest of the chromosome necessary for the formation of complete dg-type phage was supplied by recombination with the helper phage chromosome.

This question can be resolved by examining the phage genes contained in the transformed gal⁺ cells. For this purpose, helper phage are used which differ from λdg, not only in regard to the dg region, but also at the mi locus, and/or in the c region (see Fig. 1). For example, a phage called λi^{434} may be used as helper. This phage is identical with ordinary λ except that it contains the immunity region (i^{434}) of the 434 phage (see Fig. 2) instead of that of λ itself (i^{λ}). Consequently, bacteria lysogenic for λi^{434} are immune to the 434 phage and, of course, to λi^{434}, but are not immune to phage carrying the i^{λ} immunity region (e.g., λdg and λ). If gal⁻ E. coli lysogenic for λi^{434} are infected with λi^{434} helper phage and exposed to λdg DNA, we can ask whether the resulting gal⁺ transformants contain phage chromosomes bearing the i^{λ} immunity region contained in the λdg DNA. Examination reveals that over 97 per cent of the gal⁺ formed in this way produce i^{λ}-type phage. Similar experiments, in which both the c region (which includes i^{λ}) and the mi locus were marked differently in the helper phage than in the λdg DNA, showed that a majority of the transformed gal⁺ cells produced phage carrying the λdg DNA markers for the c region and the mi locus. Thus bacteria which incorporate the dg region from λdg DNA have a high probability of receiving both the c region and the mi locus from this DNA.

The interval between mi and the farthest end of the dg region is about 90 per cent of the known chromosome map of λdg (see Fig. 1). Since the linkage between these components of the λdg chromosome has been observed for DNA concentrations as low as 0.1 λdg DNA equivalents per recipient bacterium, and since the number of gal⁺ bacteria is a linear function of the DNA concentration, the simplest interpretation of these results is that the active molecules comprise at least 90 per cent of the λdg chromosome. If this chromosome contains all of the DNA of the phage, the active DNA molecules should contain about 2×10^5 bases, i.e., have a molecular weight of about 6×10^7. We are presently engaged in physical studies to determine the actual size of these active DNA molecules.

It should be noted that these experiments demonstrating the existence of the gal$^+$ genes in the λdg DNA are analogous to the transduction experiments demonstrating that λdg phage particles contain the gal$^+$ genes. That is, both require the stable association of such genes with the recipient bacterial chromosome in order to observe the resulting gal$^+$ clones. The alternate experiments with λdg phage, in which the synthesis of one of the galactose enzymes is observed following phage infection, have not yet been performed with the λdg DNA system. There is no reason, in principle, why these experiments cannot be performed with success. Indeed such an assay of gene function should prove quite valuable for the λdg DNA system. For example, it is now known that large DNA molecules, such as those extractable from T2 phage having an estimated molecular weight of 6×10^7 (Thomas and Berns, 1961), can be broken by exposure to high shear gradients (Hershey and Burgi, 1960). This breakage is relatively specific in that the highest probability of breakage is near the center of the DNA molecule. If the λdg map (Fig. 1) approximately represents the physical distribution of genes in the active DNA molecules, then breakage near the center should yield halves with the *gal* region intact. It would be of interest to compare the activity of such half-chromosomes containing the *gal* region, in regard to their ability to form stable associates with the recipient bacterial chromosomes (i.e., transformed gal$^+$ clones), with their ability to cause the synthesis of the galactose enzymes. Thus if one supposes that the C_I cistron is a necessary site for the lysogenic association of the λdg chromosome with the bacterial chromosome, separation of the C_I cistron from the *gal* region by breakage would yield half-chromosomes containing the *gal* region which would not form stable associates with the recipient bacterial chromosomes. There is, however, no equally valid reason to suppose that they could not function in the synthesis of the galactose enzymes. In addition to testing these suppositions, such experiments lead in the general direction of one of the criteria for the idealized system mentioned earlier, namely, the isolation of single genetic units of function.

Finally, it should be mentioned that the present system for demonstrating the genetic activity of λdg DNA can be adapted to the measurement of the activity of DNA isolated from ordinary λ (λ DNA). *E. coli* cells infected with helper phage λi^{434} are exposed to λ DNA and then poured onto Petri plates containing a nutrient agar medium. After incubation at 37°C, one observes phage plaques against a confluent background of cells lysogenic for the λi^{434} helper phage. Since these background bacteria are immune to phage carrying the i^{434} immunity region, the plaques must contain phage with a different immunity region. Examination reveals that such plaques contain ordinary λ. Since the λ DNA is the only source of the i^{λ} component of these phages, the number of plaques represents a measure of the activity of the λ DNA. The number of plaques that are formed is directly proportional to the amount of λ DNA employed, and this activity of λ DNA is sensitive to pancreatic DNase.

As one would expect from the results with λdg DNA, the active molecules in the λ DNA preparations appear to represent most of the λ chromosome. Dr. Kaiser has found that if the λi^{434} helper phage and the λ DNA are differently marked at the mi and h loci (see Fig. 1), the vast majority of the plaques contain phage having the mi and h markers from the λ DNA. By the same arguments that have been applied to the λdg DNA experiments, this result implies that the active DNA molecules contain at least that portion of the λ chromosome lying between h and mi, i.e., about 70 per cent of the known map length.

The T-even Bacteriophages

The DNA of the T-even group (T2, T4, T6) is unique in that it does not contain the cytosine (C) found in all other DNA (Chargaff, 1955). In place of cytosine, the DNA of these phages contains 5-hydroxymethyl cytosine (HMC) in which the 5-hydroxymethyl group is variously substituted with one or two glucose residues. The glucosidic linkage to the hydroxymethyl group may be either α or β for the monoglucosides and is α for the diglucoside. The amount of each of the four possible HMC bases (i.e., nonglucosylated, α-monoglucosylated, β-monoglucosylated, and α-diglucosylated) contained in the DNA is a hereditary characteristic of the phage and is given for the three T-even phages in Table 2. Except for the substitution of HMC (and its glucosylated derivatives) for C, the base composition of the T-even phages is normal in that the expected equalities of A and T, and of G and total HMC are observed.

This difference between the DNA of the T-even phages and that of E. coli (Table 2), their host cell, implies that upon infection of the host cell a new mechanism, or mechanisms, for the synthesis of phage DNA must become available to the cell. Examination of DNA synthesis immediately following T-even phage infection has revealed that synthesis of C containing DNA stops at the time of infection and, after a lag of five to seven minutes, HMC-containing DNA com-

TABLE 2

The Base Content of DNA from *E. coli* and the T-even Phages

DNA	Per cent of total bases								Reference
						HMC-containing bases			
	A	T	G	C	HMC	HMC-α-G	HMC-β-G	HMC-α-diG	
E. coli	25	25	24	26	0	0	0	0	(a) (b)
T2	32	32	18	0	4	12	0	1	(c)(d)(e)(f)(g)(h)
T4	32	33	18	0	0	12	5	0	(c)(f)(g)(h)(i)
T6	32	33	18	0	4	1	0	12	(c) (e) (g) (h) (j)

The following abbreviations have been used: A = adenine; T = thymine; G = guanine; C = cytosine; HMC = 5-hydroxymethyl cytosine; HMC-α-G = 5-cytosine-methyl-α-glucoside; HMC-β-G = 5-cytosine-methyl-β-glucoside; and HMC-α-diG = 5-cytosine-methyl-α-glucosyl-β-glucoside.

References: (a) Gandelman et al., 1952; (b) Lehman et al., 1958; (c) Wyatt and Cohen, 1953; (d) Hershey et al., 1953; (e) Mayers and Spizizen, 1954; (f) Sinsheimer, 1956; (g) Jesaitis, 1957; (h) Lehman and Pratt, 1960; (i) Volkin, 1954; (j) Loeb and Cohen, 1959.

mences (Hershey et al., 1953; Vidaver and Kozloff, 1957). This means that not only must infection provide the cell with a mechanism for the synthesis of phage DNA, but it must also provide a means of stopping the synthesis of *E. coli* DNA. One might suppose that these mechanisms are provided by new enzyme activities attendant upon injection of the phage DNA into the host cell. Thus the possibility arises that infection results in the synthesis of many more new proteins than are contained in the structure of the mature phage; proteins which, for our purposes, would have the advantage of being easily assayed by virtue of their catalytic properties.

Recent work on the metabolism of phage-infected cells indicates that such a possibility is, indeed, an actuality. Thus, twelve different enzyme activities have been observed to increase within a short time (two to four minutes) after *E. coli* cells are infected with T-even phages.

The formation of the HMC residue was found to occur at the deoxynucleotide level when Flaks and Cohen (1957, 1959) reported that a reaction between deoxycytidine-5'-phosphate (dC-5'-P), formaldehyde, and tetrahydrofolic acid to yield 5-hydroxymethyl-deoxycytidine-5'-phosphate (dHMC-5'-P) was catalyzed by an enzyme present in T2-phage-infected cells, but absent in uninfected cells (<0.5 per cent of infected cells; Flaks et al., 1959). With this observation as a stimulus, and based on an understanding of the general parameters of DNA synthesis elucidated by Kornberg and his associates (Chap.

9), the other reactions referred to in Fig. 4 were found to be increased by T-even phage infection.

The synthesis of DNA, catalyzed by DNA polymerase, involves a reaction between "primer" DNA and the 5'-triphosphates of deoxyadenosine (dATP), deoxythymidine (dTTP), deoxyguanosine (dGTP), and deoxycytidine (dCTP). It is therefore reasonable to suppose that the dHMC-5'-P must first be raised to the triphosphate level (dHMC-TP) before it can be incorporated into DNA by the polymerase. This supposition has been found to be correct. Thus, cells infected with T-even phage contain an enzyme activity necessary for the phosphorylation of dHMC-5'-P to dHMC-TP by ATP (reaction 2), whereas such a kinase activity is not detectable in uninfected cells (<0.5 per cent of infected cells).

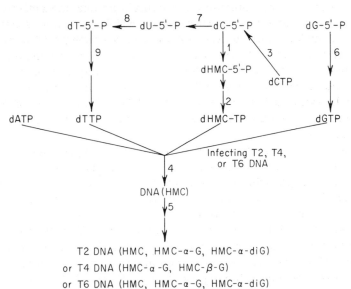

FIG. 4. Enzyme reactions involved in T-even DNA synthesis that are affected by phage infection. See the text for the meaning of the numbers and abbreviations that are used. Two arrows in sequence (reactions 8, 5, 6, and 9) indicate the reaction is known or thought to occur in two steps. References to the numbered reactions are given below:

(1) Flaks and Cohen, 1957, 1959a; Flaks et al., 1959; Kornberg et al., 1959. (2) Kornberg et al., 1959; Sommerville et al., 1959. (3) Kornberg et al., 1959; Koerner et al., 1960; Zimmerman and Kornberg, 1961. (4) Kornberg et al., 1959; Aposhian and Kornberg, 1961. (5) Kornberg et al., 1959; Kornberg et al., 1961. (6) Kornberg et al., 1959; Bessman, 1959; Bessman and Van Bibben, 1959. (7) Keck et al., 1960. (8) Flaks and Cohen, 1959b; Barner and Cohen, 1959. (9) Kornberg et al., 1959; Bessman, 1959.

Reactions 1 and 2 are sufficient to explain the ability of HMC to be incorporated into DNA, but they do not explain why the synthesis of cytosine-containing DNA stops after infection. This latter fact can be explained by reaction 3. An enzyme, deoxycytidine triphosphatase (dCTPase), which hydrolyzes dCTP to yield dC-5′-P and pyrophosphate, is found after T-even infection of *E. coli*, but is absent (<1 - 2 per cent) prior to infection. The supposition is that the high activity of this dCTPase is sufficient to reduce the steady-state concentration of dCTP in infected cells to such a low level that it is no longer operative as a substrate for the polymerase. This supposition is enhanced by the finding that the level of kinase activity by which dC-5′-P is converted to dCTP in uninfected cells, is not altered following phage infection (Kornberg et al., 1959; Bessman, 1959). Furthermore, infected cells contain an enzyme activity, not present before infection, by which deoxycytidine-5′-diphosphate (dCDP) is broken down to dC-5′-P and orthophosphate (Zimmerman and Kornberg, 1961). Since dCDP is the proposed intermediate in the formation of dCTP from dC-5′-P, this activity would further decrease the concentration of dCTP in infected cells. It appears that the breakdown of dCTP and of dCDP to dC-5′-P is catalyzed by the same enzyme, the dCTPase referred to above (Zimmerman and Kornberg, 1961).

While reactions 1, 2, and 3 are sufficient to explain the incorporation of HMC residues in place of C residues, they do not explain why T-even phage DNA is replicated preferentially to the replication of *E. coli* DNA in which HMC is substituted for C. The DNA polymerase present before phage infection does not itself discriminate either between dHMC-TP and dCTP, or between *E. coli* and T2 DNA (Lehman et al., 1958; Kornberg et al., 1959). While this remains a moot question, the following two phenomena may be involved.

There is a considerable degradation of *E. coli* DNA a few minutes after infection (Hershey et al., 1953), which one would suppose to be due to an increased DNase activity in the vicinity of that DNA within the cell. Indeed, an increase in DNase activity has been observed in extracts of cells following their infection with T-even phage (Kozloff, 1953; Kunkee and Pardee, 1956). It is doubtful, however, that this increase in over-all DNase activity is necessarily relevant to the mechanism of specific breakdown of *E. coli* DNA following infection. Thus the increase in activity can be observed using T-even phage DNA as a substrate as well as using cytosine-containing DNA as substrate (Kozloff, 1953; Lehman, personal communication). Furthermore, infection of cells with ultraviolet-irradiated phage yields an increase in the DNase activity of extracts, but does not result in breakdown of *E. coli* DNA within the infected cell (Kunkee and Pardee, 1956). The observed increase in over-all DNase activity is attributable to a decrease in the concentration of an inhibitor (probably RNA) in the extracts (Kozloff, 1953). Such a decrease of inhibitor concentration could be peculiar to the extracts and not exhibited within the cells from which the extracts are derived; e.g., a decrease in RNA inhibitors could result from RNase activity released from ribosomes (Elson, 1958) during extraction, were ribosomes less stable in infected-cell extracts than in noninfected-cell extracts. Given such a possibility, it may be that the formation of a specific DNase (not acting on T-even phage DNA) is hidden within the larger increase of the nonspecific DNase activity observed in infected-cell extracts.

A second possible factor in an explanation of the switchover from *E. coli* to phage DNA replication is the appearance of a new DNA polymerase activity (reaction 4) shortly after infection with T2. This new DNA polymerase is differentiable from that in uninfected cells by the specificity it exhibits to "primer" DNA, by its antigenicity, and by the fact that the two polymerases are separable by fractionation (Aposhian and Kornberg, 1961). The present data on the specific requirements of "primer" DNA for the two polymerases are too preliminary to allow any definitive conclusions as to the possibility that the newly formed DNA polymerase is the directive agent in the switchover of DNA synthesis in phage-infected cells. Even if this possibility were a reality, it does not necessarily include an explanation for the breakdown of *E. coli* DNA following infection, unless, of course, the newly formed DNA polymerase is bifunctional, acting to degrade *E. coli* DNA while accepting T2 DNA as a "primer" for synthesis. In any case, the formation of this new polymerase marks a fourth new enzyme activity resulting from T2 infection.

The glucose residues are attached to the HMC after its incorporation into DNA (reaction 5). A total of four different glucosylating enzymes have been found in cells infected with T-even phage (Kornberg et al., 1961). In each case the reaction catalyzed is between HMC-containing DNA and UDPG with the result that a glucose residue is transferred to the HMC of the DNA. Infection with T2 results in the appearance of an enzyme which catalyzes the formation of HMC-α-glucoside residues in the HMC-containing DNA. Infection with T4 yields two enzymes; one which causes the synthesis of HMC-α-glucosides and another which produces HMC-β-glucosides. The α-glucosylating enzyme preparation of T4-infected cells is different from that of T2-infected cells in that it can further glucosylate T2 DNA, while the T2 enzyme cannot.

Finally, the cells infected with T6 contain an α-glucosylating enzyme like that found in T4-infected cells, and an enzyme which forms

HMC-α-diglucoside residues by adding another glucose in β linkage to HMC-α-glucoside residues in the DNA. Although one would suppose this latter enzyme to be present in T2-infected cells (see Table 2), it has not yet been detected. With this exception, of these four types of glucosylating enzymes, a given phage produces two.

There are four additional enzyme activities which are increased as a result of T-even phage infection. These are involved in the synthesis of either dGTP or dTTP. The deoxyguanosine-5'-phosphate (dG-5'-P) kinase activity (reaction 6: dG-5'-P reacts with ATP to yield dGTP) increases from eleven to forty-fivefold upon infection with T-even phage. The dG-5'-P kinase activity that appears subsequent to infection can be differentiated from that present in uninfected cells by (1) the fact that it does not require monovalent cations for activation as does the enzyme present before infection (Bessman and Van Bibber, 1959); and (2) these two activities are separable by fractionation (Bessman, 1960). Thus the increase in dG-5'-P kinase would appear to have the same basis as the increase in the previous enzyme activities, i.e., the formation of a new enzyme subsequent to phage infection.

The dC-5'-P present in infected cells is used for the synthesis of both dHMC-TP (reaction 1 and 2) and for the synthesis of dTTP (reactions 7, 8, and 9). Thus, infection of *E. coli* with T2 causes the formation of an enzyme which deaminates dC-5'-P (reaction 7) to yield deoxyuridine-5'-phosphate (dU-5'-P). The dU-5'-P can then be converted to deoxythymidine-5'-phosphate (dT-5'-P) by reaction with formaldehyde, tetrahydrofolic acid, and an enzyme called thymidylate synthetase (reaction 8) present in uninfected wild-type *E. coli* (Friedkin and Kornberg, 1957). Infection of wild-type *E. coli* by T2 phage results in an approximate sevenfold increase in the activity of this enzyme (Flaks and Cohen, 1959b). Of more significance is the fact that *E. coli* cells damaged by mutation so that they contain no thymidylate synthetase activity, will, upon infection with T2 phage, form such activity (Barner and Cohen, 1959). Finally, the kinase activity necessary for the conversion of dT-5'-P to dTTP (reaction 9) is increased from ten to twentyfold upon infection with T-even phage. It should be pointed out that this last case is the only one of the preceding twelve enzyme activities in which the increasing activity has not been demonstrated to start from a value which is essentially zero in the uninfected cell.

This series of twelve enzyme increases provides most of the components necessary for an explanation of the specific shunting mechanism whereby T-even DNA synthesis is turned on, and *E. coli* DNA synthesis turned off, shortly after infection. As intriguing as this mechanism is, the aspect of the phenomena that is most pertinent to this discussion is the means by which such increases are accomplished. The following two alternative hypotheses are apparent:

(1) The infecting phage DNA contains the genes which specify the structure of the given proteins. These structural genes are not present in the uninfected bacteria. The injection of these genes into the host cytoplasm allows their expression.

(2) The structural genes are contained in the uninfected bacteria where their expression is repressed (see Pardee, Chap. 11). The phage DNA does not contain the structural genes, but the injection of this DNA, or some other co-injected material, relieves this repression and results in expression of these genes.

Both hypotheses are based on the assumption that the new activity present in infected cells is the result of de novo synthesis of a given enzyme, and is not due to the activation of preexisting protein. While this has not been rigorously demonstrated, the fact that chloramphenicol, 5-methyl tryptophan, or tryptophan starvation reversibly blocks the increase in each of the enzyme activities where these tests have been applied, provides support for this assumption (Flaks et al., 1959; Flaks and Cohen, 1959b; Keck et al., 1960; Bessman, 1959).

At present neither of these two hypotheses can be eliminated. The latter hypothesis is similar to the prevalent model of induced enzyme synthesis (see Chap. 11) whereby small-molecular-weight inducer molecules relieve a state of repressed enzyme synthesis present in the uninduced cell. Flaks, Lichtenstein, and Cohen, (1959) examined T2 phage for possible small-molecular-weight inducer molecules and found about one, or less, molecules of free dC-5'-P, dHMC-5'-P, and dT-5'-P per phage particle. This, of course, does not eliminate the idea of small-molecular-weight inducers being injected into the cell with the phage DNA, although it effectively eliminates these molecules as inducers. Furthermore, the phage DNA itself could conceivably act as a derepressant, either by causing the synthesis of molecules which antagonize a repressor substance present in uninfected cells, or by directly activating an inactive structural gene in the bacterium. There is little, if any, precedent for such speculative DNA functions, although the operator-gene theory of Jacob, Perrin, Sanchez, and Monod (1960) does provide for a gene function (operator gene) which triggers the expression of closely linked structural genes.

In at least two of the cases of increased enzyme activity following phage infection (dG-5'-P kinase and DNA polymerase) two separable enzymes are involved; that present in uninfected cells and that synthesized after infection. One would therefore suppose that two different structural genes must be involved in each case. The first hypothesis designates one structural gene to the bacterium and one to the phage. The second hypothesis places both structural genes in the bacterium and imposes the added condition that the function of one of these is repressed. Precedents exist for both states. The λdg infection of gal_k^- cells would appear to involve a gal_k^+ structural gene in the phage and a gal_k^- structural gene in the bacterium. The phase variation in *Salmonella* flagellar protein involves two distinct structural genes for flagellar protein within a single bacterium, only one of which is operative at a given time (Lederberg and Iino, 1956).

Lacking any definite evidence for a preferential adoption of either of these hypotheses, one may select the preferred hypothesis on the basis of simplicity, i.e., selection of the hypothesis involving the least number of required components. On this basis, the preferred hypothesis is obviously that involving the presence of the structural genes in the phage DNA. The alternate, or repressor hypothesis, demands a repression and activation mechanism in addition to the structural genes demanded by each hypothesis.

Proof of the preferred hypothesis depends upon the isolation of mutant phage which can cause the synthesis of a structurally different enzyme from that produced by infection with wild-type phage. Such mutants have not, of course, been identified for any of the twelve enzymes involved in phage DNA synthesis. However, there is another enzyme, a lysozyme, which is synthesized upon T-even phage infection, and for which such mutants have been identified (Streisinger, 1960; Dreyer, 1960). Similarly, other mutants involving a change in structure of one of the tail proteins and of the head protein of the phage particle have been identified (Brenner and Barnett, 1959). These observations increase the preference rating of the proposition that the phage DNA contains the structural genes specifying the enzymes involved in the synthesis of that DNA.

If this supposition is accepted, and it is assumed that the structural genes for all six of the proteins present in mature phage particles [head, core, sheath, plate, fibre (Brenner et al., 1959), and internal proteins (Levine et al., 1958; Murakami et al., 1959)] are likewise in the phage DNA, then the DNA of a given phage must contain at least seventeen distinct structural genes involved in the synthesis of seventeen different proteins. Thus, this seemingly simple particle becomes a very compact information center for protein synthesis. Since there are about 4×10^5 bases in the DNA of a T-even phage particle, there would be an average of 2×10^4 bases per structural gene at the level of twenty such genes per phage. This allows for twenty bases per amino acid if the average protein is assumed to contain 10^3 amino acids. Thus there is more than enough

DNA to account for these structural genes, even if a coding ratio of base pairs per amino acid is postulated to be as high as ten.

From the standpoint of size, genetic analysis, and availability of proteins whose synthesis is specified by the phage DNA, it would appear that the T-even phages represent a potentially valuable source of DNA for our idealized system. However, the T-even phage system suffers from the fact that attempts to demonstrate the genetic activity of DNA isolated from these phages have met with considerable frustration and little success.

Treatment of T2 phage with high concentrations of urea yields particles (Pi particles) which have lost their ability to infect normal *E. coli* cells, but which have also gained the ability to infect cells whose cell walls have been disrupted by the action of egg-white lysozyme (*E. coli* "protoplasts") (Spizizen, 1957; Mahler and Frazer, 1959). These Pi particles are clearly differentiable from intact T2 phage, but apparently still retain phage components other than the phage DNA. Thus, while Pi particles are slowly inactivated by pancreatic DNase, they are much more sensitive to the action of trypsin, which has no affect on the activity of λdg DNA or on the transforming activity of *H. influenzae* DNA (Zamenhof, 1957). Similarly, Pi particles are more thermolabile than one would expect were DNA the only necessary component for their activity.

The difficulty in obtaining a demonstration of the genetic activity of DNA isolated from T-even phage by an infection assay probably lies in the necessity of getting an entire phage chromosome into a single bacterium. Thus, if the estimated molecular weight of T2 DNA isolated by the phenol technique of about 6×10^7 is correct (Thomas and Berns, 1961), such molecules would consist of one-half of the phage complement of DNA. If these molecules also represent only one-half of the phage chromosome, then a successful infection could occur only if the alternate halves entered the same "protoplast" or bacterium. The probability of this event may be so low that DNA isolated from T-even phage would appear inactive by this type of assay. Consequently one would suppose that the demonstration of the genetic activity of isolated T-even phage DNA might have a better chance of success if the activity of a single gene were investigated with respect to the synthesis of a single protein, e.g., one of the enzymes involved in the synthesis of phage DNA. Furthermore, with such an assay of activity, one might increase the probability of success by employing smaller DNA molecules obtained by breakage of large molecules isolated by the phenol technique (Hershey and Burgi, 1960).

Bacteriophage ϕX174

One of the main considerations for the emphasis of phage as a source of DNA in the study of gene function, has been the relatively small amount of DNA per reproducing unit. If this were the only consideration, the phage ϕX174 would be the only one necessary to mention, since it has about one-fortieth the DNA content of λ and about one-eightieth that of the T-even phages (Table I). The DNA of this phage, whether in association with the phage protein as the mature particle, or as isolated by the phenol technique, appears to exist as a single polynucleotide strand rather than as a double-stranded molecule typical of native DNA from other sources (Sinsheimer, 1959a and b; Tessman, 1959). The observed equivalence between the DNA content per particle and the molecular weight of the isolated DNA ($1.6 - 1.8 \times 10^6$) would indicate that the isolated DNA consists of like molecules, assuming no heterogeneity among the complete phage (Sinsheimer, 1959a and b).

DNA isolated from ϕX174 will infect $E.$ $coli$ "protoplasts" to yield new phage (Guthrie and Sinsheimer, 1960; Hofschneider, 1960; Sekiguchi et al., 1960). The infecting activity of the isolated DNA preparation and the DNA itself form coincident bands during cesium chloride density-gradient centrifugation with a mean buoyant density of 1.72 g cm^{-3} (Guthrie and Sinsheimer, 1960). Since the complete phage particle exhibits a buoyant density of 1.40 g cm^{-3} that is consistent with its 25 per cent DNA content (Sinsheimer, 1959a), these data indicate that the active units in the DNA preparation are molecules of DNA essentially free of phage protein.

The efficiency of infection (number of infected protoplasts yielding plaques per phage equivalent of DNA) can be as high as 0.03 if very low DNA concentrations are employed (3×10^{-8} μg DNA per ml). However, the number of infected protoplasts is not a linear function of the DNA concentration, the efficiency of infection decreasing to about 10^{-4} at DNA concentrations just prior to saturation (3×10^{-4} μg DNA per ml) (Guthrie and Sinsheimer, 1960). In spite of this nonlinear kinetics of infection, the fact that efficiencies of about 0.03 are observed when the ratio of ϕX174 DNA molecules to recipient protoplasts is less than 10^{-4} would indicate that contact of a protoplast with a single DNA molecule is sufficient for infection. The nonlinear kinetics can be explained by assuming a heterogeneity in the recipient protoplast population with respect to the probability of infection. Thus it would appear that the active DNA molecules contain the entire genome of the mature phage.

One may now ask, what proteins, if any, have their structure determined by the DNA of ϕX174? It is to be supposed that this DNA contains the structural genes which specify the nature of the phage protein(s) associated with the mature phage particle. However, the genetic analysis of ϕX174 and the identification of mutants which affect the structure of a specific protein are at their infancy. Genetic recombination among several different negative host-range mutants of ϕX174 has been reported (Pfeifer, 1961). The negative host-range mutants are partial revertants to wild-type ϕX174, in that they were derived from a three-step host-range mutant able to infect three strains of *E. coli*, which the wild-type phage cannot infect. The negative host-range mutants have lost the ability to infect one of these three strains and, consequently, recombinants derived from crosses between them can be recognized by their ability to infect this E. coli strain, the frequency of recombination being between 10^{-3} and 10^{-4}. If it turns out that such mutants have altered host ranges because of altered capacities to adsorb to the various host cells, as in the case of the T2 host-range mutants (Streisinger and Franklin, 1956), one would suspect that the responsible mutations involve a gene(s) controlling the structure of a protein(s) present in the mature phage particle.

Genetic recombination has also been reported in phage S 13 (Tessman and Tessman, 1959), which is closely related to ϕX174 in size, serological and host-range properties, and in DNA content (Zahler, 1958; Tessman, 1959). Some of the recombinable mutants of S 13 are less sensitive to inactivation at 60° C than is the wild-type strain (Tessman and Tessman, 1959). If this observation can be repeated with purified virus, it would indicate that the genetic difference between mutant and wild-type involves a structural difference in the protein coat of these phages, since the phage DNA should be stable to such heating. This, again, would imply the existence of a structural gene that defines a protein of the phage particle.

It is clear that we shall have to await further genetic and protein analysis of these phages before we have a clear answer to their structural gene content. There appears to be no reason why this will not be forthcoming. Consequently, the ϕX174 (or S 13) phage system may be the closest approximation to the ideal we set at the beginning of this article. Whether or not the ϕX174 DNA molecule represents one structural gene, it certainly contains considerably less than λ or the T-even phages. Indeed, with a minimum coding ratio of three nucleotides per amino acid, ϕX174 can specify only about 2,000 amino acid positions, or enough for two different proteins of molecular weight about 10^5.

CONCLUDING REMARKS

These phage sources of DNA have been emphasized over cellular sources mainly on the basis of the more limited size of their DNA genome. This methodology of simplicity is a formal one which has general significance only within a series of structurally similar molecules. It is doubtful that it should be applied among such dissimilar types of DNA as are contained within these three phages, thereby selecting out the ϕX174 system to the exclusion of the other two. Thus, for example, our knowledge of the relative roles played by DNA in the single-stranded (ϕX174) versus the double-stranded state (λ and T-even phages) is so negligible that a comparative prediction of the usefulness of each system is meaningless. Similarly, the existence of up to six different bases in the HMC-containing DNA of the T-even group (Table 2) may yield particular advantage in problems of base-sequence analysis.

Furthermore, the extension of this methodology to the isolation of single units of function remains limited by the assumption that a single unit of function as defined, when linked to other such units, can indeed function when freed of such linkage. The validity of this assumption may be variable. Thus, in some cases the coordinate expression of several closely linked structural genes may be necessary for the expression of any one of them (Jacob et al., 1960). In other cases a single structural gene may be able to act independently. Since it seems likely that λdg DNA contains a genetic unit of coordinate expression in the closely linked genes that specify the galactose enzymes (Buttin, 1961), it should be useful in the analysis of such coordinate expression. On the other hand, the smaller ϕX174 DNA may afford an example of independent gene expression, and not be useful in analysis of coordinate expression.

These speculations emphasize that at this stage the relative usefulness of these phage DNA systems can be determined only by the further development of each system in the test of more specific hypotheses. This marks a point of diminishing return for the general methodological approach that forms the basis of this article.

REFERENCES

1. Aposhian, H. V., and A. Kornberg (1961),*Federation Proc.*,20:361. Also personal communication.
2. Arber, W. (1958), Transduction des caractères Gal par bé bactériophage lambda. *Arch. Sci. (Genève)*, 11:259.
3. —— and G. Kellenberger (1958), Study of the properties of seven defective-lysogenic strains derived from *Escherichia coli* K12 (λ). *Virology*, 5:458-475.
4. Avery, O. T., C. M. MacLeod, and M. McCarty (1944), Studies on the chemical nature of the substance inducing transformation of pneumococcal types. Induction of transformation by a deoxyribonucleic acid fraction isolated from Pneumococcus Type III. *J. Exp. Med.*, 79:137-158.
5. Barner, H. D., and S. S. Cohen (1959), Virus-induced acquisition of metabolic function. IV. Thymidylate synthetase in thymine-requiring *Escherichia coli* infected by T2 and T5 bacteriophage. *J. Biol. Chem.*, 234:2987-2991.

6. Bertani, G. (1958), Lysogeny, in *Advances in Virus Research*, vol. V, K. M. Smith and M. A. Lauffer, eds., Academic Press, Inc., New York, pp. 151-193.
7. Bessman, M. J. (1959), Deoxyribonucleotide kinases in normal and virus-infected *Escherichia coli*. *J. Biol. Chem.*, 234:2735-2740.
8. —— (1960), Personal communication.
9. —— and M. J. Van Bibber (1959), A change in properties of deoxyguanylate kinase of *E. coli* caused by viral infection. *Biochem. Biophys. Res. Comm.*, 1:101-104.
10. Brenner, S. (1959), Physiological aspects of bacteriophage genetics, in *Advances in Virus Research*, vol. 6, K. M. Smith and M. A. Lauffer, eds., Academic Press, Inc., New York, pp. 137-158.
11. —— and L. Barnett (1959), Genetic and chemical studies on the head protein of bacteriophages T2 and T4. *Brookhaven Symposia Biol.*, 12:86-94.
12. ——, G. Streisinger, R. W. Horne, S. P. Champe, L. Barnett, S. Benzer, and M. W. Rees (1959), Structural components of bacteriophage. *J. Mol. Biol.*, 1:281-292.
13. Buttin, G. (1961), *Compt. Rend. Acad. Sci. Paris* (in press).
14. ——, F. Jacob, and J. Monod (1960), Synthèse constitutive de galactokinase consécutive au développement des bactériophages λ chez *Escherichia coli* K12. *Compt. Rend. Acad. Sci. Paris*, 250:2471-2473.
15. Campbell, A. (1957), Transduction and segregation in *Escherichia coli* K12. *Virology*, 4:366-384.
16. —— (1959), Ordering of genetic sites in bacteriophage λ by the use of galactose-transducing defective phages. *Virology*, 9:293-305.
17. Chargaff, E. (1955), Isolation and composition of the deoxypentose nucleic acids and of corresponding nucleoproteins, in *The Nucleic Acids*, vol. 1, E. Chargaff and J. N. Davidson, eds., Academic Press, Inc., New York, chap. 10.
18. Dreyer, W. J. (1960), in *Structure and Function of Proteins, Brookhaven Symposia Biol.*, June, 1960.
19. Elson, D. (1958), Latent ribonuclease activity in ribonucleoprotein. *Biochim. Biophys. Acta*, 27:216-217.
20. Flaks, J. C., and S. S. Cohen (1959b), Virus-induced acquisition of metabolic function. III. Formation and some properties of thymidylate synthetase of bacteriophage-infected *Escherichia coli*. *J. Biol. Chem.*, 234:2981-2986.
21. —— and —— (1957), The enzymic synthesis of 5-hydroxymethyldeoxycytidylic acid. *Biochim. Biophys. Acta*, 25:667-668.
22. —— and —— (1959a), Virus-induced acquisition of metabolic function. I. Enzymatic formation of 5-hydroxymethyldeoxycytidylate. *J. Biol. Chem.*, 234:1501-1506.
23. ——, J. Lichtenstein, and S. S. Cohen (1959), Virus-induced acquisition of metabolic function. II. Studies on the origin of the deoxycytidylate hydroxymethylase of bacteriophage-infected *E. coli*. *J. Biol. Chem.*, 234:1507-1511.
24. Friedkin, M., and A. Kornberg (1957), The enzymatic conversion of deoxyuridylic acid to thymidylic acid and the participation of tetrahydrofolic acid, in *The Chemical Basis of Heredity*, W. D. McElroy and B. Glass, eds., Johns Hopkins Press, Baltimore, pp. 609-614.
25. Fuerst, C. R., and G. S. Stent (1956), Inactivation of bacteria by decay of incorporated radioactive phosphorus. *J. Gen. Physiol.*, 40:73-90.
26. Gandelman, B., S. Zamenhof, and E. Chargaff (1952), The deoxypentose nucleic acids of three strains of *Escherichia coli*. *Biochim. Biophys. Acta*, 9:399-401.
27. Guthrie, G. D., and R. L. Sinsheimer (1960), Infection of protoplasts of *Escherichia coli* by subviral particles of φX174. *J. Mol. Biol.*, 2:297-305.
28. Hershey, A. D. (1955), An upper limit to the protein content of the germinal substance of bacteriophage T2. *Virology*, 1:108-127.

29. —— and E. Burgi (1956), Genetic significance of the transfer of nucleic acid from parental to offspring phage. *Cold Spring Harbor Symposia Quant. Biol.*, 21: 91-101.

30. —— and —— (1960), Molecular homogeneity of deoxyribonucleic acid of phage T2. *J. Mol. Biol.*, 2:143-152.

31. —— and M. Chase (1952), Independent functions of viral protein and nucleic acid in growth of bacteriophage. *J. Gen. Physiol.*, 36:39-56.

32. ——, J. Dixon, and M. Chase (1953), Nucleic acid economy in bacteria infected with bacteriophage T2. I. Purine and pyrimidine composition. *J. Gen. Physiol.*, 36:777-789.

33. —— and N. E. Melechen (1957), Synthesis of phage-precursor nucleic acid in the presence of chloramphenicol. *Virology*, 3:207-236.

34. Hoagland, M. B. (1960), The relationship of nucleic acid and protein synthesis as revealed by studies in cell-free systems, *The Nucleic Acids*, vol. 3, E. Chargaff and J. N. Davidson, eds., Academic Press, Inc., New York, chap. 37.

35. Hofschneider, P. H. (1960), *Z. Naturforsch.*, 156:441.

36. Hogness, D. S. (1959), Induced enzyme synthesis, in *Biophysical Science – A Study Program*, J. F. Oncley, ed., John Wiley and Sons, Inc., New York, pp. 256-268. Also in *Revs. Mod. Phys.*, 31:256-268.

37. Horecker, B. L., J. Thomas, and J. Monod (1960), Galactose transport in *Escherichia coli*. I. General properties as studied in a galactokinaseless mutant. *J. Biol. Chem.*, 235:1580-1585.

38. Jacob, F., and C. R. Fuerst (1958), The mechanism of lysis by phage studied with defective lysogenic bacteria. *J. Gen. Microbiol.*, 18:518-526.

39. ——, D. Perrin, C. Sanchez, and J. Monod (1960), L'opéron: groupe de gène à l'expression coordinnée par un opérateur. *Compt. rend. Acad. Sci. Paris*, 250: 1727-1729.

40. —— and E. L. Wollman (1956), Sur les processus de conjugaison et de recombinaison chez *Escherichia coli*. I. L'induction par conjugaison au induction zygotique. *Ann. Inst. Pasteur*, 91:486-510.

41. —— and —— (1957), Genetic aspects of lysogeny, in *The Chemical Basis of Heredity*, W. D. McElroy and B. Glass, eds., Johns Hopkins Press, Baltimore, pp. 468-498.

42. —— and —— (1958a), The relationship between the prophage and the bacterial chromosome in lysogenic bacteria, in *Recent Progress in Microbiology. Symposia Intern. Congr. Microbiol.*, 7th Congr., Stockholm, pp. 15-30.

43. —— and —— (1958b), Sur les processus de conjugaison et de recombinaison génétique chez *Escherichia coli*. IV. Prophages inductibles et mesure des segments génétiques transférés au cours de la conjugaison. *Ann. Inst. Pasteur*, 95:497-519.

44. Jesaitis, M. A. (1957), The nucleic acids of T2, T4, and T6 bacteriophages. *J. Exp. Med.*, 106:233-246.

45. Kaiser, A. D. (1957), Mutations in a temperate bacteriophage affecting its ability to lysogenize *Escherichia coli*. *Virology*, 3:42-61.

46. —— and D. S. Hogness (1960), The transformation of *Escherichia coli* with deoxyribonucleic acid isolated from bacteriophage λdg. *J. Mol. Biol.*, 2:392-415.

47. —— and F. Jacob (1957), Recombination between related temperate bacteriophages and the genetic control of immunity and prophage localization. *Virology*, 4:509-521.

48. Kalckav, H. M., K. Kurahashi, and E. Jordan (1959), Heriditary defects in galactose metabolism in *Escherichia coli* mutants. I. Determination of enzyme activities. *Proc. Natl. Acad. Sci. U.S.*, 45:1776-1786.

49. Keck, K., H. R. Mahler, and D. Fraser (1960), *Arch. Biochem. Biophys.*, 86:85.

50. Koerner, J. F., M. S. Smith, and J. M. Buchanan (1960), Deoxycytidine triphosphatase, an enzyme induced by bacteriophage infection. *J. Biol. Chem.*, 235: 2691-2697.

51. Kornberg, A., S. B. Zimmerman, S. R. Kornberg, and J. Josse (1959), Enzymatic synthesis of deoxyribonucleic acid. VI. Influence of bacteriophage T2 on the synthetic pathway in host cells. *Proc. Natl. Acad. Sci. U.S.*, 45:772-785.

52. Kornberg, S. R., S. B. Zimmerman, and A. Kornberg (1961), *J. Biol. Chem.*, 236:1487.

53. Kozloff, L. M. (1953), Origin and fate of bacteriophage material. *Cold Spring Harbor Symposia Quant. Biol.*, 18:209-220.

54. Kunkee, R. E., and A. B. Pardee (1956), Studies on the role of deoxyribonuclease in T2 bacteriophage development. *Biochim. Biophys. Acta*, 19:236-246.

55. Lacks, S., and R. D. Hotchkiss (1960), Formation of amylomaltase after genetic transformation of pneumococcus. *Biochim. Biophys. Acta*, 45:155-163.

56. Lederberg, E. M. (1958), Fine structure of the *Gal* loci in *Escherichia coli* K12. *Proc. Intern. Congr. Genet., 10th Congr., Montreal*, 2:161.

57. —— (1960), Genetic and functional aspects of galactose metabolism in *Escherichia coli* K12. *Microbial Genetics. Symposium Soc. Gen. Microbiol., 10th, London*, pp. 115-131.

58. Lederberg, J., and T. Iino (1956), Phase variation in *Salmonella. Genetics*, 41: 743-757.

59. Lehman, I. R., and E. A. Pratt (1960), On the structure of the glucosylated hydroxymethylcytosine nucleotides of coliphages T2, T4 and T6. *J. Biol. Chem.*, 235:3254-3259.

60. ——, S. B. Zimmerman, J. Adler, M. J. Bessman, E. S. Simms, and A. Kornberg (1958), Enzymatic synthesis of deoxyribonucleic acid. V. Chemical composition of enzymatically synthesized deoxyribonucleic acid. *Proc. Natl. Acad. Sci. U.S.*, 44:1191-1196.

61. Levine, L., J. L. Barlow, and H. Van Vunakis (1958), An internal protein in T2 and T4 bacteriophages. *Virology*, 6:702-717.

62. Loeb, M. R., and S. S. Cohen (1959), The origin of purine and pyrimidine deoxyribose in T6r^+ bacteriophage. *J. Biol. Chem.*, 235:364-369.

63. Lwoff, A. (1953), Lysogeny. *Bact. Revs.*, 17:269-337.

64. Mahler, H. R., and D. Frazer (1959), Studies in partially resolved bacteriophage-host system. IV. Some properties of the protoplast-infecting agent derived from T2 bacteriophage. *Virology*, 8:401-424.

65. Mayers, V. L., and J. Spizizen (1954), The isolation of deoxyribonucleic acid from bacteriophages by an improved method. *J. Biol. Chem.*, 210:877-884.

66. Marmur, J., and R. D. Hotchkiss (1955), Mannitol metabolism, a transferable property of pneumococcus. *J. Biol. Chem.*, 214:383-396.

67. Morse, M. L., E. M. Lederberg, and J. Lederberg (1956a), Transduction in *Escherichia coli* K-12. *Genetics*, 41:142-156.

68. ——, ——, and —— (1956b), Transductional heterogenotes in *Escherichia coli. Genetics*, 41:758-779.

69. Murakami, W. T., H. Van Vunakis, and L. Levine (1959), Synthesis of T2 internal protein in infected *Escherichia coli*, strain B. *Virology*, 9:624-635.

70. Pfeifer, D. (1961), Genetic recombination in bacteriophage ϕX174. *Nature*, 189: 422-423.

71. Riley, M., A. B. Pardee, F. Jacob, and J. Monod (1960), On the expression of a structural gene. *J. Mol. Biol.*, 2:216-225.

72. Sekiguchi, M., A. Taketo, and Y. Takagi (1960), An infective deoxyribonucleic acid from bacteriophage ϕX174. *Biochim. Biophys. Acta*, 45:199-200.

73. Sinsheimer, R. L. (1956), The glucose content of deoxyribonucleic acids of certain bacteriophages. *Proc. Natl. Acad. Sci. U.S.*, 42:502-504.
74. —— (1959a), Purification and properties of bacteriophage ϕX174. *J. Mol. Biol.*, I:37-42.
75. —— (1959b), A single-stranded deoxyribonucleic acid from bacteriophage ϕX174. *J. Mol. Biol.*, 1:43-53.
76. Smith, J. D., and L. Siminovitch (1953), "Preliminary data" quoted by A. Lwoff. *Bact. Revs.*, 17:320.
77. Soffer, R. (1960), Personal communication.
78. Sommerville, R., K. Ebisuzaki, and G. R. Greenberg (1959), Hydroxymethyldeoxy-cytidylate kinase formation after bacteriophage infection of *Escherichia coli. Proc. Natl. Acad. Sci. U.S.*, 45:1240-1245.
79. Spizizen, J. (1957), Infection of protoplasts by disrupted T2 virus. *Proc. Natl. Acad. Sci. U.S.*, 43:694-701.
80. —— (1959), Genetic activity of deoxyribonucleic acid in the reconstitution of biosynthetic pathways, in *Symposium on Biochem. Aspects of Cell Structure and Function, Federation Proc.*, 18:957-965.
81. Starlinger, P. (1959), Zur Winkungsweise der Gene. *Habilitationsschr.*, University of Cologne.
82. Stent, G. S., and C. R. Fuerst (1955), Inactivation of bacteriophages by decay of incorporated radioactive phosphorus. *J. Gen. Physiol.*, 38:441-458.
83. Streisinger, G. (1960), Personal communication.
84. —— and N. C. Franklin (1956), Mutation and recombination at the host range genetic region of phage T2. *Cold Spring Harbor Symposia Quant. Biol.*, 21:103-111.
85. Tessman, I. (1959), Some unusual properties of nucleic acid in bacteriophages S 13 and ϕX174. *Virology*, 7:263-275.
86. Tessman, E. S., and I. Tessman (1959), Genetic recombination in phage S 13. *Virology*, 7:465-467.
87. Thomas, C. A., and K. I. Berns (1961), The physical characterization of DNA molecules released from T2 and T4 bacteriophage. Personal communication.
88. Vendrely, R. (1955), The deoxyribonucleic acid content of the nucleus, in *The Nucleic Acids*, vol. 2, E. Chargaff and J. N. Davidson, eds., Academic Press, Inc., New York, chap. 19.
89. Vidaver, G. A., and L. M. Kozloff (1957), The rate of synthesis of deoxyribo-nucleic acid in *Escherichia coli* B infected with T2r$^+$ bacteriophage. *J. Biol. Chem.*, 225:335-347.
90. Volkin, E. (1954), The linkage of glucose in coliphage nucleic acids. *J. Am. Chem. Soc.*, 76:5892-5893.
91. Weigle, J., M. Meselson, and K. Paigen (1959), Density alterations associated with transducing ability in bacteriophage lambda. *J. Mol. Biol.*, 1:379-386.
92. Wyatt, G. R., and S. S. Cohen (1953), The bases of the nucleic acids of some bacterial and animal viruses: the occurrence of 5-hydroxymethyl cytosine. *Biochem. J.*, 55:774-782.
93. Zahler, S. A. (1958), Some biological properties of bacteriophages S 13 and ϕX174. *J. Bacteriol.*, 75:310-315.
94. Zamenhof, S. (1957), Properties of the transforming principle, in *The Chemical Basis of Heredity*, W. D. McElroy and B. Glass, eds., Johns Hopkins Press, Baltimore, pp. 351-396.
95. Zimmerman, S. B., and A. Kornberg (1961), *J. Biol. Chem.*, 236:1480.

Chapter Eight

The Structure of DNA and RNA

ROBERT 1. SINSHEIMER

*Division of Biology, California Institute
of Technology, Pasadena, California.*

INTRODUCTION

One of the classic areas of biochemical research is that of the
structure of the substances of living matter. Starting with urea, many
and more complex substances have been analyzed, through glucose
and the steroids and vitamin B_{12}, until now even the smaller proteins
are yielding to modern techniques. As structural research has en-
compassed the more complex substances, a new dimension—that of
function and the relation of structure to function—has been encountered and the science has become truly *bio*chemical. The largest
specific molecules—and thus the most complex—of living matter are
the nucleic acids. It is with these substances—which pose problems
of structure and intimately related function still well beyond our
grasp—that this chapter will be concerned.

To summarize the knowledge of the structure of the nucleic acids
in the spring of the year 1960 is both inspiring and tantalizing. It is
inspiring and instructive to look back a decade to 1950 and see how
far our knowledge of nucleic acid structure has progressed, even
more so to see how our understanding of the profound biological role
of these substances has grown and become more securely based.

However, it is tantalizing to realize that only the broad outlines
of the structure of the nucleic acids have been sketched; that the details elude us, yet that it is the nuances of detail that must provide
the basis of the most fascinating features of the biological function
of these macromolecules. We glimpse some broad and sweeping
principles, but dimly.

Today the basic framework for nucleic acid structures is well
established. It is a sequence of purine and pyrimidine nucleoside
residues linked by phosphate ester bridges between the 5'-carbon of
one residue and the 3'-carbon of the next (Fig. 1). It is interesting
to recall that ten years ago, in 1950, it was by no means clear that
this was the basic structure. Waldo Cohn and his collaborators (19)
had just isolated 2'-, 3'-, and 5'- phosphorylated nucleosides from

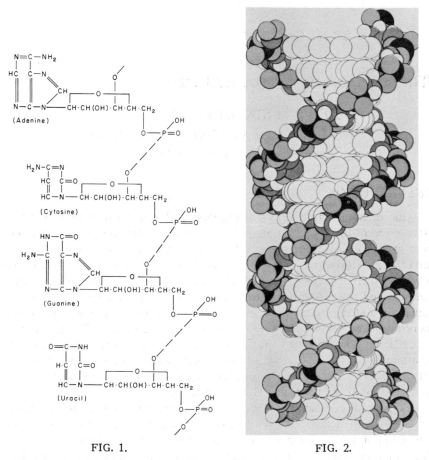

FIG. 1.   FIG. 2.

FIG. 1. General structure of a polynucleotide chain (in this instance a poly-ribonucleotide). FIG. 2. Model of the Watson-Crick structure of deoxyribose-nucleic acid. (*Courtesy Dr. L. D. Hamilton.*)

RNA, and several years of perplexity, with proposals of branched structures of various types, were to ensue before the artifacts were explained and the present concept firmly established. The methods available in 1950 for the isolation of deoxyribonucleotides from DNA gave yields of only a few per cent, and proposals for the existence of special types of linkage to explain the action of various enzymes upon DNA persisted until means for the quantitative degradation of DNA to nucleotides could be achieved (50, 78), and until the physico-chemical events attendant to such degradation could be explained.

With this fairly simple and regular structure well established one might inquire as to what the current and pending problems of DNA and RNA structure are. They are many. We should like to know how long these chains of nucleotides in nucleic acids of various types are; what the proportions are, and above all what the sequences of the purines and pyrimidines in various nucleic acids are. Are there modified nucleic acids with other types of substituents coupled to the polynucleotide chains through covalent bonds? Is there secondary structure involving secondary linkages within parts of a given nucleic acid strand, or regular linkages to a second or third strand? What features of structure are of significance in various biological situations? And more recently we have begun to ask questions as to the structure of the nucleic acids when they are embodied in chromosomes, or in ribosomal particles, or in viruses, as contrasted to their structure when free in solution.

Structure of DNA

The structure of what is by far the most common form of DNA is the complementary two-stranded helix first proposed by Watson and Crick (90). That this is the elementary structure of DNA, when isolated from almost all sources at all times, is clear. This structure is known to be present not only in solution but in the DNA of intact sperm and of certain species of bacteriophage. In cells, this structure may be incorporated into more complex superstructures. The principal features of the Watson-Crick structure are shown in Fig. 2.

Evidence that this is the correct structure is of many sorts (70). There is the X-ray diffraction data of Wilkins, Stokes, and Wilson (93), and of Franklin and Gosling (40), that first led Watson and Crick to its formulation. Electron microscope pictures of Hall and Litt (45) indicate that the mass per unit length of DNA is in agreement with the expectation of the structure. The structure neatly accounts for the molar equalities of adenine and thymine and of guanine and cytosine first discovered by Chargaff to be true of almost all DNA (14). In addition there is now an abundance of physicochemical data to support this model. Specifically, kinetic studies of the decline of molecular weight upon enzyme digestion (68,84) confirm nicely the concept of a cross-linked multiple-stranded structure.

In addition, a variety of effects of such diverse agents as acid (11,23,33,85), alkali (39), heat (11,22,64), or low ionic strength (21, 69) can be most neatly explained by the postulate that the DNA, originally in a firm, relatively rigid, helical two-stranded structure can be converted by a cooperative transition to a "denatured" state, i.e., to a collapsed, single-stranded, flexible structure which may have, dependent upon conditions, some random cross links between chains (31,59). This transition from native to denatured state is usually abrupt, is accelerated by agents that act to disrupt hydrogen bonds, and is in general irreversible (31).

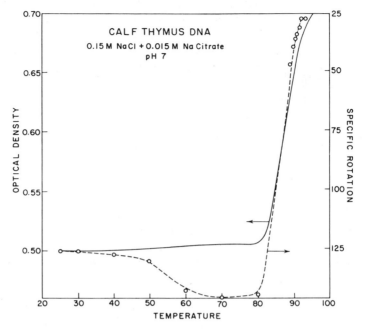

FIG. 3. Dependence of the optical rotatory power and ultraviolet absorption of calf thymus DNA upon temperature. (*From Doty, Boedtker, Fresco, Haselkorn, and Litt,* 1959.)

Thus, upon heating a DNA sample in a given ionic environment, at a critical temperature the ultraviolet absorption will begin to rise (Fig. 3), the optical rotation and the viscosity correspondingly to fall (28,29,30), and over a narrow temperature range the entire transition will be completed. Upon cooling there will be some reversal of the effect of heat upon optical density, optical rotation, or viscosity, but the original state is never fully regained. This melting of the hydrogen bonds between the two DNA strands is a cooperative action analogous to the melting of a one-dimensional crystal. The temperature of melting can be lowered by the addition of hydrogen-bond-rupturing agents such as urea, or by destabilization of the double helix by increasing its net charge by a reduction of the ionic strength of the solution.

Denaturation can also readily be brought about by the addition of acid or alkali to an extent sufficient to weaken adequately the hydrogen-bonded structure. In this case, the denaturation is observed as an abrupt and irreversible change in the titration curve (11,23). At higher temperatures or in the presence of urea the denaturation will occur with a lower increment of charge upon the double helix.

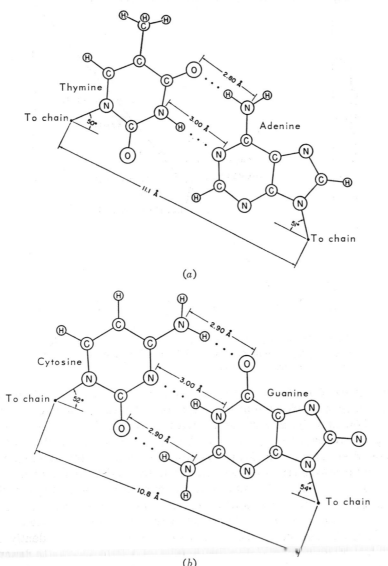

(a)

(b)

FIG. 4. (a and b) Dimensions of the adenine-thymine and guanine-cytosine pairs of DNA. (*From Pauling and Corey*, 1956.)

In the Watson–Crick structure there are two types of hydrogen-bonded pairs (Fig. 4)—the adenine-thymine pair and the guanine-cytosine pair (63). These might be expected to be of unequal strength, and indeed, a priori, the triple hydrogen-bonded guanine-cytosine pair might be expected to be stronger. Doty and collaborators (58) have shown that this is the case. By a study of the thermal denatur-

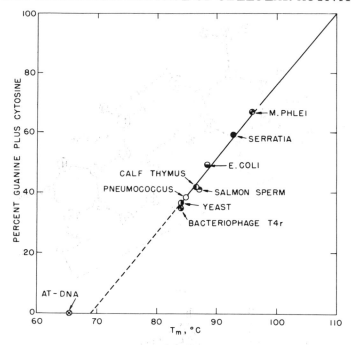

FIG. 5. Relationship between the "melting" temperature of various DNA preparations and their content of guanine-cytosine pairs. (*From Marmur and Doty,* 1959.)

ation curves of DNAs with varying proportions of GC and AT pairs (obtained from various sources, especially bacterial species) they could show that the melting temperature increased as the fraction of GC pairs increased (Fig. 5). This being so, the fact that the melting curves of several of the DNA preparations from bacterial sources are remarkably sharp implies that the individual DNA molecules of these preparations are remarkably uniform in purine and pyrimidine composition, or, more specifically, uniform as to the ratio of GC to AT pairs. A clear-cut confirmation of this was obtained when it was discovered by Sueoka, Marmur, and Doty (82), and independently by Rolfe and Meselson (65), that the density of a DNA molecule depends slightly, but measurably, upon the ratio of GC to AT pairs within the molecule. Thus when banded in a cesium chloride density gradient, the DNAs of several bacterial species form very narrow bands, which are for diverse species completely non-overlapping (Fig. 6). This result implies that there are no, or almost no, DNA molecules in pneumococcal DNA with the same nucleotide composition as any molecules of DNA from *Serratia marcescens*.

While this is acutely true of bacterial DNA, it is not so true of mammalian DNA. The melting curve of thymus DNA is broad, in-

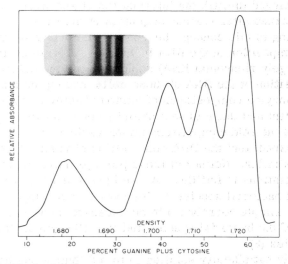

FIG. 6. An illustration of the differences in density
and therefore differences in banding position in a
CsCl density gradient of several DNA preparations
of differing guanine-cytosine content. From left to
right the bands are those of AT polymer, *Pneumococ-*
cus DNA *E. coli* DNA, and *Serratia marcescens* DNA.
(*From Doty, Marmur, and Sueoka, 1959.*)

dicating a considerable range of composition, and indeed some years
ago Chargaff and collaborators (13) were able to fractionate calf
thymus DNA into fractions with AT/GC ratios ranging from 1.0 to
1.8. Among the DNAs of the so far investigated bacterial species,
the AT/GC ratio ranges from 0.45 to 2.7 (3,54). This is an enormous
range, and coupled with relative homogeneity of each DNA gives rise
to a serious dilemma in our thinking about the relation of structure
to function in DNA.

Since the formulation of the concept that the DNA molecules are
the bearers of hereditary information, and serve in some manner as
molecular templates, it has been assumed that this information is
carried as the sequence of the purine and pyrimidine nucleotides
comprising each molecule. At least one major portion of the information content of the genome is composed, presumably, of the speci-
fications for the formation of the peptide chains of the many enzymes
and proteins of cellular metabolism. This line of reasoning has led
to the development of a coding concept, by which is merely meant
the idea that the sequence of nucleotides in DNA molecules is a code
which specifies the sequence of amino acids in various proteins. It
has been widely proposed that the direction of protein synthesis by

DNA is achieved through the intervention of secondary RNA templates patterned after various segments of the DNA.

According to this concept then, we should expect on the one hand that the composition of the RNA in various cells (in bacteria the RNA is very largely ribosomal RNA) should bear some evident relation to the composition of the DNA of those cells, and on the other hand, since the enzyme compositions of various bacterial cells are not very different and there is no a priori reason to expect vast differences in amino acid composition among various bacterial species, we might expect that the DNA composition of varied species would be rather similar. Neither of these perhaps naive but straightforward expectations is fulfilled. As we have seen, the composition of the DNA of bacterial species varies over a wide range. Further, there is no simple correlation to be observed between the DNA compositions of the bacterial species and the RNA compositions of the same species (3).

No really satisfactory solution to this dilemma has been proposed. Sinsheimer (77), and independently, Sueoka, Marmur, and Doty (82) have proposed one possible solution which is that the nucleic acid code is really written in two symbols instead of four as it had seemed to be; specifically, that the only structural feature of importance is the presence of an amino or keto group in the 6-position of each ring, and thus that adenine is equivalent to cytosine and guanine to thymine and thus the adenine-thymine pair is equivalent to a cytosine-guanine pair. This formulation would thus permit the same message to be expressed with any ratio of AT to CG pairs.

Other conceivable solutions (26) are that only a part of the DNA of each molecule carries the message while the remainder, which must be at least 40 per cent, is of no consequence for this purpose, or that the basic code is not universal but differs in different species, or that RNA has an existence and replication independent of DNA in the same cell. It is clear that a resolution of this problem will await a much more detailed knowledge of the mode of action of DNA in influencing cellular processes.

So far we have considered only variations in the AT/GC ratio of DNA. Other obvious types of variation are in the presence of unusual nucleotides, and of course in patterns of sequence. Actually, most DNAs contain at least small amounts of an unusual nucleotide. The most common variations are to substitute a modified cytosine for cytosine (Fig. 7). These will, of course, still pair with guanine as does cytosine.

Hydroxymethylcytosine and its glucosylated derivatives with one or two glucoses are found in the DNAs of the T-even bacteriophages, where they completely replace cytosine (51,57,71,74,89). The extent

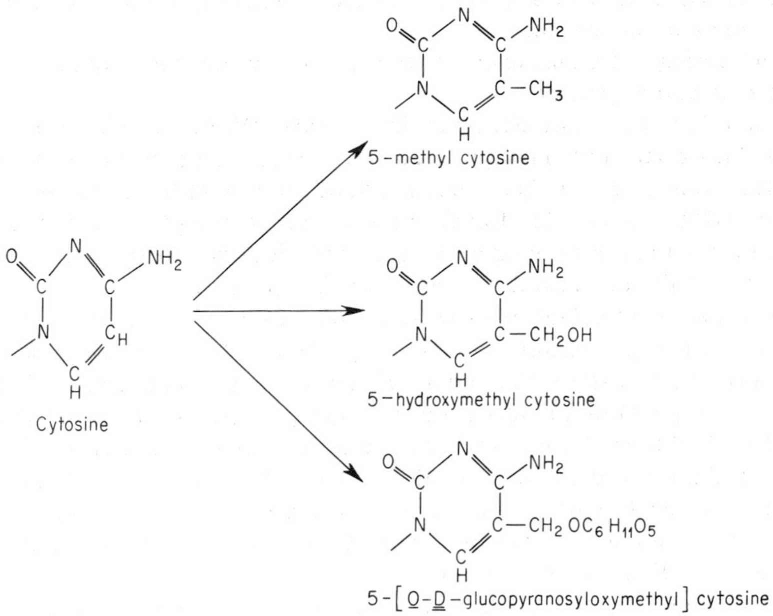

FIG. 7. Formulas of modified cytosines found in various DNA preparations.

of glucosylation, single or double, is known to vary among the different T phages, and there is evidence from the chromatographic fractionation of T2 DNA by Brown (6), that the glucose substitution is not a random one, i.e., that there are DNA fractions with greater glucose substitution than others. These observations appeared to create an awkward problem as to how, during the replication of these DNA molecules, the replicating mechanism could decide whether to use a glucosylated or a nonglucosylated hydroxymethylcytosine. Fortunately, this problem has been neatly resolved by the evidence from Kornberg's laboratory (52) that the glucose residues are coupled to the hydroxymethylcytosine only after the DNA molecules are built, and thus the specificity of location of the glucose is dependent in some presently unknown way upon the specificity of the enzyme concerned (which is known to be different among the different T-even bacteriophages).

5-methylcytosine (94), which is found in mammalian DNA to the extent of about 6 per cent of the cytosine and in plant DNA to about 30 per cent of the cytosine is again nonrandomly distributed. Indeed, in calf thymus DNA, it is known to be present only following guanine, although in wheat germ DNA it is more widely distributed (72,73,81). Here again it is now at least conceivable that the methyl is attached after the DNA molecule is made and the specificity would then reside in the enzyme concerned.

The biological significance of these substitutes for cytosine is quite obscure at present.

The other substitute observed in various DNAs, especially of bacterial origin, is 6-methylaminopurine (37). This substitutes in small amounts (2.4 residues per hundred adenines) for adenine in *E. coli* DNA and possibly for thymine in the pathological situation wherein thymine-requiring cells are dying for lack of thymine. Little is known of the detailed distribution of this purine.

Deliberate modification of DNA composition can be made by offering purine and pyrimidine analogues, particularly in combination with measures that restrict the supply of the natural components. Thus, it has been possible to substitute to varying degrees the halogenated uracils, 5-chloro, 5-iodo, and particularly 5-bromo-uracil for thymine in the DNA of various species (92,36,97,98,17,16,56). There is at least indirect evidence that it is possible to substitute 2-amino-purine for adenine (41). Such substitutions are found to be highly mutagenic and frequently lethal.

It is suspected that the mutagenic properties of such analogues are due to significant alterations of their pK's of ionization, as compared with those of the natural components, leading then to occasional erroneous substitutions (91). Thus, normally, 5-bromo-uracil would pair with adenine as does thymine but as its pK of ionization is lower than that of thymine, it could occasionally ionize and pair with guanine, and thus in effect, result in replacement of a hydroxymethylcytosine by a thymine. Chemical mutations of this sort either as a consequence of analogue substitution, of alkylation, or of deamination, are proving to be a powerful tool for the correlation of genetic maps and DNA structure. It is of unusual interest, but at present rather inexplicable, that some of these mutagens appear to be especially effective at certain sites on the genetic maps (5,41).

It is clear that very detailed knowledge of both the genetic and functional behavior of DNA will have to await the development of improved methods for the determination of nucleotide sequences in DNA. Several new techniques of great promise have recently been developed in this area. One of the most powerful is that of Burton and Peterson (10), who have found that by treatment of DNA with acid in the presence of diphenylamine, under appropriate conditions, it is possible to remove all of the purines and to cleave all the phosphate links to the former purine nucleotides, resulting in the liberation of the exclusively pyrimidine tracts in unaltered form. Fractionation and analysis of these tracts, have so far provided evidence for the existence of sequences of five thymines and of three cytosines, and of mixtures of thymine and cytosine up to six nucleotides in length. This data will be of increasing interest as comparisons are made among various types of DNA, but it is already of interest to note that the existence of a tract of five consecutive thymines would be impossible according to the three letter, comma-free code proposal of Crick et al. (25), and would seem then to rule out such a code.

A technique which can potentially provide information concerning the complementary purine tracts by destruction of the pyrimidines by hydrazine, followed by appropriate use of phosphomonoesterase and alkali has been developed by Takemura (83).

These newer techniques for the determination of the proportions of specific sequences offer great promise, most particularly if they can be applied to preparations containing relatively homogeneous sets of DNA molecules. The haploid DNA complement of a calf genome contains some 300,000 DNA molecules. As far as we know, these could be all different in composition and sequence. They appear also to vary in size. As Butler and Shooter (8) first demonstrated, the sedimentation constants of the molecules of calf thymus DNA preparations cover a range from 10 to 40 svedbergs. This range of sedimentation rate could, in principle, be due to variations of shape or of weight or both, but studies of preparations of various mean molecular weights, and of preparations altered in various ways, have led to the conclusion that the principal factor responsible for this spread in sedimentation is a range of molecular weight (9).

If this spread were due *entirely* to a range of molecular weight, which is unlikely, the range of weight would be as enormous as $S \propto M^{\frac{1}{3}}$ for molecules of this type (32). A fourfold range of S would correspond to a sixty-fourfold range of molecular weight. The mean molecular weights of most DNA preparations appear to range from 4 to 10 to 15 million.

Bacterial DNAs and particularly bacteriophage DNAs appear to be more homogeneous as to size (61) and composition (24,58,65,82), while presumably the ultimate in homogeneity is reached in the DNA of the small bacteriophage of ϕX174 which has but one molecule of DNA (75,76). This DNA is, however, atypical in another respect.

Since the development and confirmation of the two-stranded Watson-Crick structure it has become accepted that all DNAs are of this form. Recently this view has been challenged, and from two directions. On the one hand a single-stranded form of DNA has been found in an obviously viable organism, the ϕX174 bacteriophage. On the other hand, the contention has been raised that possibly many DNA preparations are really four-stranded structures, pairs of double helices.

This latter suggestion arose indirectly from the outcome of the experimental attempt by Meselson and Stahl (60) to analyse the process of DNA replication in bacteria. Watson and Crick had proposed that DNA replicates by a process involving the separation of the two strands of the double helix, with the formation of a new strand to pair with each of the old strands. By an ingenious use of heavy isotopes, Meselson and Stahl demonstrated that the DNA molecules did separate into two components at each replication (Fig. 8), and that the daughter molecules were composed of equal amounts of old and new components. Further, it could be shown that the two components of each new daughter DNA molecule were continuous, and could be separated by heating. If these components were the single DNA

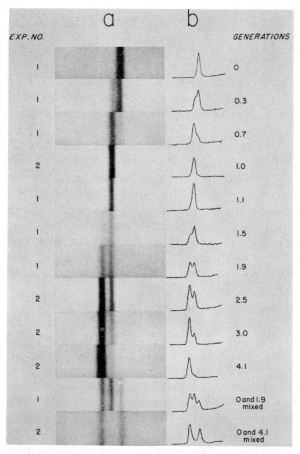

FIG. 8. Sequence of changes in the density of bacterial DNA molecules observed at various times after the bacteria are removed from an N^{15} medium to an N^{14} medium. (*From Meselson and Stahl, 1958.*)

strands, the result would be exactly that predicted by Watson and Crick.

However, Cavalieri and collaborators (12) have investigated the structure of the DNA in preparations of the type used by Meselson and Stahl, and they have concluded that this structure is very complicated; specifically, that it consists of eight subunits each in itself a double helix, linked into blocks of four by protein ligaments, and with the blocks of four coupled to each other by four heat-sensitive bonds of unidentified nature. Such a structure is really properly a portion of a chromosome. The conclusions that Cavalieri has drawn are open to some argument, but it does seem clear that the structure of the DNA molecules obtained by various means cannot be taken for granted. It may well be that the presence of varying residues of the chromosomal structure may be responsible for the variation of the physicochemical properties of DNAs prepared in various ways from various sources. The uncertainty as to the structure of the DNA concerned has, of course, created a corresponding uncertainty in the interpretation of the Meselson-Stahl experiment.

Cavalieri's result also brings forceably to our attention the fact that we know very little indeed as to the configuration of DNA when in a functional chromosome, or as to the nature of its couplings to other chromosomal constituents.

The single-stranded DNA form appears in a bacterial virus, ϕX174, which is of the same size range as many of the RNA-containing plant or animal viruses, and indeed the DNA content of this virus, 1.7 million in molecular weight, is quite similar to the RNA content of such viruses. As such this DNA may be rather distinct from other DNAs in its mode of action. That this DNA is not double-stranded is demonstrated by a variety of properties including a noncomplementary base composition, hypochromic studies, light-scattering data, and an analysis of the kinetics of degradation.

Structure of RNA

It has now become clear that cells may contain several kinds of RNA which have different functions, and probably different structures to perform these functions. We can certainly now distinguish soluble RNA, ribosomal RNA, viral RNA, and nuclear RNA. Unfortunately this development has rather vitiated much of the earlier work which was done on total cellular RNA.

The soluble RNA is quite arbitrarily defined as that RNA left in a cell homogenate after the nuclei and the mitochondria and microsomes or ribosomes have been centrifuged out. It comprises perhaps 10 to 20 per cent of the cellular RNA. In the few cases analysed it is composed of relatively small nucleic acid molecules of molecular weight 25 to 30 thousand (86). These molecular weights are derived from sedimentation and diffusion studies and are confirmed by end-group analysis. These are the acceptor RNAs which act as acceptors of the activated amino acids. Over 90 per cent of these molecules are known to terminate in an adenosine moiety (47) to which the amino acid is coupled. The end-group analysis, by alkaline digestion, releases one adenosine per 80 or 90 nucleotides, suggesting again a chain weight of 25 to 30 thousand (38). The nucleotide next to the terminal adenosine is invariably cytidylic acid (47).

There is good evidence that there are specific types of RNA molecules in the soluble RNA, perhaps one type for each amino acid, and some success has been achieved in the fractionation of different types (7,48,96), but no data on structural features among different types are yet available.

While composed largely of the four principal ribonucleotides, adenylic, guanylic, cytidylic, and uridylic acids, the soluble RNAs are the major home of a veritable zoo of odd minor nucleotides (Fig. 9). The most abundant of these is the pseudo-uridine (62) discovered independently by Cohn (18) and by Allen (66,95). Others include the various methylated adenines and guanines (1,27, 55,80), the methylated pyrimidines (2,55), thymine and 5-methylcytosine, and a class of nucleotides with a new sugar, 2'-0-methylribose (79). Not all of these are found in the soluble RNA from any one source, and differences are observed in the occurrence and proportions of these in the few soluble RNAs that have been analysed. The biological sig-

RELATIVE PROPORTIONS OF ADDITIONAL COMPONENTS IN RNA
FROM RAT LIVER MICROSOMES AND SOLUBLE FRACTION

Values are mole/100 moles uridine.

Component	Microsomes	Soluble
Pseudo-uridine	7.5	25
5-Methylcytosine	0.4	10
6-Methylaminopurine	0.5	8.1
6-Dimethylaminopurine	0.1	0.1
1-Methylguanine	0.1	3.3
2-Methylamino-6-hydroxypurine	0.1	2.3
2-Dimethylamino-6-hydroxypurine	0.1	3.0

FIG. 9. Comparison of the proportions of minor nucleotides in soluble and microsomal RNA of rat liver. (*From Dunn*, 1959.)

nificance of these oddities, and it is very likely that not all have yet been discovered, is quite unknown.

It is perhaps of interest that exclusive of these odd nucleotides the major constituents of soluble RNA are present in nearly complementary proportions. Thus, in one of the best analysed soluble RNAs (38), that of *E. coli* (Fig. 10), adenine is nearly equivalent to uracil and guanine nearly equivalent to cytosine. The composition of the soluble RNA bears no simple relation to that of the ribosomal RNA of the same organism.

The ribosomal particles contain a large fraction of the RNA of a cell, in bacteria perhaps 80 per cent (87). These particles, whether from animals (46), plants (88), or bacteria (87), are observed to split reversibly into two unequal, smaller units upon removal of divalent ions. Thus, in bacteria the intact ribosomes (70S) can be dissociated into equal numbers of 50S and 30S particles.

If RNA is prepared from intact animal or bacterial ribosomes and examined in the ultracentrifuge, two distinct components are observed (43,44,53), with sedimentation rates about 28S and 17S (Fig. 11). They are usually present in proportions of 1.5 to 2 to 1. The 28S component is of a molecular weight of about 1.3 million; the 17S component about 600,000. The 30S and 50S components of *E. coli* ribosomes have been separated and RNA isolated from each (53). The 30S particles yield only the 17S component. The 50S par-

Nucleotide composition of S-RNA

	mol/100 mols identified nucleotides
Adenylic acid†	20·3 ± 0·5‡
Guanylic acid	32·1 ± 0·1
Cytidylic acid	28·9 ± 0·3
Uridylic acid	15·0 ± 0·4
Pseudouridylic acid	2·1
Thymine ribonucleotide	1·1
2-Methyladenylic acid	0·0
6-Methylaminopurine ribonucleotide	0·1
1-Methylguanylic acid	0·1
Ratios	
Purines/pyrimidines	1·12
6-amino/6-keto	0·98

† Value includes terminal adenosine.

‡ Errors are expressed as standard deviations from the mean of four estimations.

FIG. 10. Composition of soluble RNA of *E. coli*. (*From Dunn, Smith, and Spahr*, 1960.)

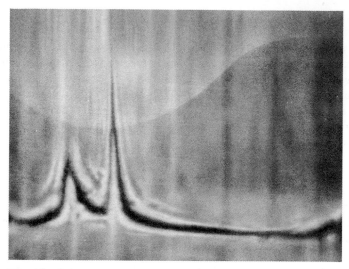

FIG. 11. Ultracentrifuge sedimentation pattern of ribosomal RNA. (*From Gierer*, 1958.)

ticles yield 28S component and a variable amount of 17S component. The nucleotide compositions of the RNAs of these 30S, 50S, and 70S particles, are very similar, and it has been proposed that 28S RNA component is derived by the coupling of two 17S RNA components in the 50S particles. Apparently, however, there is no further coupling when the 30S and 50S particles are linked to form the 70S particles. Again, the biological significance of this RNA arrangement is quite obscure.

Hall and Doty (44) have presented evidence suggesting that these larger ribosomal RNAs from calf-liver ribosomes are actually composed of a set of loosely linked smaller RNA molecules of molecular weight of around 120,000. This evidence is derived from a study of the consequences to ribosomal RNA of varied periods of heating. However, Kurland (53) was unable to find evidence for such discrete subunits in the RNA of the *E. coli* ribosomes.

Preparations of the ribosomal RNA usually have small amounts of the odd nucleotides previously mentioned (4,34). These are found, however, much more abundantly in the soluble RNA. Since the soluble RNA is thought by some to shuttle in and out of the ribosomes, bearing amino acids, it is conceivable that some is trapped within the ribosomes at time of isolation, and that this trapped fraction is the source of the odd bases. Alternatively, they may be an integral part of the ribosomal RNA.

Studies of the hypochromicity of ribosomal RNA both after isolation (29) and when in the ribosomes (44,67), suggest that this RNA has a considerable degree of intramolecular hydrogen bonding, and thus, of secondary structure. However, the exact nature of this structure is unknown.

Viral RNA, either that of the plant viruses (29,42,49), or of such animal viruses as polio (20), appears to be a distinct type. In amount, 1.7 to 2 million in molecular weight, it is equivalent to the total RNA of a ribosome. However, it does *not* split into two components equivalent to those of the ribosomes, nor does it contain any of the odd nucleotides, being composed exclusively of the four major components (55). Recent studies by Doty et al. (29), have indicated that the viral RNA also has an intramolecular structure, as evidenced (Fig. 12) by the changes that take place in the ultraviolet absorption and optical rotation of these molecules upon heating. These effects are attributed to intramolecular hydrogen bonding with the formation of helical regions including some 60 per cent of the nucleotides. A linear structure is envisioned with hairpin-like helical sections. It is conceivable that a structure of this type, with regions specifically susceptible to cleavage may account for the observations, that the

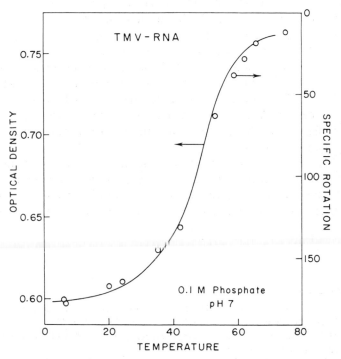

FIG. 12. Dependence of the optical rotatory power and ultraviolet adsorption of tobacco mosaic virus RNA upon temperature. (*From Doty, Boedtker, Fresco, Hall, and Haselkorn, 1959.*)

tobacco mosaic virus RNA, during degradation does not break down randomly, but appears to yield more or less discrete centrifugal components.

All too little is known about nuclear RNA. Cheng has isolated an RNA fraction from calf-thymus nuclei (15) that gives a centrifugal pattern very like that of ribosomal RNA. While this is of very considerable interest, this RNA fraction accounted for only 13 per cent of the nuclear RNA and so is conceivably, at least in part, a contaminant. The nature of the great bulk of the nuclear RNA is thus quite unknown.

SUMMARY

The major features—the gross features of nucleic acid molecules as they exist in isolated form—are well established. Most of the in vitro properties of DNA and RNA can be understood in terms of the established primary polynucleotide structure, with secondary structure imposed by hydrogen-bonding and helix formation. Yet this knowledge is at present hardly sufficient to account for the biological functions of these molecules. There are two principal reasons for this which point the ways in which we must proceed.

For the first, the nucleic acids are in almost all cases large molecules. They are also intimately concerned with a broad class of phenomena that we may group as biological specificities. It thus is not really surprising that as these molecules are examined in more detail, we tend to discover more and more subleties of structure—more and more variations upon the major themes. The significance of these variations will become apparent only when they can be linked to function.

Secondly, in vivo these molecules usually exist in an organized structure—in chromosomes, or ribosomes, or nucleoli, or probably in as yet undescribed objects. It is the structure of the nucleic acids within these superstructures that is functional—and concerning this we are as yet quite uninformed.

REFERENCES

1. Adler, M., B. Weissman, and D. B. Gutman (1958), Occurrence of methylated purine bases in yeast ribonucleic acid. *J. Biol. Chem.*, 230:717-723.
2. Amos, H., and M. Korn (1958), 5-methyl cytosine in the RNA of *Escherichia coli. Biochim. Biophys. Acta,* **29**:444-445.
3. Belozersky, A. N. (1957), On the species specificity of the nucleic acids of bacteria, in *International Symposium on the Origin of Life on Earth,* Publishing House of the Academy of Sciences of the USSR, pp. 194-201.

4. Bergquist, P. L., and R. E. F. Matthews (1959), Distribution of methylated purines in cell fractions from mouse liver and tumour. *Biochim. Biophys. Acta*, 34:567-569.

5. Brenner, S., S. Benzer, and L. Barnett (1958), Distribution of proflavin-induced mutations in the genetic fine structure. *Nature*, 182:983-985.

6. Brown, G. L. (1957), in *The Chemical Basis of Heredity*, W. D. McElroy and B. Glass, eds., Johns Hopkins Press, Baltimore, p. 743.

7. ——, A. V. W. Brown, and J. Gordon (1959), DNA mediation in protein synthesis, *Brookhaven Symposia Biol.*, 12:47-60.

8. Butler, J. A. V., and K. V. Shooter (1956), The physical heterogeneity of DNA, in *The Chemical Basis of Heredity*, W. D. McElroy and B. Glass, eds., Johns Hopkins Press, Baltimore, pp. 540-543.

9. ——, D. J. R. Laurence, A. B. Robins, and K. V. Shooter (1959), Comparison of the molecular weights of deoxyribonucleic acids as determined from light scattering and from sedimentation and viscosity. *Proc. Roy. Soc.* (London) A, 250:1-21.

10. Burton, K., and G. B. Petersen (1960), The frequencies of certain sequences of nucleotides in deoxyribonucleic acid. *Biochem. J.*, 75:17-27.

11. Cavalieri, L. F., and B. H. Rosenberg (1957), Studies on the structure of nucleic acids. XI. The roles of heat and acid in deoxyribonucleic acid denaturation. *J. Am. Chem. Soc.*, 79:5352-5357.

12. ——, ——, and J. F. Deutsch (1959), The subunit of deoxyribonucleic acid. *Biochem. Biophys. Res. Comm.*, 1:124-128.

13. Chargaff, E., C. F. Crampton, and R. Lipshitz (1953), Separation of calf thymus deoxyribonucleic acid into fractions of different composition. *Nature*, 172:289-292.

14. —— (1955), Isolation and composition of the deoxypentose nucleic acids and of the corresponding nucleoproteins, in *The Nucleic Acids*, vol. 1, E. Chargaff and J. N. Davidson, eds., Academic Press, Inc., New York, pp. 307-371.

15. Cheng, P. (1959), High molecular weight ribonucleic acids from the nuclei of calf thymus. *Nature*, 184:190-191.

16. Cheong, L., M. A. Rug, and M. L. Eidinoff (1960), Introduction of the 5-halogenated uracil moiety into deoxyribonucleic acid of mammalian cells in culture. *J. Biol. Chem.*, 235:1441-1447.

17. Cohen, S. S., and H. D. Barner (1956), Studies on the induction of thymine deficiency and on the effects of thymine and thymidine analogues in *Escherichia coli*. *J. Bacteriol.*, 71:588-597.

18. Cohn, W. E. (1959), 5-ribosyl uracil, a carbon-carbon ribofuranosyl nucleoside in ribonucleic acids. *Biochim. Biophys. Acta*, 32:569-571.

19. Cohn, W. D., and E. Volkin (1951), Nucleoside-5'-phosphates from ribonucleic acid. *Nature*, 167:483-484.

20. Colter, J. S., H. H. Bird, A. W. Moyer, and R. A. Brown (1957), Infectivity of ribonucleic acid isolated from virus-infected tissues. *Virology*, 4:522-532.

21. Cox, R. A., and A. R. Peacocke (1956), Electrometric titration of the sodium salts of deoxyribonucleic acids. Part III. The effect of sodium chloride. *J. Chem. Soc.*, 2499-2512.

22. —— and —— (1956), Electrometric titration of the sodium salts of deoxyribonucleic acids. Part IV. Denaturation by heat in aqueous solution. *J. Chem. Soc.*, 2646-2651.

23. —— and —— (1957), Application of the titration method to studies on the denaturization of sodium deoxyribonucleate. *J. Polymer Sci.*, 23:765-779.

24. Crampton, C. F., R. Lipshitz, and E. Chargaff (1954), Studies of nucleoproteins. II. Fractionation of deoxyribonucleic acids through fractional dissociation of their complexes with basic proteins. *J. Biol. Chem.*, 211:125-142.

25. Crick, F. H. C., J. S. Griffith, and L. E. Orgel (1957), Codes without commas. *Proc. Natl. Acad. Sci. U.S.*, 43:416-421.
26. —— (1959), The present position of the coding problem. *Brookhaven Symposia Biol.*, 12:35-38.
27. Davis, F. F., A. F. Carlucci and I. F. Roubein (1959), Trace nucleotides in certain ribonucleic acids from yeast. *J. Biol. Chem.*, 234:1525-1529.
28. Doty, P., H. Boedtker, J. R. Fresco, B. D. Hall, and R. Haselkorn (1959), Configurational studies of polynucleotides and ribonucleic acid. *Ann. N.Y. Acad. Sci.*, 81:693-708.
29. ——, ——, ——, R. Haselkorn, and M. Litt (1959), Secondary structure in ribonucleic acids. *Proc. Natl. Acad. Sci. U.S.*, 45:482-499.
30. ——, J. Marmur, and N. Sueoka (1959), The heterogeneity in properties and functioning of deoxyribonucleic acids. *Brookhaven Symposia Biol.*, 12:1-16.
31. ——, ——, J. Eigner, and C. Schildkraut (1960), Strand separation and specific recombination in deoxyribonucleic acids: Physical chemical studies. *Proc. Natl. Acad. Sci. U.S.*, 46:461-476.
32. ——, B. B. McGill, and S. A. Rice (1958), The properties of sonic fragments of deoxyribose nucleic acid. *Proc. Natl. Acad. Sci. U.S.*, 44:432-438.
33. Dove, W. F., F. A. Wallace, and N. Davidson (1959), Spectrophotometric study of the protonation of undenatured DNA. *Biochem. Biophys. Research Comm.*, 1:312-317.
34. Dunn, D. B. (1959), Additional components in ribonucleic acid of rat-liver fractions. *Biochim. Biophys. Acta*, 34:286-288.
35. —— (1960), the isolation of 5-methyl cytidine from RNA. *Biochim. Biophys. Acta*, 38:176-178.
36. —— and J. D. Smith (1957), Effects of 5-halogenated uracils on the growth of *Escherichia coli* and their incorporation into deoxyribonucleic acids. *Biochem. J.*, 67:494-506.
37. —— and —— (1958), The occurrence of 6-methylaminopurine in deoxyribonucleic acids. *Biochem. J.*, 68:627-636.
38. ——, ——, and P. F. Spahr (1960), Nucleotide composition of soluble ribonucleic acid from *Escherichia coli*. *J. Mol. Biol.*, 2:113-117.
39. Ehrlich, P., and P. Doty (1958), The alkaline denaturation of deoxyribose nucleic acid. *J. Am. Chem. Soc.*, 80:4251-4255.
40. Franklin, R. E., and R. G. Gosling (1953), Molecular configuration in sodium thymonucleate. *Nature*, 171:740-741.
41. Freese, E. (1959), The specific mutagenic effect of base analogues in phage T4. *J. Mol. Biol.*, 1:87-105.
42. Gierer, A. (1958), Grösse und struktur der ribosenucleinsäure des tabakmosaikvirus. *Z. Naturforsch.*, 13b:477-484.
43. —— (1958), Vergleichende untersuchungen an hochmolekular ribosenucleinsäure. *Z. Naturforsch.*, 13b:788-792.
44. Hall, B. D., and P. Doty (1959), The preparation and physical chemical properties of ribonucleic acid from microsomal particles. *J. Mol. Biol.*, 1:111-126.
45. Hall, C. E., and M. Litt (1958), Morphological features of DNA macromolecules as seen with the electron microscope. *J. Biophys. Biochem. Cytol.*, 4:1-4.
46. Hamilton, M. G., and M. L. Petermann (1959), Ultracentrifugal studies on ribonucleoprotein from rat-liver microsomes. *J. Biol. Chem.*, 234:1441-1446.
47. Hecht, L. I., P. C. Zamecnik, M. L. Stephenson, and J. F. Scott (1958), Nucleoside triphosphates as precursors of ribonucleic acid end groups in a mammalian system. *J. Biol. Chem.*, 233:954-963.
48. Holley, R. W. and B. P. Doctor (1960), Countercurrent distribution of amino acid acceptor ribonucleic acids. *Federation Proc.*, 19:348.

49. Hopkins, G. R., and R. L. Sinsheimer (1955), Visible and ultraviolet light scattering by tobacco mosaic virus nucleic acid. *Biochim. Biophys. Acta*, 17:476-484.

50. Hurst, R. O., J. A. Little, and G. C. Butler (1951), The enzymatic degradation of thymonucleic acid. II. The hydrolysis of oligonucleotides. *J. Biol. Chem.*, 188: 705-715.

51. Jesaitis, M. A. (1957), The nucleic acids of T2, T4, and T6 bacteriophages. *J. Exp. Med.*, 106:233-246.

52. Kornberg, A., S. B. Zimmerman, S. R. Kornberg, and J. Josse (1959), Enzymatic synthesis of deoxyribonucleic acid. VI. Influence of bacteriophage T2 on the synthetic pathway in host cells. *Proc. Natl. Acad. Sci. U.S.*, 45:772-785.

53. Kurland, C. G. (1960), Molecular characterization of ribonucleic acid from *Escherichia coli* ribosomes. I. Isolation and molecular weights. *J. Mol. Biol.*, 2:83-91.

54. Lee, K. Y., R. Wahl, and E. Barber (1956), Contenu en bases puriques et pyrimidiques des acides désoxyribonucléiques des bactéries. *Ann. Inst. Pasteur*, 91: 212-224.

55. Littlefield, J. W., and D. B. Dunn (1958), The occurrence and distribution of thymine and three methylated adenine bases in ribonucleic acids from several sources. *Biochem. J.*, 70:642-651.

56. —— and E. A. Guild (1960), The toxic effect of 5-bromodeoxyuridine on cultured epithelial cells. *J. Biol. Chem.*, 235:1129-1133.

57. Loeb, M. R., and S. S. Cohen (1959), The origin of purine and pyrimidine deoxyribose in T6r⁺ bacteriophage. *J. Biol. Chem.*, 234:364-369.

58. Marmur, J., and P. Doty (1959), Heterogeneity in deoxyribonucleic acids. I. Dependence on composition of the configurational stability of deoxyribonucleic acids. *Nature*, 183:1427-1429.

59. ——, and D. Lane (1960), Strand separation and specific recombination in deoxyribonucleic acids: Biological studies. *Proc. Natl. Acad. Sci. U.S.*, 46:453-461.

60. Meselson, M., and F. W. Stahl (1958), The replication of DNA in *Escherichia coli. Proc. Natl. Acad. Sci. U.S.*, 44:671-682.

61. ——, ——, and J. Vinograd (1957), Equilibrium sedimentation of macromolecules in density gradients. *Proc. Natl. Acad. Sci. U.S.*, 43:581-588.

62. Otaka, E., Y. Hotta, and S. Osawa (1959), Occurrence of the fifth nucleotide in soluble ribonucleic acid in yeast. *Biochim. Biophys. Acta*, 35:266-267.

63. Pauling, L., and R. B. Corey (1956), Specific hydrogen-bond formation between pyrimidines and purines in deoxyribonucleic acids. *Arch. Biochem. Biophys.*, 65:164-181.

64. Rice, S. A., and P. Doty (1957), The thermal denaturation of desoyribose nucleic acid. *J. Am. Chem. Soc.*, 79:3937-3947.

65. Rolfe, R., and M. Meselson (1959), The relative homogeneity of microbial DNA. *Proc. Natl. Acad. Sci. U.S.*, 45:1039-1043.

66. Scannell, J. P., A. M. Crestfield, and F. W. Allen (1959), Methylation studies on various uracil derivatives and on an isomer of uridine isolated from ribonucleic acids. *Biochim. Biophys. Acta*, 32:406-412.

67. Schlessinger, D. (1960), Hypochromicity in ribosomes from *Escherichia coli. J. Mol. Biol.*, 2:92-95.

68. Schumaker, V. N., E. G. Richards, and H. K. Schachman (1956), A study of the kinetics of the enzymatic digestion of deoxyribonucleic acid. *J. Am. Chem. Soc.*, 78:4230-4236.

69. Shack, J. (1958), On the recognition and estimation of denatured deoxyribonucleate. *J. Biol. Chem.*, 233:677-680.

70. Shooter, R. V. (1957), The physical chemistry of deoxyribosenucleic acid, in *Prog. Biophys. and Biophys. Chem.*, 8:309-346.

71. Sinsheimer, R. L. (1954), Nucleotides from T2r+ bacteriophage. *Science*, 120: 551-553.

72. —— (1954), The action of pancreatic desoxyribonuclease. I. Isolation of Mono- and Dinucleotides. *J. Biol. Chem.*, 208:445-459.

73. —— (1955), The action of pancreatic deoxyribonuclease. II. Isomeric dinucleotides. *J. Biol. Chem.*, 215:579-583.

74. —— (1956), The glucose content of the deoxyribonucleic acids of certain bacteriophages. *Proc. Natl. Acad. Sci.,U.S.*, 42:502-504.

75. —— (1959), Purification and properties of bacteriophage φX174. *J. Mol. Biol.*, 1:37-42.

76. —— (1959), A single-stranded deoxyribonucleic acid from bacteriophage φX174. *J. Mol. Biol.*, 1:43-53.

77. —— (1959), Is the nucleic acid message in a two-symbol code? *J. Mol. Biol.*, 1:218-220.

78. —— and J. F. Koerner (1922), A purification of venom phosphodiesterase. *J. Biol. Chem.*, 198:293-296.

79. Smith, J. D., and D. B. Dunn (1959), An additional sugar component of ribonucleic acids. *Biochim. Biophys. Acta*, 31:573-575.

80. —— and —— (1959), The occurrence of methylated guanines in ribonucleic acid from several sources. *Biochem. J.*, 72:294-301.

81. —— and R. Markham (1952), Polynucleotides from deoxyribonucleic acids. *Nature*, 170:120-121.

82. Sueoka, N., J. Marmur, and P. Doty (1959), Heterogeneity in deoxyribonucleic acids. II. Dependence of the density of deoxyribonucleic acids on guanine-cytosine. *Nature*, 183:1429-1431.

83. Takemura, S. (1959), Hydrazinolysis of nucleic acids. I. The formation of deoxyribo-apyrimidinic acid from herring sperm deoxyribonucleic acid. *Bull. Chem. Soc. Japan*, 32:920-926.

84. Thomas, C. A., Jr. (1956), The enzymatic degradtion of desoxyribose nucleic acid. *J. Am. Chem. Soc.*, 78:1861-1868.

85. —— and P. Doty (1956), The mild acidic degradation of desoxyribose nucleic acid. *J. Am. Chem. Soc.*, 78:1854-1860.

86. Tissieres, A. (1959), Some properties of soluble ribonucleic acid from *Escherichia coli. J. Mol. Biol.*, 1:365:374.

87. ——, J. D. Watson, D. Schlessinger, and B. R. Hollingsworth (1959), Ribonucleoprotein particles from *Escherichia coli. J. Mol. Biol.*, 1:221-233.

88. Ts'o, P. O. P., J. Bonner, and J. Vinograd (1958), Structure and properties of microsomal nucleoprotein particles from pea seedlings. *Biochim. Biophys. Acta*, 30:570-582.

89. Volkin, E. (1954), The linkage of glucose in coliphage nucleic acids. *J. Am. Chem. Soc.*, 76:5892-5893.

90. Watson, J. D., and F. H. C. Crick (1953), A structure for deoxyribosenucleic acid, *Nature*, 171:737-738.

91. —— and —— (1953), The structure of DNA. *Cold Spring Harbor Symposia Quant. Biol.*, 18:123-131.

92. Weygand, F., and A. Wacker (1952), Stoffwechseluntersuchungen bei Mikroorganismen mit Hilfe radioaktiver Isotope. III. Aufnahme von $5^{82}B_r$-Uracil durch Enterococcus und B. coli. *Z. Naturforsch.*, 7b:26-28.

93. Wilkins, M. H. F., A. R. Stokes, and H. R. Wilson (1953), Molecular structure of deoxypentose nucleic acids. *Nature*, 171:738-740.

94. Wyatt, G. R. (1951), The purine and pyrimidine composition of deoxypentose nucleic acids. *Biochem. J.*, 48:584-590.

95. Yu, C. T., and F. W. Allen (1959), Studies on an isomer of uridine isolated from ribonucleic acids. *Biochim. Biophys. Acta*, 32:393-406.
96. Zamecnik, P. C., and M. L. Stephenson (1960), Enrichment of specific activity of aminoacyl RNA. *Federation Proc.*, 19:346.
97. Zamenhof, S., B. Reiner, R. De Giovanni, and K. Ruh (1956), Introduction of unnatural pyrimidines into deoxyribonucleic acid of *Escherichia coli*. *J. Biol. Chem.*, 219:165-173.
98. ——, K. Ruh, and R. De Giovanni (1958), Further studies on the introduction of pyrimidines into deoxyribonucleic acids of *Escherichia coli*. *J. Biol. Chem.*, 232: 651-657.

Chapter Nine

Biologic Synthesis of Deoxyribonucleic Acid*

ARTHUR KORNBERG

Professor and executive head of the Department of Biochemistry at Stanford University School of Medicine, Palo Alto, California.

The knowledge drawn in recent years from studies of bacterial transformation (1) and viral infection of bacterial cells (2), combined with other evidence (3), has just about convinced most of us that deoxyribonucleic acid (DNA) is the genetic substance. We shall assume then that it is DNA which not only directs the synthesis of the proteins and the development of the cell but which must also be the substance which is copied so as to provide for a similar development of the progeny of that cell for many generations. Deoxyribonucleic acid, like a tape recording, carries a message in which there are specific instructions for a job to be done. Also, exact copies can be made from it, as from a tape recording, so that this information can be used again and elsewhere in time and space.

Are these two functions, the expression of the code (protein synthesis) and the copying of the code (preservation of the race), closely integrated or are they separable? What we have learned from our studies over the past 5 years is that the replication of DNA can be examined and at least partially understood at the enzymatic level even though the secret of how DNA directs protein synthesis is still locked in the cell.

Structure

First I should like to review very briefly some aspects of DNA structure which are essential for this discussion. Analysis of the composition of samples of DNA from a great variety of sources, and by many investigators (4), has revealed the remarkable fact that the purine content always equals the pyrimidine content. Among the purines, the adenine content may differ considerably from the guanine,

*Published with the permission of the Nobel Foundation.

245

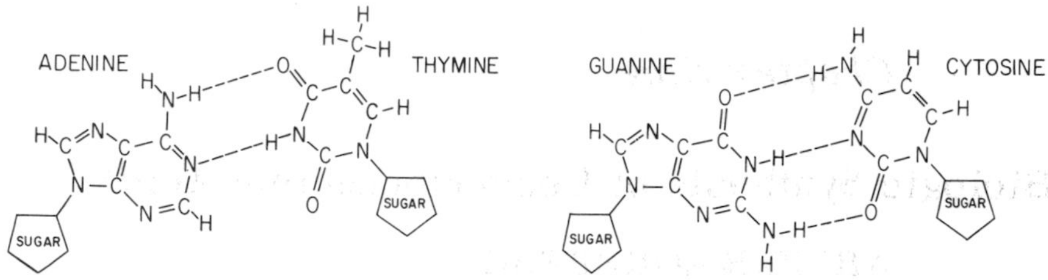

FIG. 1. Hydrogen bonding of bases.

and among the pyrimidines, the thymine from the cytosine. However, there is an equivalence of the bases with an amino group in the 6-position of the ring to the bases with a keto group in the 6-position. These facts were interpreted by Watson and Crick (5) in their masterful hypothesis of the structure of DNA. As shown in Fig. 1, they proposed in connection with their double-stranded model for DNA, discussed below, that the 6-amino group of adenine is linked by hydrogen bonds to the 6-keto group of thymine and that in a like manner guanine is hydrogen-bonded to cytosine, thus accounting for the equivalence of the purines to the pyrimidines.

On the basis of these considerations and the results of x-ray crystallographic measurements by Wilkins and his associates (6), Watson and Crick proposed a structure for DNA in which two long strands are wound about each other in a helical manner. Figure 2 is a diagrammatic representation of a fragment of a DNA chain about 10 nucleotide units long. According to physical measurements, DNA chains are, on the average, 10,000 units long. We see here the deoxypentose rings linked by phosphate residues to form the backbone of the chain; the purine and pyrimidine rings are the planar structures emerging at right angles from the main axis of the chain. Figure 3 is a more detailed molecular model (7) and presents a better picture of the packing of the atoms in the structure. The purine and pyrimidine bases of one chain are bonded to the pyrimidine and purine bases of the complementary chain by the hydrogen bonds described in Fig. 1.

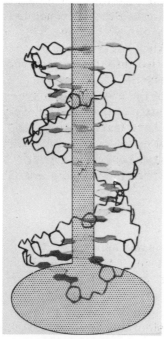

FIG. 2. Double helical structure of DNA (Watson and Crick model).

The x-ray measurements have indicated that the space between the
opposing chains in the model agrees
with the calculated value for the hydrogen-bond linkage of a purine to a
pyrimidine; it is too small for two
purines and too large for two pyrimidines. Most rewarding from the
biological point of view, the structure provides a useful model to explain how cellular replication of DNA
may come about. For, if you imagine that these two chains separate
and that a new chain is formed complementary to each of them, the result will be two pairs of strands,
each pair identical to the original
parent duplex and each member of
the pair identical to the other.

Enzymatic Approach to Replication

Although we have in the Watson
and Crick proposal a mechanical
model of replication, we may at this
point pose the question: What is the
chemical mechanism by which this
super molecule is built up in the cell?
Some 60 years ago the alcoholic fermentation of sugar by a yeast cell
was a "vital" process inseparable
from the living cell, but through the
Buchner discovery of fermentation
in extracts and the march of enzy-

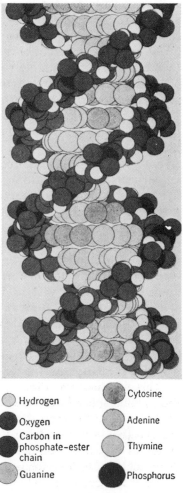

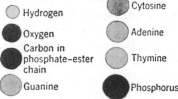

⬤ Hydrogen	◓ Cytosine
⬤ Oxygen	◯ Adenine
⬤ Carbon in phosphate-ester chain	◯ Thymine
◯ Guanine	⬤ Phosphorus

FIG. 3. Molecular model of DNA
[*After M. Feughelman et al.* (7)].

mology during the first half of this century, we understand fermentation by yeast as a (now familiar) sequence of integrated chemical
reactions.

Five years ago the synthesis of DNA was also regarded as a
"vital" process. Some people considered it useful for biochemists
to examine the combustion chambers of the cell, but tampering with
the very genetic apparatus itself would surely produce nothing but
disorder. These gloomy predictions were not justified then, nor are
similar pessimistic attitudes justified now with regard to the problems of cellular structure and specialized function which face us.
High adventures in enzymology lie ahead, and many of the explorers

will come from the training fields of carbohydrate, fat, amino acid, and nucleic acid enzymology.

I feel now, as we did then, that for an effective approach to the problem of nucleic acid biosynthesis it is essential to understand the biosynthesis of the simple nucleotides and the coenzymes and to have these concepts and methodology well in hand. It was from these studies that we developed the conviction that an activated nucleoside 5'-phosphate is the basic biosynthetic building block of the nucleic acids (8). You will recall that the main pathways of purine and pyrimidine biosynthesis all lead to the nucleoside 5'-phosphate (8): they do not usually include the free bases or nucleosides, except as salvage mechanisms. While the 2' and 3' isomers of the nucleotides are known, they probably arise mainly from certain types of enzymatic degradation of the nucleic acids. You will also recall from the biosynthesis of coenzymes (9), the simplest of the nucleotide condensation products, that it is adenosine triphosphate (ATP) which condenses with nicotinamide mononucleotide to form diphosphopyridine nucleotide, with riboflavin phosphate to form flavine adenine dinucleotide (FAD), with pantetheine phosphate to form the precursor of coenzyme A, and so forth. This pattern has been amplified by the discovery of identical mechanisms for the activation of fatty acids and amino acids, and it has been demonstrated further that uridine, cytidine, and guanosine coenzymes are likewise formed from the respective triphosphates of these nucleosides.

This mechanism (Fig. 4), in which a nucleophilic attack (10) on the pyrophosphate-activated adenyl group by a nucleoside monophosphate leads to the formation of a coenzyme, was adopted as a working hypothesis for studying the synthesis of a DNA chain. As illustrated in Fig. 5, it was postulated that the basic building block is deoxynucleoside 5'-triphosphate which is attacked by the 3'-hydroxyl group at the growing end of a polydeoxynucleotide chain; inorganic pyrophosphate is eliminated, and the chain is lengthened by one unit. The results of our studies of DNA synthesis, as is shown below, are in keeping with this type of reaction.

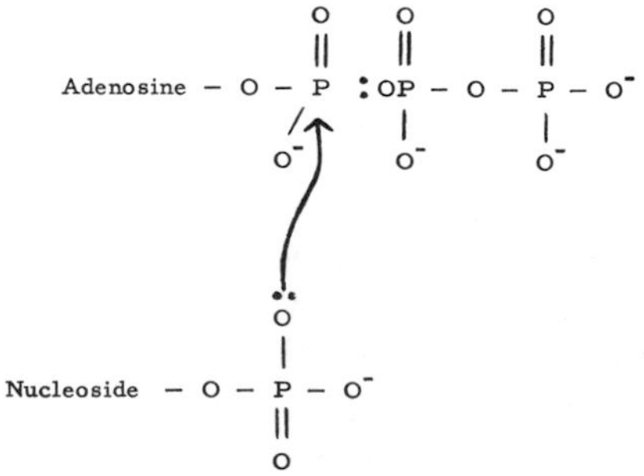

FIG. 4. Nucleophilic attack of a nucleoside monophosphate on ATP.

Properties of the Enzyme

First let us consider the enzyme and comment on the way in which it was discovered (8, 11). Mixing the triphosphates of the four deoxynucleosides which commonly occur in DNA with an extract of thymus or of bone marrow or of *Escherichia coli* would not be expected to lead to the net synthesis of DNA. Instead, as might be expected, the destruction of DNA by the extracts of such cells and tissues was by far the predominant process, and one had to resort to more subtle devices to detect such a biosynthetic reaction. We used a C^{14}-labeled substrate of high specific radioactivity and incubated it with adenosine triphosphate and extracts of *Escherichia coli*, an organism which reproduces itself every 20 minutes. The first positive results represented the conversion of only a very small fraction of the acid-soluble substrate into an acid-insoluble fraction (50 or so counts out of a million added). While this represents only a few micromicromoles of reaction, it was something. Through this tiny crack we tried to drive a wedge, and the hammer was enzyme purification (12).

This has been and still is a major preoccupation. Our best preparations are several thousandfold en-

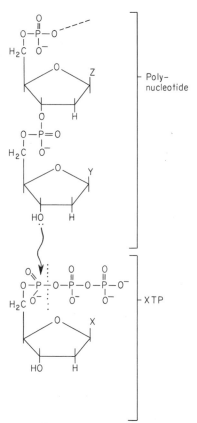

FIG. 5. Postulated mechanism for extending a DNA chain.

riched with respect to protein over the crude extracts, but there are still contaminating quantities of one or more of the many varieties of nuclease and diesterase present in the *E. coli* cell. The occurrence of what appears to be a similar DNA-synthesizing system in animal cells as well as in other bacterial species has been observed (13). We must wait for purification of the enzymes from these sources in order to make valid comparisons with the *E. coli* system.

The requirements for net synthesis of DNA with the purified *E. coli* enzyme (14) are shown in the equation in Fig. 6. All four of the deoxynucleotides which form the adenine-thymine and guanine-cytosine couples must be present. The substrates must be the tri- and not the diphosphates, and only the deoxy sugar compounds are active. Deoxyribonucleic acid, which must be present, may be obtained from animal, plant, bacterial, or viral sources, and the best indications are that all these DNA samples serve equally well in

$$\begin{matrix} n & TPPP \\ n & dGPPP \\ n & dAPPP \\ n & dCPPP \end{matrix} \; + DNA \rightleftharpoons DNA - \begin{bmatrix} TP \\ dGP \\ dAP \\ dCP \end{bmatrix}_n \; + \; 4(n)PP$$

FIG. 6. Equation for enzymatic synthesis of DNA.

DNA synthesis provided their molecular weight is high. The product, which I discuss below in further detail, accumulates until one of the substrates is exhausted and may be 20 or more times greater in amount than the DNA added, and thus is composed to the extent of 95 per cent or more of the substrates added to the reaction mixture. Inorganic pyrophosphate is released in quantities equimolar to the deoxynucleotides converted to DNA.

Should one of these substrates be omitted, the extent of the reaction is diminished by a factor of more than 10^4, and special methods are then required to detect it. It turns out that when one of the deoxynucleotide substrates is lacking, an extremely small yet significant quantity of nucleotide is linked to the DNA primer. My coworkers and I have described this so-called "limited reaction" (15) and have shown that under these circumstances a few deoxynucleotides are added to the nucleoside ends of some of the DNA chains but that further synthesis is blocked for lack of the missing nucleotide. Current studies suggest that this limited reaction represents the repair of the shorter strand of a double helix in which the strands are of unequal length, and that the reaction is governed by the hydrogen-bonding of adenine to thymine and of guanine to cytosine.

When all four triphosphates are present, but when DNA is omitted, no reaction takes place at all. What is the basis for this requirement? Does the DNA function as a primer in the manner of glycogen, or does it function as a template in directing the synthesis of exact copies of itself? We have good reason to believe that it is the latter, and as the central and restricted theme of this article, I should like to emphasize that it is the capacity for base pairing by hydrogen-bonding between the preexisting DNA and the nucleotides added as substrates that accounts for the requirement for DNA.

The enzyme we are studying is thus unique in our experience to date in that it takes directions from a template—it adds the particular purine or pyrimidine substrate which will form a hydrogen-bonded pair with a base on the template (Fig. 7). There are five major lines of evidence that support this thesis.

Physical Properties of Enzymatically Synthesized DNA

The first line of evidence is derived from studies of the physical nature of the DNA produced by the enzyme. I might mention again that in these descriptions as in those of the chemical nature of DNA,

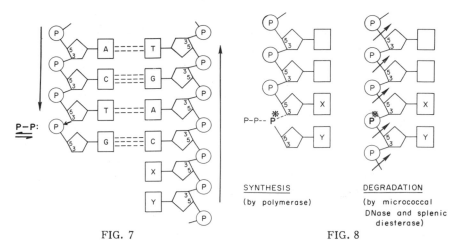

FIG. 7   FIG. 8

SYNTHESIS
(by polymerase)

DEGRADATION
(by micrococcal
DNase and splenic
diesterase)

FIG. 7. Mechanism for enzymatic DNA replication. FIG. 8. Method for determining sequences in DNA.

discussed below, 90 to 95 percent of the DNA sample comes from the substrates used in the reaction. From collaborative studies with Howard K. Schachman, to whom we are greatly indebted, it can be said that the enzymatic product is indistinguishable from high-molecular-weight, double-stranded DNA isolated from natural sources (16). It has sedimentation coefficients in the neighborhood of 25 and reduced viscosities of 40 deciliters per gram, and on the basis of these measurements we believe it to be a long, stiff rod with a molecular weight of about 6 million. When the DNA is heated, the rod collapses and the molecule becomes a compact, randomly coiled structure; it may be inferred that the hydrogen bonds holding the strands together have melted, and this is borne out by charac-teristic changes in the viscometric and optical properties of the molecule. Similar results are found upon cleavage of the molecule by pancreatic deoxyribonuclease. In all these respects the enzymat ically synthesized DNA is indistinguishable from the material iso-lated from natural sources and may thus be presumed to have a hy-drogen-bonded structure similar to that possessed by natural DNA.

Would one imagine that the collapsed, jumbled strands of heated DNA would serve as a primer for DNA synthesis? Very likely one would think not. Guided by everyday experience with a jumbled strand of twine, one might regard this as a hopeless template for replication. It turns out that the collapsed DNA is an excellent primer and that the nonviscous, randomly coiled, single-stranded DNA leads to the synthesis of highly viscous, double-stranded DNA

(17). Sinsheimer has isolated from the tiny ϕX174 virus a DNA which appears to be single-stranded (18). Like heated DNA, it has proved to be an excellent primer (17) and a useful material in current studies (19) for demonstrating in density-gradient sedimentations its progressive conversion to a double-stranded condition during the course of enzymatic synthesis.

While a detailed discussion of the physical aspects of replication is not feasible in this article, it should be mentioned that the DNA in the single-stranded condition is not only a suitable primer but is the only active form when the most purified enzyme preparations are used. With such preparations of *E. coli*, the native, double-stranded DNA is inert unless it is heated or pretreated very slightly with deoxyribonuclease. Bollum has made similar observations with the enzyme that he has purified from calf thymus (20).

Substitution of Analogs

The second line of evidence is derived from studies of the activity of the substrates when substitutions are made in the purine and pyrimidine bases. From the many interesting reports on the incorporation of bromouracil (21), azaguanine (22), and other analogs into bacterial and viral DNA, it might be surmised that some latitude in the structure of the bases can be tolerated provided there is no interference with their hydrogen bondings. When experiments were carried out with deoxyuridine triphosphate or 5-bromodeoxyuridine triphosphate, it was found that these compounds supported DNA synthesis when used in place of thymidine triphosphate but not when substituted for the triphosphates of deoxyadenosine, deoxyguanosine, or deoxycytidine. As already described (23), 5-methyl- and 5-bromocytosine specifically replaced cytosine; hypoxanthine substituted only for guanine; and, as just mentioned, uracil and 5-bromo-uracil specifically replaced thymine. These findings are best interpreted on the basis of hydrogen bonding of the adenine-thymine and guanine-cytosine type.

Along these lines it is relevant to mention the existence of a naturally occurring "analog" of cytosine, hydroxymethyl cytosine (HMC), which is found in place of cytosine in the DNA of the *E. coli* bacteriophages of the T-even series (24). In this case the DNA contains equivalent amounts of HMC and guanine and, as usual, equivalent amounts of adenine and thymine. Of additional interest is the fact that the DNA's of T2, T4, and T6 bacteriophages contain glucose linked to the hydroxymethyl groups of the HMC in characteristic ratios (25, 26), although it is clear that in T2 and T6 some of the HMC groups contain no glucose (26).

These characteristics have posed two problems regarding the synthesis of these DNA's which might appear to be incompatible with the simple base-pairing hypothesis. First, what mechanism is there for preventing the inclusion of cytosine in a cell which under normal conditions has deoxycytidine triphosphate and incorporates it into its DNA? Second, how does one conceive of the origin of the constant ratios of glucose to HMC in DNA if the incorporation occurs via glucosylated and nonglucosylated HMC nucleotides? Our recent experiments have shown that the polymerase reaction in the virus-infected cell is governed by the usual hydrogen-bonding restrictions but with the auxiliary action of several new enzymes developed specifically in response to infection with a given virus (27, 28). Among the new enzymes is one which splits deoxycytidine triphosphate and thus removes it from the sites of polymerase action (28). Another is a type of glucosylating enzyme that transfers glucose from uridine diphosphate glucose directly and specifically to certain HMC residues in the DNA (28).

Chemical Composition

The third line of evidence is supplied by an analysis of the purine and pyrimidine base composition of the enzymatically synthesized DNA. We may ask two questions. First, will the product have the equivalence of adenine to thymine and of guanine to cytosine that characterize natural DNA? Second, will the composition of the natural DNA used as primer influence and determine the composition of the product? In Table 1 are the results which answer these

Table 1. Chemical composition of enzymatically synthesized DNA, synthesized with different primers. A, adenine; T, thymine; G, guanine; C, cytosine.

DNA	A	T	G	C	$\dfrac{A+G}{T+C}$	$\dfrac{A+T}{G+C}$
Mycobacterium phlei						
Primer	0.65	0.66	1.35	1.34	1.01	0.49
Product	0.66	0.65	1.34	1.37	0.99	0.48
Escherichia coli						
Primer	1.00	0.97	0.98	1.05	0.98	0.97
Product	1.04	1.00	0.97	0.98	1.01	1.02
Calf thymus						
Primer	1.14	1.05	0.90	0.85	1.05	1.25
Product	1.12	1.08	0.85	0.85	1.02	1.29
Bacteriophage T2						
Primer	1.31	1.32	0.67	0.70	0.98	1.92
Product	1.33	1.29	0.69	0.70	1.02	1.90
A-T copolymer	1.99	1.93	<0.05	<0.05	1.03	>40

two questions (29). The experiments are identical except that in each case a different DNA primer was used: *Mycobacterium phlei, Escherichia coli,* calf thymus, and phage T2 DNA, respectively.

In answer to the first question, it is clear that in the enzymatically synthesized DNA, adenine equals thymine and guanine equals cytosine, so the purine content is in every case identical to the pyrimidine. In answer to the second question, it is again apparent that the characteristic ratio of adenine-thymine pairs to guanine-cytosine pairs of a given DNA primer is imposed rather faithfully on the product that is synthesized. Whether the net DNA increase in only 1 per cent, as measured with isotopic tracers, or 1000 per cent, the results are the same.

It can be said further that it has not been possible to distort these base ratios by using widely differing molar concentrations of substrates or by any other means. In the last line of Table 1 is a rather novel "DNA" which is synthesized under conditions that I will not describe here (17, 30). Suffice it to say that after very long lag periods, a copolymer of deoxyadenylate and thymidylate (A-T) develops which has the physical size and properties of natural DNA and in which the adenine and thymine are in a perfectly alternating sequence. When this rare form of DNA-like polymer is used as a primer, new A-T polymer synthesis starts immediately, and even though all four triphosphates are present, no trace of guanine or cytosine can be detected in the product. The conclusion thus seems inescapable that the base composition is replicated in the enzymatic synthesis and that hydrogen-bonding of adenine to thymine and of guanine to cytosine is the guiding mechanism.

Enzymatic Replication of Nucleotide Sequences

The fourth line of evidence which I should like to cite is drawn from current studies of base sequences in DNA and their replication. As I have suggested already, we believe that DNA is the genetic code; the four kinds of nucleotides make up a four-letter alphabet, and their sequence spells out the message. At present we do not know the sequence; what Sanger has done for peptide sequence in protein remains to be done for nucleic acids. The problem is more difficult, but not insoluble.

Our present attempts at determining the nucleotide sequences (31) will be described in detail elsewhere, and I will only summarize them here. Deoxyribonucleic acid is enzymatically synthesized, with phosphorus-32 as label, in one of the deoxynucleoside triphosphates; the other three substrates are unlabeled. This radioactive phosphorus, attached to the 5-carbon of the deoxyribose, now becomes the bridge between that substrate molecule and the nucleotide at the growing end of the chain with which it has reacted (Fig. 8). At the end of the synthetic reaction (after some 10^{16} diester bonds have been formed), the DNA is isolated and digested enzymatically to yield the 3'-deoxynucleotides quantitatively. It is apparent (Fig. 8) that the phosphorus atom formerly attached to the 5-carbon of the deoxynucleoside triphosphate substrate is now attached to the 3-carbon of the nucleotide with which it reacted during the course of synthesis of the DNA chains. The phosphorus-32 content of each of the 3'-deoxynucleotides, isolated by paper electrophoresis, is a measure of the relative frequency with which a particular substrate reacted with each of the four available nucleotides in the course of synthesis of the DNA chains. This procedure, when carried out four times with a different labeled substrate in each case, yields the relative frequencies of all the 16 possible kinds of dinucleotide (nearest neighbor) sequences.

Such studies have, to date, been carried out with DNA primer samples from six different natural sources. The conclusions are as follows: (i) All 16 possible dinucleotide sequences are found in each case; (ii) the pattern of relative frequencies of the sequences is unique and reproducible in each case and is not predicted from the base composition of the DNA; (iii) enzymatic replication involves base pairing of adenine to thymine and of guanine to cytosine; and, most significantly (iv) the frequencies also indicate clearly that the enzymatic replication produces two strands of opposite direction, as predicted by the Watson and Crick model.

These studies and anticipated extensions of them should yield the dinucleotide frequencies of any DNA sample which can serve as an effective primer for enzymatic replication and thus provide some clues for deciphering the DNA code. Unfortunately, this method does not provide information about trinucleotide frequencies, but we are hopeful that, with the improvement of enzymatic tools for analysis and chromatographic techniques for isolation, some start can be made in this direction.

Requirement for Four Triphosphates and DNA for DNA Synthesis

Returning to the earlier-stated requirement for all four deoxynucleoside triphosphates and DNA for DNA synthesis, we can now regard and understand this requirement as another and final line of evidence for hydrogen bonding. Without added DNA there is no template for hydrogen bonding, and without all four triphosphates, synthesis stops early and abruptly for lack of a hydrogen-bonding mate for one of the bases in the template.

SUMMARY

I have sketched the enzymatic approaches to the problem of DNA replication and the properties of the DNA-synthesizing enzyme purified from *Escherichia coli*. The unifying and basic generalization about the action of this enzyme is that it catalyzes the synthesis of a new DNA chain in response to directions from a DNA template; these directions are dictated by the hydrogen-bonding relationship of adenine to thymine and of guanine to cytosine. The experimental basis for this conclusion is derived from the observations of: (i) the double-stranded character of the enzymatically synthesized DNA and its origin from a single-stranded molecule, (ii) the pattern of substitution of analogs for the naturally occurring bases, (iii) the replication of the chemical composition, (iv) the replication of the nucleotide (nearest neighbor) sequences and the antiparallel direction of the strands, and (v) the requirement for all four deoxynucleoside triphosphates (adenine, thymine, guanine, and cytosine) and for DNA for DNA synthesis (32).

REFERENCES

1. Avery, O. T., C. M. MacLeod, and M. McCarty (1944), *J. Exp. Med.*, 79:137; R. D. Hotchkiss, in *The Chemical Basis of Heredity*, W. D. McElroy and B. Glass, eds., Johns Hopkins Press, Baltimore (1957), p. 321.
2. Hershey, A. D. (1953), *Cold Spring Harbor Symposia Quant. Biol.*, 18:135.
3. Beadle, G. W., in *The Chemical Basis of Heredity*, W. D. McElroy and B. Glass, eds., Johns Hopkins Press, Baltimore, 1957, p. 3.
4. Chargaff, E., in *Nucleic Acids*, E. Chargaff and J. N. Davidson, eds., Academic Press, Inc., New York (1955), vol. 1, pp. 307-371.
5. Watson, J. D., and F. H. C. Crick (1953), *Nature*, 171:737; (1953), *Cold Spring Harbor Symposia Quant. Biol.*, 18:123.
6. Wilkins, M. H. F. (1957), *Biochem. Soc. Symposia (Cambridge, Engl.)*, 14:13.
7. Feughelman, M., R. Langridge, W. E. Seeds, A. R. Stokes, H. R. Wilson, C. W. Hooper, M. H. F. Wilkins, R. K. Barclay, and L. D. Hamilton (1955), *Nature*, 175:834.
8. Kornberg, A., in *The Chemical Basis of Heredity*, W. D. McElroy and B. Glass, eds., Johns Hopkins Press, Baltimore, 1957, p. 579; (1959), *Revs. Modern Phys.*, 31:200.
9. —— in *Phosphorus Metabolism*, W. D. McElroy and B. Glass, eds., Johns Hopkins Press, Baltimore (1951), p. 392; (1957), *Advances in Enzymol.*, 18:191.
10. Koshland, D. E., Jr., in *The Mechanism of Enzyme Action*, W. D. McElroy and B. Glass, eds., Johns Hopkins Press, Baltimore (1954), p. 608.
11. Kornberg, A., I. R. Lehman, and E. S. Simms (1956), *Federation Proc.*, 15:291; A. Kornberg (1957-58), *Harvey Lecture Ser.*, 53:83.
12. Lehman, I. R., M. J. Bessman, E. S. Simms, A. Kornberg (1958), *J. Biol. Chem.*, 233:163.
13. Bollum, F. J., and V. R. Potter (1957), *J. Am. Chem. Soc.*, 79:3603; C. G. Harford and A. Kornberg (1958), *Federation Proc.*, 17:515; F. J. Bollum (1958), *ibid.*, 17:193; —— (1959), *ibid.*, 18:194.

14. Bessman, M. J., I. R. Lehman, E. S. Simms, and A. Kornberg (1958), *J. Biol. Chem.*, 233:171.
15. Adler, J., I. R. Lehman, M. J. Bessman, E. S. Simms, and A. Kornberg (1958), *Proc. Natl. Acad. Sci. U.S.*, 44:641.
16. Schachman, H. K., I. R. Lehman, M. J. Bessman, J. Adler, E. S. Simms, and A. Kornberg (1958), *Federation Proc.*, 17:304.
17. Lehman, I. R. (1959), *Ann. N.Y. Acad. Sci.*, 81:745.
18. Sinsheimer, R. L. (1959), *J. Mol. Biol.*, 1:43.
19. Lehman, I. R., R. L. Sinsheimer, and A. Kornberg, unpublished observations.
20. Bollum, F. J. (1959), *J. Biol. Chem.*, 234:2733.
21. Weygand, F., A. Wacker, and H. Dellweg (1952), *Z. Naturforsch.*, 7b:19; D. B. Dunn and J. D. Smith (1954), *Nature*, 174:305; S. Zamenhof and G. Griboff (1954), *ibid.*, 174:306.
22. Heinrich, M. R., V. C. Dewey, R. E. Parks, Jr., and G. W. Kidder (1952), *J. Biol. Chem.*, 197:199.
23. Bessman, M. J., I. R. Lehman, J. Adler, S. B. Zimmerman, E. S. Simms, and A. Kornberg (1958), *Proc. Natl. Acad. Sci. U.S.*, 44:633.
24. Wyatt, G. R., and S. S. Cohen (1953), *Biochem J.*, 55:774.
25. Sinsheimer, R. L. (1954), *Science*, 120:551; E. Volkin (1954), *J. Am. Chem. Soc.*, 76:5892; G. Streisinger and J. Weigle (1956), *Proc. Natl. Acad. Sci. U.S.*, 42:504.
26. —— (1956), *Proc. Natl. Acad. Sci. U.S.*, 42:502; M. A. Jesaitis (1957), *J. Exp. Med.*, 106:233; (1958), *Federation Proc.*, 17:250.
27. Flaks, J. G., and S. S. Cohen (1959), *J. Biol. Chem.*, 234:1501; J. G. Flaks, J. Lichtenstein, and S. S. Cohen (1959), *ibid.*, 234:1507.
28. Kornberg, A., S. B. Zimmerman, S. R. Kornberg, and J. Josse (1959), *Proc. Natl. Acad. Sci. U.S.*, 45:772.
29. Lehman, I. R., S. B. Zimmerman, J. Adler, M. J. Bessman, E. S. Simms, and A. Kornberg (1958), *ibid.*, 44:1191.
30. Schachman, H. K., J. Adler, C. M. Radding, J. K. Lehman, and A. Kornberg (1960), *J. Biol. Chem.*, 235:3242.
31. Josse, J., A. D. Kaiser, and A Kornberg (1961), *J. Biol. Chem.*, 236:864.
32. Any credit for the work cited here is shared by my colleagues in New York, Bethesda, St. Louis, and Stanford, and by the whole international community of chemists, geneticists, and physiologists, which is truly responsible for the progress in nucleic acid biochemistry.

Chapter Ten

Soluble Ribonucleic Acid and Protein Synthesis*

PAUL C. ZAMECNIK

*From the John Collins Warren Laboratories
of the Huntington Memorial Hospital of Harvard University, at the Massachusetts General Hospital, Boston, Massachusetts.*

It has become a main objective in biochemistry today to try to discover the steps by which the message inherent in the sequence of bases in deoxyribonucleic acid becomes translated into the sequence of amino acids which determine the specificity of function of proteins in the cell. At two points in the synthesis of a protein molecule, ribonucleic acid (RNA) has been found to be directly involved — first in esterification of activated amino acids to the soluble RNA (S-RNA) or transfer RNA, and secondly in the ribosomes of the cell, the site at which amino acids line up in proper order prior to formation of a long peptide chain. In this progression from free amino acid to completed protein, a key step is the esterification of an activated amino acid to a particular S-RNA molecule. Lack of competition of amino acids for attachment to this S-RNA fraction, the specificity of activating enzymes in catalyzing this esterification, and partial separations of S-RNA into fractions with enhanced abilities to accept individual amino acids — all suggest that separate S-RNA molecules exist, each coded for a specific amino acid. It has been our aim, during the past year, to devise procedures whereby a species of S-RNA molecule with a single amino acid attached may be separated from the bulk of the other S-RNA molecules. Were this goal to be accomplished, it would then become practicable to try to determine the sequence of bases in a particular S-RNA molecule. Such a sequence may be called the "translation signature" of an amino acid. The goal of complete isolation of a single amino acyl S-RNA molecule has also attracted much attention from other investigators recently. Efforts to achieve separations have been based on the use of

*This is publication No. 1011 of the Cancer Commission of Harvard University. The work described herein was supported by grants from the National Institutes of Health, the United States Atomic Energy Commission, and the American Cancer Society.

resin columns (Smith et al., 1959), countercurrent distribution
(Holley and Merrill, 1959), electrophoresis (Lipmann et al., 1959),
and removal of tyrosine-RNA by attachment to a diazotized resin
(Brown et al., 1959).

It has become clear that successful fractionation of S-RNA will
depend upon the availability of a ready source of this material. For
a year or two in our laboratory we had used RNA from yeast (Hecht
et al., 1959) for amino acid labeling experiments. When Roger
Monier arrived from Paris in 1958 for a year's stay, he undertook
to fractionate this RNA in order to free it from what we thought
would be a heavy contamination of yeast ribosomal RNA. Surprisingly,
it turned out that the direct phenol extraction procedure which we had
employed on live baker's yeast preferentially extracted the small-
molecular-weight RNA of the yeast (molecular weight 25,000 to 30,000)
(Monier et al., 1960), and left behind the microsomal RNA. The
sedimentation constant, chromatographic behavior on DEAE-cellu-
lose columns, base composition, and the valine and adenylate accepting functions of this RNA obtained by direct phenol extraction
were indistinguishable from those of yeast S-RNA obtained by the
more laborious grinding, centrifugation technique. The rare base
content (i.e., uracil-5-ribosyl phosphate, thymine ribotide, and 6-
methylaminopurine ribotide) of this RNA was also the same as that
of S-RNA and very much greater than that of yeast ribosomal RNA.
In addition, this directly extracted RNA could be labeled with C^{14}-
valine and with C^{14}-ATP somewhat better than could the S-RNA obtained by rupture of cells and differential centrifugation prior to
exposure to phenol (Monier et al., 1960).

Our own approach to the problem of fractionating S-RNA depends
upon the observation that an amino acid esterified to the 3' or 2'
hydroxyl position of the terminal ribose moiety of the S-RNA molecule blocks the periodate reaction which, in the absence of esterified
amino acid, can oxidize the terminal ribose to the dialdehyde. This
dialdehyde in turn can be used as a site of attachment of a histochemical dye, which so alters the solubility of the RNA that it can
then be separated from the RNA which has an amino acid attached
(Zamecnik et al., 1960; Zamecnik and Stephenson, 1960).

The sequence of reactions involved is illustrated in Fig. 1. Our
objective is to refine this procedure, which presently shows some
promise, and to carry out nucleotide sequence determinations on a
particular purified S-RNA molecule when sufficient purification has
been achieved. Thus far we have approximately a twelvefold enrichment of specific activity for valine-RNA and a ninefold enrichment
for leucine-RNA. On the assumption that valine-acceptor RNA may
comprise a twentieth of the total amino acid acceptor RNA, a further

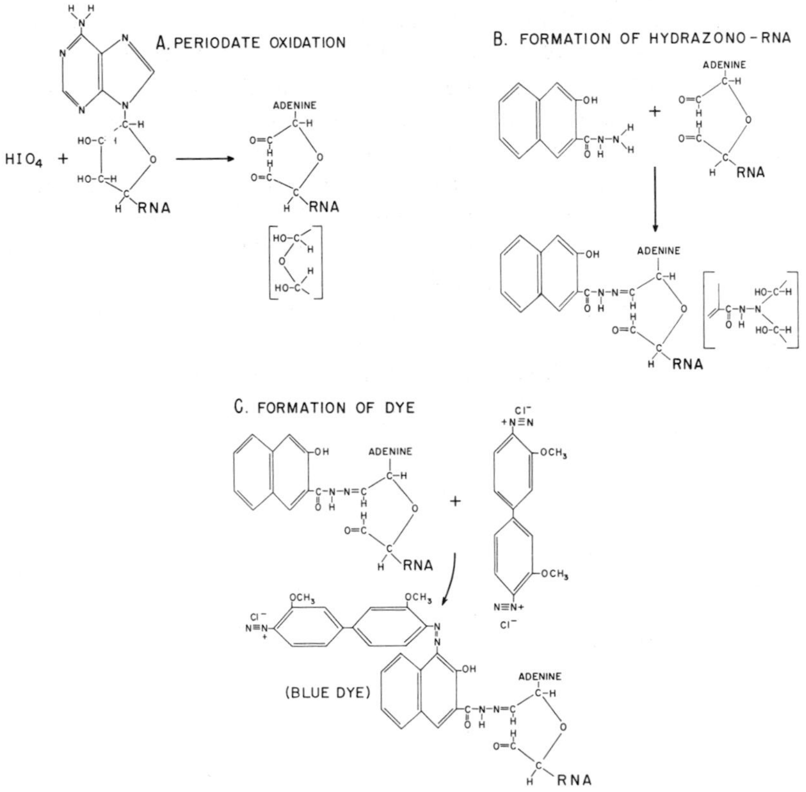

FIG. 1. Steps in formation of dye-bound RNA.

purification of the order of at least twofold would be needed to get a pure valine-RNA. This simplified assumption may of course be far from the truth, since all the S-RNA may not accept amino acids.

We have also carried out exploratory efforts to attach a dye molecule to a particular amino acyl RNA. This type of procedure is the reverse of the one outlined above, with the objective of pulling out a single amino-acyl RNA species from the mass of non-dye-bound RNA molecules. For this purpose we have tried S^{35}-cysteine-RNA, and dihydroxy-dinaphthyl-disulfide. According to Barrnett and Seligman (1952), this latter reagent may be used for the histochemical identification of protein-SH groups by combining with the protein-SH to form one molecule of protein-naphthyl disulfide and one of free naphthyl mercaptan, in a sulfide exchange reaction. Tetrazotized o-dianisidine then combines with the naphthyl moiety of the protein-naphthyl disulfide to form a blue azo dye. Theoretically, this method should offer promise as a way of distinguishing cysteine-

RNA from the family of S-RNAs, with the histochemical dye attaching to the sulfhydryl group of the cysteine. We have, however, encountered practical difficulties with this procedure due to the tendency of the SH-group of cysteine to bind nonspecifically with both protein and RNA. The azo-dye-hydrazono-RNA procedure has therefore been a more useful one for purification of aminoacyl-RNA.

At the present time our objectives are to scale up the direct phenol extraction procedure of yeast S-RNA to the gram quantity level, to adapt the azo-dye-hydrazono-RNA procedure to this level of S-RNA separation, and to work out a plan for sequential degradation of the nucleotides in a purified aminoacyl-RNA.

Toward this latter goal, we have devised a hydrolytic procedure, the key to which goes back to an observation of Barry and Mitchell (1953) that when cyclohexylamine is added to an aqueous solution of periodate-oxidized starch, the double Schiff base of glyoxal sepa-

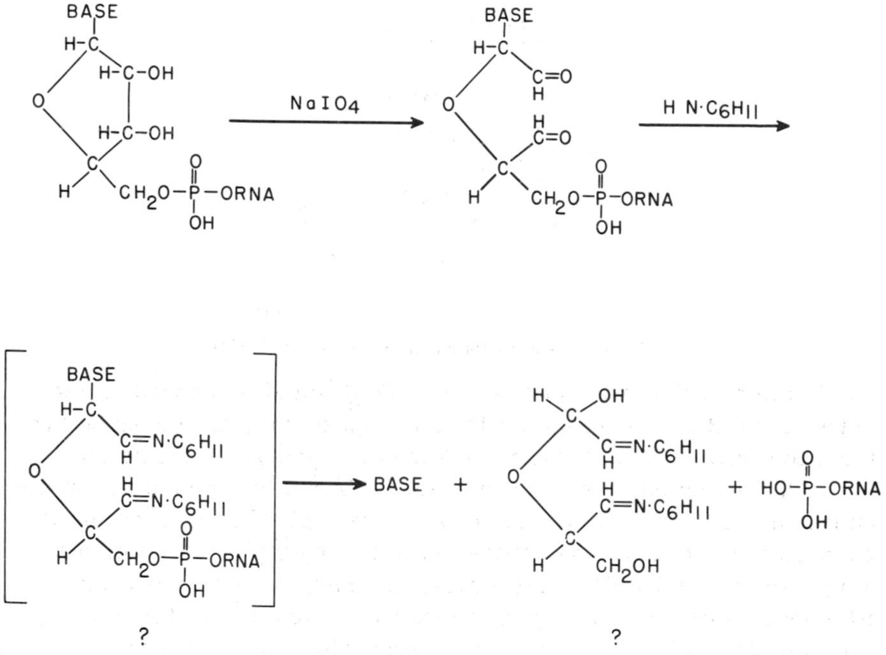

FIG. 2. Steps in cyclohexylamine degradation of RNA.

rates. Hakomori (1959) suggests in a brief abstract that this may serve as the basis for a sequential degradation of RNA.

We have found, however, (Yu and Zamecnik, 1960) that while addition of cyclohexylamine to periodate-oxidized S-RNA results in release of the terminal base, further degradation cannot be achieved by a second addition of periodate and cyclohexylamine, at least under the conditions we have used. The degradative sequence can be repeated though, if phosphomonoesterase is added prior to the second treatment with periodate and cyclohexylamine. The possible sequence of steps is illustrated in Fig. 2. Sequential degradation has been carried out in a qualitative way as far as four nucleotide residues in from the end of an S-RNA preparation.

There is some reason to hope that studies in other laboratories and those mentioned above will in time provide us with information on how a soluble RNA molecule can be coded to a particular amino acid. The answer to this question would furnish a key piece in the puzzle as to how genetic information stored in the nucleotide sequence of the gene manifests itself in the metabolism of the cell.

The author wishes to express his indebtedness to his colleagues, Drs. Mary Stephenson, Jesse Scott, and Robert Loftfield for helpful advice and criticism.

REFERENCES

Barrnett, R. J., and A. M. Seligman (1952), Demonstration of protein-bound sulfhydral and disulfide groups by two new histochemical methods. *J. Natl. Cancer Inst.*, 13:215-216.

Barry, V. C., and P. W. D. Mitchell (1953), Properties of periodate-oxidized polysaccharide, Part I; The preparation of polymeric substances containing nitrogen from oxidized starches. *J. Chem. Soc.*, pp.3610-3612.

Brown, G. L., A. V. W. Brown, and J. Gordon (1959), DNA mediation in protein synthesis, *Brookhaven Symposia Biol.*, 12; Structure and function of genetic elements. *Brookhaven Natl. Lab. Symposium*, June 1-3, pp. 47-62.

Hakomori, S. (1959), Determination of the bases of terminal nucleotide and of their sequence in the molecule of ribonucleic acid. *Symposium on Nucleic Acids*, Kyoto, Japan, pp. 16-17.

Hoshi, Li Ti, M. L. Stephenson, and P. C. Zamecnik (1959), Binding of amino acids to the end group of a soluble ribonucleic acid. *Proc. Natl. Acad. Sci. U.S.*, 45: 505-518.

Holley, R. W., and S. H. Merrill (1959), Countercurrent distribution of an active ribonucleic acid. *J. Am. Chem. Soc.*, 81:753.

Lipmann, F., W. C. Hülsmann, G. Hartmann, H. G. Boman, and G. Acs (1959), Amino acid activation and protein synthesis. *J. Cell. and Comp. Physiol.*, Suppl. 1, 54:75-88.

Monier, R., M. L. Stephenson, and P. C. Zamecnik (1960), The preparation and some properties of a low molecular weight ribonucleic acid from baker's yeast. *Biochim. Biophys. Acta* (in press).

Smith, K. C., E. Cordes, and R. S. Schweet (1959), Fractionation of transfer ribonucleic acid, *Biochim. Biophys. Acta,* 33:286-287.

Yu, C-T., and P. C. Zamecnik (1960), A hydrolytic procedure for ribonucleosides and
its possible application to the sequential degradation of RNA. *Biochim. Biophys.
Acta,* 45:148.

Zamecnik, P. C., and M. L. Stephenson (1960), Partial purification of transfer RNA.
Ann. N.Y. Acad. Sci. 88:708.

——, ——, and J. F. Scott (1960), Partial purification of soluble RNA. *Proc. Natl.
Acad. Sci. U.S.,* 46:811-822.

Chapter Eleven

Aspects of Genetic and Metabolic Control of Protein Synthesis

ARTHUR B. PARDEE
*Associate Professor of Biochemistry and
Virology, University of California at Berkeley*

The Quantitative Problem of Enzyme Synthesis

Some enzyme activities are found in large amounts and some in small in living creatures. This fact immediately raises two sorts of questions. First, since growth and function require the harmonious operation of the multitude of reactions catalyzed by these enzymes, one would expect the enzymes to be present in amounts which in some way correspond to the need for them. So we can ask how well the amounts of individual enzymes fit the needs of the organism. We will not dwell on this question here, but will proceed to a second question: What chemical and genetic mechanisms regulate the amounts of the individual enzymes? It is worth noting that this problem of enzyme formation conveniently permits us to ask two such dissimilar questions—one about the physiological needs of the cell and the other about its regulatory machinery. Studies of enzyme formation would seem to provide a bridge across the borderlines of cell chemistry and biology.

The problem of interest in this article will be how cells regulate their rates of enzyme formation. A number of observations made in the past few years permit us to outline in a general way the modes of regulation whereby enzyme balances are maintained. Some of the components of the enzyme-forming apparatus have been identified, and a number of specific stimulatory or inhibitory effects of small molecules on the production of enzymes have been described. Our task is to examine present information regarding the components of the system and their interactions.

Parts of the Cell Involved in Enzyme Formation

Components of the cell that are important for the synthesis of proteins are necessarily important in the synthesis of enzymes, since all known enzymes are largely protein in composition. Many of the processes of protein synthesis appear to be the same for all proteins, therefore their study cannot inform us about the specificity of enzyme synthesis. The initial steps of conversion of nutrients to amino acids, and the activation of the latter and their transfer to soluble RNA—those steps so beautifully worked out in recent years (see recent issues of *Annual Review of Biochemistry*) are of this sort, and will merely be indicated in Fig. 1, which shows parts of the enzyme-synthesizing apparatus.

When the amino acids are assembled to form a protein, presumably on some large molecular-weight "template," possibilities for regulation of synthesis exist. Some evidence has been obtained recently that these templates are ribonucleoproteins, recently named ribosomes (Schweet, 1959; McQuillan, 1960). If each ribosome is specific for the synthesis of an individual enzyme, any factor that interferes with a specific ribosome's function should alter the rate of synthesis of the corresponding enzyme. If the above is true, the ribosomes would be promising sites for specific action of agents that regulate enzyme synthesis.

Another component of the cell which plays a role in specific enzyme synthesis is genetic material. We recall the now well-accepted one gene-one enzyme hypothesis which can be stated, for our purpose, as meaning that a given enzyme can be produced only when the appropriate gene or genes are present. Certain genes can control synthesis of specific enzymes in an all-or-none way; further evidence for the association of genes with enzyme synthesis will be provided below. There is little to indicate at what point in the process of enzyme formation the gene exerts its influence. The most popular view is that genes control the synthesis of corresponding ribosomes; therefore they are shown as guiding ribosome formation (Fig. 1).

Genes alone cannot fix the rate of enzyme synthesis; such a mechanism could not fit the varying needs of the cell under changing conditions. Other compounds might interact with genes so as to make the latter temporarily more or less active; these responses might be associated with the nutritional needs of the cell. One of the major points to be made in this article is that the factors which function in regulation of enzyme synthesis might act on the genes themselves.

The data to be discussed here refer to the bacterium *Escherichia coli*. Of course there must be regulatory mechanisms for all organisms. Most of the experiments on

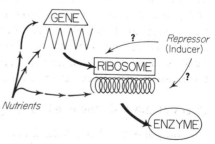

FIG. 1. Parts of the enzyme-synthesizing apparatus.

regulation of enzyme synthesis have been performed with *E. coli*, but experiments on regulation should be carried out with other organisms as well.

Induction and Repression

We will now discuss briefly some instances in which altered nutritional conditions cause very large changes in the amounts of enzymes. These examples serve to show us that the amounts of enzymes are not fixed by the genetic composition of the organism alone, but that small molecules must have an extremely important function in the regulation of enzyme synthesis.

Enzyme induction (or adaptation) has been known for many years and has recently been studied intensively at the nutritional level (for a review, see Pollock, 1959). Induction refers to the great increase in the rate of synthesis of an enzyme when a low-molecular-weight compound, usually a substrate of the enzyme, is added to the growing cells. An illustration is seen in Fig. 2, in which the addition of tryptophan to *E. coli* results in a rapid, almost instantaneous synthesis of tryptophanase (Pardee, 1960b). An example of specificity of enzyme induction is shown in Table 1. Here supplementing the medium of *E. coli* with DL-serine caused a two-hundredfold increase in specific activity of D-serine deaminase in 90 min; but during this time L-serine deaminase increased only fourfold, and L-threonine deaminase did not change appreciably (Pardee, 1955).

Inducers can be produced through metabolic sequences as well as being provided directly as nutrients. This is shown by the well-

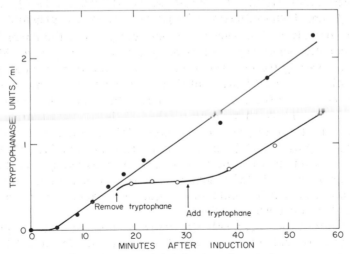

FIG. 2. Induction and deinduction of tryptophanase.

TABLE 1

Induction of Deaminases

Additions	Deaminase Activity		
Compound	D-Serine	L-Serine	L-Threonine
None	0.08	0.7	4.6
DL-Serine	16.6	2.9	3.9
L-Leucine + Glycine	0.26	4.6	3.0

The bacteria were grown on a synthetic medium containing glycerol as a carbon source. Ninety minutes before the enzyme assays, the indicated compounds were added. Enzyme activities are given as $m\mu$ moles keto acid produced per min per 0.2 ml of culture.

known sequential inductions (Stanier, 1951), in which enzymes are induced by compounds formed through the action of a series of inducible enzymes on the nutrient. Results of this sort suggested that perhaps all enzymes are under the control of intracellular metabolites (Pollock, 1953; Cohn, 1953). Such inductions by normal metabolites would be difficult to observe because most intracellular metabolites cannot be varied readily in concentration without considerable alterations of over-all metabolism and growth.

Repression is the specific inhibition of enzyme formation by low-molecular-weight metabolites. It seems at present more significant for the regulation of formation of biosynthetic enzymes than does induction by normal intracellular metabolites. Examples of repression were described almost simultaneously for enzymes of valine (Adelberg, 1953), methionine (Wijesundera, 1953; Cohn, 1953), and tryptophan (Cohn, 1953) synthesis. The product of each repressible reaction reduced formation of an enzyme considerably below the normal level. More recently, some repressible enzymes have been found which respond to lowering the concentration of a metabolite by reaching very high levels. A second feature of these observations is that the repressor is formed from the end product of the metabolic pathway, rather than being the immediate product of the enzyme action. The main examples are arginine repression of the synthesis of acetyl-ornithinase (Vogel, 1957) and ornithine transcarbamylase (Gorini, 1957), and uracil repression of aspartate transcarbamylase (Yates, 1957) formation. It is the feedback feature of repression which gives it a special interest for metabolic regulation: excess of an end product shuts off a whole pathway.

We will take as an example the repression of the first enzyme of the biosynthetic pathway of pyrimidine synthesis. The specific activity of this enzyme, aspartate transcarbamylase (and of the next two enzymes of the pathway), is low when a uracil-requiring mutant of

E. coli is grown on excess uracil. But the enzyme concentration rises rapidly when the uracil is removed and the bacteria are suspended in fresh uracil-free medium. Addition of uracil to this medium rapidly stops enzyme synthesis. By choosing a low uracil concentration in which the bacteria can grow slowly but where repression is weak, the enzyme concentration can be made to increase a thousandfold and eventually reaches about 7 per cent of the total cell protein (Shepherdson, 1960).

The increases of enzyme activity brought about in these examples of induction and derepression represent de novo synthesis from amino acids and not merely activation phenomena, at least in the investigated cases [induced β-galactosidase (Rotman, 1954, Hogness, 1955) and penicillinase (Pollock, 1958), and repressible aspartate transcarbamylase (Yates, 1957)].

Constitutivity and the Relation between Induction and Repression

As seen in the preceding section, small molecules are important in determining the rates of enzyme synthesis. Where and how do they fit into the scheme of Fig. 1? Induction and repression are at first sight similar phenomena. Recent results show that this similarity is more than superficial: repressors block enzyme formation by combining with a specific site in the cell, and inducers reverse the effect of repressors by competing for this site (Pardee, 1959b).

The clue to this problem came from studies of constitutive bacteria which form an enzyme at a rate virtually independent of the presence of inducers or repressors. *E. coli* in the wild type is inducible for β-galactosidase and carries the gene i^+. It can be converted to the constitutive (i^-) form by a single-step mutation.

Another genetic difference is important for the work to be described. The wild-type bacteria are able to form β-galactosidase and contain the z^+ allele of the gene which controls the structure of this enzyme (Perrin, 1959). Mutants with the z^- allele do not make the active form of the enzyme. Organisms can be obtained with any combination of these alleles, i.e., z^+i^+, z^-i^+, z^+i^-, and z^-i^-.

Genetic material from two bacteria can be brought together into one cell by the process of bacterial conjugation. A donor strain, designated as *Hfr*, transfers part of its chromosome into a receptor (F^-) cell (see Wollman and Jacob, 1959, for a summary). The transfer is through a narrow connection of cell material which can be seen in the electron microscope (Anderson, 1957). When the genes from a bacterium that can be induced to make active β-galactosidase (z^+i^+) are transferred into a bacterium that is constitutive but cannot make the active enzyme (z^-i^-), the z^+ and i^+ genes both enter the receptor cell at about 18 minutes, in the experiment shown

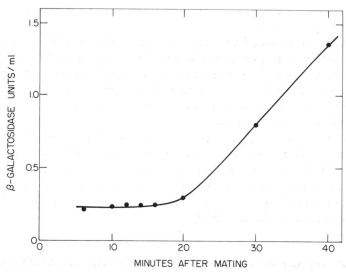

FIG. 3. Kinetics of β-galactosidase synthesis by mated bacteria.

(Fig. 3), and almost immediately thereafter β-galactosidase appears.
No inducer is required for enzyme formation (Riley, 1960). But injection of the i^- allele into a z^+i^+ bacterium, in the converse experiment, does not result in constitutive enzyme production. Therefore
the cytoplasms of donor and receptor cannot have mixed during
mating. The cytoplasm of the receptor cell must determine initially
whether the enzyme is produced inducibly or constitutively (Pardee,
1959b).

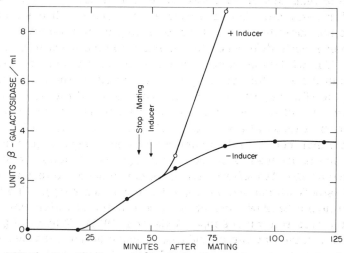

FIG. 4. Constitutive and induced β-galactosidase formation by a
mated deletion mutant.

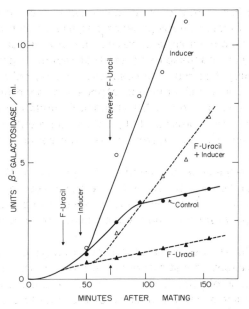

FIG. 5. Effect of F-uracil on β-galactosidase formation by mated bacteria.

The most important point for the present argument is that the mated bacteria into which the z^+i^+ genes have been injected soon become inducible; that is, they soon require an inducer in order to continue forming the enzyme (see Figs. 5 and 6 on pages 271, 274). It is believed that the i^+ gene functions by making a repressor that stops synthesis of the β-galactosidase (Pardee, 1959b).

Independent evidence that the inducible form of the gene is the active or dominant one has been obtained from a different sort of experiment (Pardee, 1960b). A mutant (W3787) of wild-type *E. coli* (z^+i^+) which behaved as if the z^+ gene had been deleted (i.e., the mutant was z^- and did not form recombinants with numerous other z^- bacteria) was obtained from the laboratory of Dr. J. Lederberg. When an organism of this genetic type was used as a receptor of the z^+i^+ genes, constitutive enzyme formation was noted at first (Fig. 4 on p. 270). Therefore the mutant must have been i^- as well as z^-. This result suggests that the i^+ gene was deleted with the adjacent z^+ gene, and one concludes that inactivity of the i gene causes constitutive enzyme formation.

Constitutivity of several enzymes of tryptophan synthesis was gained by a single mutation (Cohen, 1959). As with the β-galactosidase-forming system, repression was dominant over constitutivity. The prevention of enzyme synthesis was attributed to an intracellular repressor in the wild type which was under the control of the mutated gene—one far removed from the genes controlling specificity of enzyme structures. The repressor required tryptophan for its formation; no inducer capable of reversing this effect has been found.

The results just discussed suggest that inducers permit enzyme formation by competing with repressors. So far, only in one system have externally added inducers and repressors been shown to compete. The repression of ornithine transcarbamylase by arginine is reversed by ornithine (Gorini, 1960). How commonly this competition between inducers and repressors occurs remains a question for future study.

Since whole sequences of enzymes of tryptophan (Cohn, 1959, 1960) and histidine synthesis (Ames, 1959) are repressed by a single repressor, it is possible that one inducer, also, can act on a sequence; therefore it is possible that the inducer need not be a substrate of the enzyme.

Since the inducer has the same effect on enzyme synthesis as absence of repressor (constitutive bacteria), and the inducer does not act as a source of specificity to determine the structure of the enzyme, it does not provide a portion of the template around which the protein is molded. Rather it acts to release the enzyme-forming mechanism at some site—the one where the repressor acts.

The Nature of the Repressor

The above results raise the question of the chemical nature of repressors. In nutritional terms the repressor is the compound added to the medium; e.g., tryptophan is the repressor of the enzyme tryptophan-synthase. But constitutive mutants are obtained in which this enzyme cannot be repressed by tryptophan (Cohen, 1959). Similarly a constitutive E. coli mutant has been isolated in which aspartate transcarbamylase is not repressed by uracil (Shepherdson, 1960). The most reasonable explanation is that the added compound is built into a more complex structure which functions as the true repressor. Perhaps the repressor gene (i^+ for β-galactosidase) is involved in conversion of the added compound to the true repressor. Possibly this explains why phenyl-thio-galactoside, which inhibits β-galactosidase formation in inducible cells, does not inhibit production of this enzyme in the constitutive mutants (Herzenberg, 1959): the added compound cannot be converted into a repressor in the mutants.

Some hints as to the chemical nature of the repressor are gained from a study of the conditions which permit the mated cells (discussed above) to be converted from constitutivity to inducibility. This conversion requires about an hour (Fig. 4) and occurs even in presence of inhibitors such as 5-methyl-tryptophan (Pardee, 1959a), chloramphenicol, or 5-F-uracil (Fig. 5) (Pardee, 1960b). The state of repression (inducibility) therefore can develop in bacteria in which β-galactosidase synthesis, and presumably synthesis of other proteins, is strongly inhibited. However, it cannot be stated that the repressor itself is formed in the absence of protein synthesis because the period during which inducibility develops might be required for some process other than the formation of repressor, and the latter could be made within a few minutes after the inhibition is released.

Preliminary data obtained with enzyme synthesis in broken cell preparations suggest the action of a repressor (Nisman, 1960). These preparations, made from constitutive bacteria, are stated to form β-galactosidase. A fraction derived from inducible bacteria inhibited this increase in enzyme activity, whereas a similar fraction from constitutive bacteria did not. The inhibitory activity was not sensitive to ribonuclease, suggesting that the inhibitory substance was not made from RNA. Development of this work will be watched with great interest since it is by approaches such as this that the chemical nature of the repressor is likely to be discovered.

The release and onset of repression are rapid. This suggests that the active repressor is quickly broken down and resynthesized as the concentration of the repressing nutrient changes. If so, isolation of the repressor may not be easy.

The Site of Repressor Action

The site at which the repressor acts is as obscure as the chemical nature of the repressor. Owing to the specificity of the process, one would imagine that the inducer and repressor must combine with a site on a large molecule. Three possibilities come to mind: the enzyme itself, the specific ribosome, and the structural gene.

The inducer does not seem to have to combine with enzyme in the process of enzyme formation. Evidence on this point, based primarily on kinetic and specificity data, is summarized elsewhere (Monod, 1958) and will not be repeated here. The results show that added compounds do not have proportional affinities for the enzyme and activities as inducers. However, since the enzyme affinity data were obtained with disrupted cells and the induction data with intact cells, the evidence is not as direct as might be desired. A more recent piece of data shows that the active enzyme is not essential for induction: mutants incapable of forming β-galactosidase are able to produce proteins immunologically very like the enzyme, presumably inactive forms (Perrin, 1959).

The choice between ribosomes and genes as sites for attachment of the repressor cannot be made with any certainty. The ribosomes are at present the most popular candidates because it is easy to

visualize the repressor as blocking the laying down of amino acids
on the template or preventing the release of the finished enzyme
(Monod, 1958). The rapid release of repression or initiation of induced enzyme synthesis is readily explained on this basis. Alternatively, if the inducer acts on the gene and permits the formation of
specific ribosomes, a lag would be expected before enzyme appears
and while the ribosomes are made. The inducible enzymes β-galac-
tosidase, D-serine deaminase, and tryptophanase (Figs. 2 and 6) actually do not appear at once after addition of the inducer, but only
after a lag of about 4 minutes. This lag cannot be attributed to the
time required for entry of the inducer into the bacteria. It would
very well be long enough for formation of the ribosomes because the
genetic material introduced by bacterial conjugation became fully
functional in a very short time. Therefore, the kinetics of induction
are not easily explained if the ribosomes are sites of inducer action,
and may even favor the alternative gene-inducer model.

Enzyme formation ceases abruptly when inducer is removed from

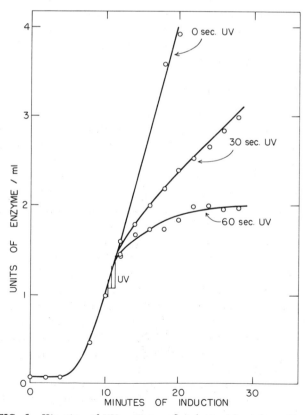

FIG. 6. Kinetics of UV action on β-galactosidase formation.

the culture (Fig. 2) or repressor is added to it. These results are readily explained if the ribosomes carry the sites on which bound repressor stops enzyme formation. The results are not so easily accounted for if the repressor combines with the gene. In this case one would expect the ribosomes made before the repressor and the gene have combined to continue enzyme production, even after new ribosome formation is stopped. But this objection would be invalid if ribosomes could not function unless the genes continually supplied something to them, and the repressor prevented production of this material. The suggestion that the ribosomes themselves are functionally unstable and must be constantly replaced is not a very appealing one because of the often demonstrated chemical stability of ribosomes, and because if the ribosomes had a half-life of only a few minutes, only a small fraction of ribosomes would be active; these would probably be insufficient to account for even one active ribosome for each kind of enzyme.

In spite of these kinetic difficulties there is some evidence to support the idea that genes are the sites with which the repressor combines. Genetic evidence has shown that the repressor acts on a group of enzymes simultaneously in the case of β-galactoside-utilizing (Jacob, 1960) and tryptophan-synthesizing enzymes (Cohen, 1959). A set of four histidine-synthesizing enzymes is repressed in proportion by histidine (Ames, 1959). The authors of the above works have suggested that the repressor combines with a genetic locus to block the whole series of genes from functioning. Genetic evidence also suggests that a special genetic locus (*o*) is the site of attachment of the repressor in the case of β-galactosidase synthesis (Jacob, 1960).

The Requirement of Intact Genes for Enzyme Formation

That the gene is important in enzyme synthesis was shown by the mutational studies that led to the one gene-one enzyme hypothesis. Also the immediate commencement of β-galactosidase synthesis on introduction of the corresponding z^+ gene (Fig. 3) suggests that the gene is closely involved. We can ask then, how directly is the gene involved in enzyme synthesis? Where should it be placed in Fig. 1? We could imagine that the gene is involved only in synthesis of the ribosomes, and once these are formed it is not important: genes might play an indirect role. Or alternatively, genes could continue to have a direct influence on enzyme synthesis, either as templates or by furnishing something to ribosomes, as suggested above.

The problem of the involvement of genes in enzyme synthesis can be approached through the effects of ultraviolet light (UV). Irradiation of bacteria with UV stops enzyme formation. The effect must be quite direct, since enzyme synthesis stops within a very few minutes after irradiation (Fig. 6). Determinations of the action spectrum and dose required for inactivation show that the sensitive unit is nucleic acid of size about 0.5 million molecular weight units (Rushizky, 1960). Therefore, the material affected could be either ribosomal RNA or genetic DNA.

That the UV-sensitive material is in the chromosome is strongly suggested by irradiation experiments on mating bacteria (Pardee, 1960a). Irradiation of the donor bacteria inactivates the ability of these cells to form β-galactosidase. It does not prevent transfer to their genetic material into recipient cells, but the ability of the transferred material to cause enzyme formation in the mated bacteria is damaged. Enzyme formation is inactivated to about the same extent in the unmated, irradiated bacteria as in the intact F^- cells to which the damaged genetic material has been transferred. Furthermore, the log plot of damage of enzyme synthesis versus UV dose is approximately three-hit for induced enzyme formation by the unmated bacteria and only one-hit for these mated bacteria. These results are easily explained by the fact that there are several nuclei in the donor and only one of these is transferred. The most direct conclusion from these data is that UV damages the genetic material, and damage in this material stops enzyme synthesis.

The inactivation of enzyme formation by P^{32} decay also suggests a continuing role of the gene. The decay of P^{32} built into bacterial DNA stops formation of several enzymes (McFall, 1958). The effect

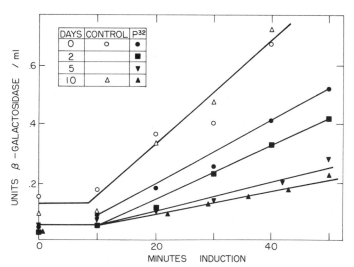

FIG. 7. Damage by P^{32} decay to β-galactosidase formation in mated bacteria.

is attributed to damage to the chromosome, and suggests that chromosomal integrity is essential for enzyme synthesis.

These P^{32}-decay experiments have recently been extended to the formation of β-galactosidase by mated bacteria (Riley, 1960). In effect, by injecting the radioactive z^+ gene into nonradioactive z^- recipient bacteria, allowing P^{32} decay to occur, and subsequently measuring ability of the mated cells to form the enzyme, one can first introduce the z^+ gene and then destroy it. As described earlier, introduction of the gene causes enzyme formation to commence virtually at once (Fig. 3). Destruction of the introduced genetic material by P^{32} decay sharply reduced the ability of the zygotes to form the enzyme (Fig. 7). Even after enzyme formation was well under way, the destruction of DNA by P^{32} decay stopped further enzyme formation. Therefore the specificity for enzyme formation had not been transferred to some new, non-P^{32}-containing material such as stable ribosomes. The enzyme-forming ability of the zygotes was stabilized only after about 100 minutes, when nonradioactive replicas of the DNA were probably formed. These results, like those obtained with UV, suggest that the genetic material must continually have a role in the synthesis of enzymes.

CONCLUDING REMARKS

We can return to Fig. 1 to summarize our thoughts on the problem of regulation of specific enzyme synthesis. The components of the specific enzyme-forming apparatus seem ample in number, perhaps too numerous to fit our facts. The problems of interaction of these components are very much with us. We can pose many broad questions regarding the system: How general is the inducer-repressor competition? What is the chemical nature of the repressor? Where is the site of action of the repressor? Is the ribosome a site of specific enzyme synthesis? Why does the gene seem to be continually necessary for enzyme synthesis? Are there modes of regulation of enzyme formation other than induction-repression? When we can pose precise questions in emporimentally testable terms, perhaps we shall progress in understanding the problem of regulation of enzyme synthesis.

REFERENCES

Adelberg, E. A., and H. E. Umbarger (1953), *J. Biol. Chem.*, 205:475-482.
Ames, B. N., and B. Garry (1959), *Proc. Natl. Acad. Sci. U.S.*, 45:1453-1461.
Anderson, T. F., E. L. Wollman, and F. Jacob (1957), *Ann. Inst. Pasteur*, 93:450-455.
Cohen, G., and F. Jacob (1959), *Compt. Rend. Acad. Sci.*, 248:3490-3492.

Cohn, M., and J. Monod (1953), in *Adaptation in Microorganisms*, E. F. Gale and R. Davis, eds., Cambridge University Press, London, pp. 132-147.

Gorini, L., and W. Masa (1957), *Biochim. Biophys. Acta*, 25:208-209.

—— (1960), *Proc. Natl. Acad. Sci. U.S.*, 46:682-690.

Herzenberg, L. A. (1959), *Biochim. Biophys. Acta*, 31:525-538.

Hogness, D. S., M. Cohn, and J. Monod (1955), *Biochim. Biophys. Acta*, 16:99-116.

Jacob, F., D. Perrin, C. Sanchez, and J. Monod (1960), *Compt. Rend. Acad. Sci.*, 250:1727-1730.

McFall, E., A. B. Pardee, and G. S. Stent (1958), *Biochim. Biophys. Acta*, 27:282-297.

McQuillen, K., R. B. Roberts, and R. J. Britten (1959), *Proc. Natl. Acad. Sci. U.S.*, 45:1437-1447.

Monod, J. (1958), *Rec. Trav. Chim. Pays-Bas*, 77:569-585.

Nisman, B., and H. Fukuhara, (1960), *Compt. Rend. Acad. Sci.*, 250:410-412.

Pardee, A. B., and L. S. Prestidge (1955), *J. Bacteriol.*, 70:667-674.

—— and —— (1959a), *Biochim. Biophys. Acta*, 36:545-547.

——, F. Jacob, and J. Monod (1959b), *J. Mol. Biol.*, 1:165-178.

—— and J. Monod (1960a), unpublished.

—— and L. S. Prestidge (1960b), unpublished.

Perrin, D., A. Bussard, and J. Monod (1959), *Compt. Rend. Acad. Sci.*, 249:778-780.

Pollock, M. R. (1953), in *Adaptation in Microorganisms*, E. F. Gale and R. Davies, eds., Cambridge University Press, London, pp. 150-177.

—— and M. Kramer (1958), *Biochem. J.*, 70:665-681.

—— (1959), in *The Enzymes*, 2d ed., vol. 1, P. D. Boyer and H. Lardy, eds., Academic Press, Inc., New York, pp. 619-680.

Riley, M., A. B. Pardee, F. Jacob, and J. Monod (1960), *J. Mol. Biol.* 2:216-225.

Rotman, B., and S. Spiegelman (1954), *J. Bacteriol.*, 68:419-429.

Rushizky, G., M. Riley, L. S. Prestidge, and A. B. Pardee (1960), *Biochim. Biophys. Acta*, 45:70-76.

Schweet, R., H. Lamfrom, and E. Allen (1958), *Proc. Natl. Acad. Sci. U.S.*, 44:1029-1035.

Shepherdson, M., and A. B. Pardee (1960), *J. Biol. Chem.*, 235:3233-3237.

Stanier, R. Y. (1951), *Ann. Rev. Microbiol.*, 5:35-56.

Vogel, H. J. (1957), in *The Chemical Basis of Heredity*, W. D. McElroy and B. Glass, eds., Johns Hopkins Press, Baltimore, pp. 276-289.

Wijesundera, S., and D. D. Woods (1953), *Biochem. J.*, 55:viii; (1960), *J. Gen. Microbiol.*, 22:229-241.

Wollman, E. L., and F. Jacob (1959), *La Sexualité des Bactéries*. Masson et Cie., Paris.

Yates, R. A., and A. B. Pardee (1957), *J. Biol. Chem.*, 227:677-692.

Chapter Twelve

Control of Cellular Metabolism

H. A. KREBS

Medical Research Council Unit for Research in Cell Metabolism, Department of Biochemistry, University of Oxford, Oxford, England

INTRODUCTION

The capacity to regulate activities according to circumstances is one of the chief characteristics of living matter and has been widely studied by biologists. Earlier investigators who were concerned with regulation looked in the first instance to the nervous system and to hormones as objects of their study. What is relatively new is the entry of biochemical considerations at the enzyme level into the study of control mechanisms. I shall limit myself here essentially to this biochemical level.

The part which enzyme biochemistry has to play in this field is twofold. First there exist, in addition to the nervous and hormonal control mechanisms, other mechanisms—called by Stadie (1954) "primitive" control mechanisms—which are composed of relatively simple chemical systems. They occur in all forms of life, including the unicellular ones which do not possess hormones or a nervous system. An example of a "primitive" control mechanism is the change of energy-giving reactions in yeast cells when conditions change from anaerobiosis to aerobiosis. As has been known since Pasteur, the fermentation of sugar is the source of energy anaerobically, but aerobically the fermentation is replaced, wholly or partly, by respiration. Among the most striking regulatory mechanisms of lower organisms are those which coordinate chemical synthesis in relation to growth. These control mechanisms see to it that the quantities of cell constituents synthesized are exactly related to requirements. Such "primitive" control mechanisms of lower organisms also occur in higher animals. They are in fact the basic systems upon which the action of hormones or of the nervous system is superimposed.

The second reason for the entry of enzymology into the study of control mechanisms stems from the fact that even behind activities of the nervous tissue invariably there are chemical mechanisms. Thus the registration of stimuli or the conduction of impulses by nervous tissue is achieved by a machinery which is essentially a chemical machinery. This implies that a biochemist will never be satisfied by ascribing control mechanisms to the function of the nervous system. This would be merely a first stage of localizing the site of control mechanisms, and this stage will have to be followed by a study of the chemical events in the nervous system which are behind the functioning of the nerve cells. At present we are still a long way from having reached this area of investigation, and what follows is therefore mainly concerned with the "primitive" types of control mechanisms. The study of these mechanisms is a field which has been opened up fairly recently as a result of the elucidation of many aspects of the chemical organization of living cells and of metabolic pathways. Control is essentially a matter of quantitative variations and before these could be studied, qualitative information on the types of chemical reactions occuring in cells had to be assembled.

It is the object of this survey to discuss different types of control mechanisms employed by living cells and to illustrate these types by specific examples.

The Role of Reversible Reactions in Control Mechanisms

The great majority of chemical reactions taking place in living organisms are readily reversible and in some cases the simple reversibility of a reaction is a component of control mechanisms. Examples are buffer systems such as those regulating the constancy of pH in the blood (see Peters and van Slyke, 1931). These particular buffer systems safeguard that the transport of oxygen and carbon dioxide occurs with the minimum pH change. A special component of this pH-controlling system (apart from several ordinary buffers like the phosphate and the bicarbonate-CO_2 systems) is hemoglobin; it is endowed with two unusual properties which make it exceptionally effective as a buffer. The first is the reversible reaction between amino groups and CO_2, forming carbamino compounds. The second is the fact that oxygenated hemoglobin is a stronger acid than reduced hemoglobin. This means that the removal of oxygen from the blood by tissue respiration and its replacement by CO_2 is automatically accompanied by a supply of alkali which reacts with CO_2 to form bicarbonate. Owing to the simultaneous rise of both bicarbonate and CO_2 the pH change is relatively slight.

Another instance where reversibility appears to play a role in controlling the rate and direction of a reaction is the glutamic dehydrogenase system. What requires control in this case is the amount of glutamic acid supplied to the organism as building material. On most diets, glutamic acid is available in excess of requirements, but glutamic acid is not an essential amino acid; it can be readily synthesized in animal tissues from ammonia, reduced pyridine nucleotide, and α-oxoglutarate, formed as an intermediate of respiration. The question arises of the mechanism which controls the degradation of any excess of glutamic acid available from the diet on the one hand, and the synthesis of glutamic acid on the other, when the dietary supply is inadequate. Experiments on liver homogenates (Table 1) and other tissue preparations indicate that the reaction catalyzed by glutamic dehydrogenase operates in the direction of degradation when glutamate is present in excess, and in the opposite direction when no glutamate has been added and ammonia and a source of α-oxoglutarate (in this experiment fumarate) is available. The data of Table 1 incidentally also demonstrate that some of the glutamate present is readily converted to aspartate. This is formed by transamination between glutamate formed first and the oxaloacetate arising in the course of the tricarboxylic acid cycle (Krebs and Bellamy, 1960). It is likely that in the intact body, mass action alone controls the direction of glutamate metabolism. If the peripheral organs remove glutamate from the blood, they automatically create conditions favoring a synthesis, and if there is an excess of glutamate this is used as a fuel of respiration.

It is not easy to assess at the present the extent to which reversible systems of this kind serve as essential components of control mechanisms. Probably they are the exception rather than the rule. Recent investigations have shown that in several cases where simple reversibility and mass action were thought to be the main elements

TABLE 1

Amino Acid Metabolism of Rat-liver Homogenate

(3 ml, 10%, 30°, 60 min, O₂

The data refer to 3 ml homogenate containing 0.3 g rot liver (fresh weight). Salino medium: 21 ml 0.155M KCl; 2 ml 0.155M KHCO₃; 2 ml 0.02M MgCl₂; 5 ml 0.1M Na-phosphate-buffer, pH 7.4. Substrates listed below. 30°. 1 hour. O₂.

Added:	Glutamate 60 μmoles	Glutamate 30 μmoles	Fumarate 60 μmoles NH₄Cl 20 μmoles
Change in:			
Glutamate	− 15.7	− 11.8	+ 4.8
Aspartate	+ 14.9	+ 11.6	+ 8.4

of the control mechanism, this is in fact not the case. Examples are the synthesis of glycogen and the synthesis of fatty acids.

Glycogen synthesis, as has been known from the work of Cori and Cori, (1939) and of Hanes (1940), can be achieved by a reversal of the action of phosphorylase which catalyses the interconversion of glycogen and glucose-1-phosphate:

glycogen + glucose-1-phosphate ⇌ glycogen + phosphate.

The direction of the reaction depends on the concentrations of glucose-1-phosphate and inorganic phosphate. Until recently, it was thought that the synthesis of glycogen or starch was entirely due to the action of this enzyme, but it is now known (Leloir and Cardini, 1957; Cardini, Leloir, and Chiriboga, 1955; Leloir and Goldemberg, 1960) that there is a second mechanism of glycogen synthesis which is quantitatively much more important. This involves reactions in which uridine derivatives are key reactants:

uridine triphosphate + glucose-1-phosphate ⇌ uridine
        diphosphoglucose + pyrophosphate
uridine diphosphoglucose + glycogen ⇌ uridine diphosphate
        + glycogen
uridine diphosphate + ATP ⇌ uridine triphosphate + ADP
Sum:
glycogen + glucose-1-phosphate + ATP ⇌ glycogen
        +ADP + pyrophosphate.

This mechanism requires the expenditure of an additional pyrophosphate bond of ATP for the incorporation of each glucose unit into glycogen, and this is responsible for the fact that the equilibrium in this system is much more in favor of synthesis than in the phosphorylase system. The enzymes concerned are present in high activity in muscle and other tissues (Robbins, Traut, and Lipmann, 1959) and they are no doubt chiefly responsible for glycogen synthesis. It follows, then, that glycogen synthesis and glycogen breakdown are not brought about by a simple reversal of the same reaction but by a cyclic mechanism where synthesis and breakdown follow different routes, phosphorylase catalyzing breakdown and the uridine diphosphoglucose system the synthesis.

An analogous situation has recently come to light in respect to the synthesis of fatty acids from acetate. The intermediary stages of fatty acid degradation have been firmly established within the last ten years (Lynen, 1952, 1953, 1959; Green, 1960) subsequent to the discovery of coenzyme A and the acyl coenzyme A derivatives of fatty acids. The four steps of fatty acid degradation—α,β-saturation, hydroxylation of the unsaturated fatty acid in β-position, dehydrogenation of the β-hydroxy acyl coenzyme A, and finally the thiolysis of the β-keto acids by coenzyme A:

$$
\begin{array}{c}
CH_3 \\
| \\
(CH_2)_n \\
| \\
CH_2 \\
| \\
CH_2 \\
| \\
CO \\
| \\
S-CoA
\end{array}
\quad
\underset{\pm\,2H}{\longleftrightarrow}
\quad
\begin{array}{c}
CH_3 \\
| \\
(CH_2)_n \\
| \\
CH \\
\| \\
CH \\
| \\
CO \\
| \\
S-CoA
\end{array}
\quad
\underset{\pm\,H_2O}{\longleftrightarrow}
\quad
\begin{array}{c}
CH_3 \\
| \\
(CH_2)_n \\
| \\
CHOH \\
| \\
CH_2 \\
| \\
CO \\
| \\
S-CoA
\end{array}
$$

$$
\underset{\pm\,2H}{\longleftrightarrow}
\quad
\begin{array}{c}
CH_3 \\
| \\
(CH_2)_n \\
| \\
CO \\
| \\
CH_2 \\
| \\
CO \\
| \\
S-CoA
\end{array}
\quad
\underset{\pm\,HS-CoA}{\longleftrightarrow}
\quad
\begin{array}{c}
CH_3 \\
| \\
(CH_2)_n \\
| \\
CO \\
| \\
S-CoA
\end{array}
\quad + \quad
\begin{array}{c}
CH_3 \\
| \\
CO \\
| \\
S-CoA
\end{array}
$$

are all readily reversible and it was first thought that the synthesis was achieved by a reversal of degradation. This would mean that fat synthesis occurs when the products of degradation, viz., acetyl coenzyme A and reduced pyridine nucleotides, are present in excess, as would be the case when the supply of carbohydrate is abundant.

However, a detailed study of the fatty acid synthesis has shown that its enzymic mechanism is very different from that of the degradation. This was first suggested by observations of Brady and Gurin (1952) and of Klein (1957) and more recently established by Wakil and his collaborators (1958) and by Lynen (1959). The enzyme systems for the synthesis show very different cofactor requirements from those bringing about degradation. In contrast to the degradation the synthesis requires bicarbonate, TPN, and biotin. The bicarbonate is fixed to form malonyl coenzyme A. This is subsequently decarboxylated and the fixed carbon is again set free. The purified preparations bringing about fatty acid synthesis are free from some of the enzymes required for fatty acid oxidation, and this is conclusive proof that synthesis is not a simple reversal of degradation. In other words, fatty acid synthesis and fatty acid degradation again represent a cyclic mechanism.

Control by Specific Enzyme Inhibition

In reversible systems, the product inhibits the enzyme by mass action, according to the laws of equilibria, i.e., thermodynamics. Of much greater importance in control mechanisms are other kinds of enzyme inhibition where a metabolite inhibits an enzyme in which the metabolite itself is not a direct reactant as substrate or product.

Many microorganisms can synthesize all or most of the required amino acids, purines, and pyrimidines from ammonia and a carbon source such as glucose, glycerol, or lactate. Much is known about the pathways of synthesis and the properties of the enzymes concerned with the synthesis, and it is also known that in many cases the capacity of the enzymes to synthesize cell constituents is much greater than required. Although, then, the enzymes and the starting materials for the synthesis are available, the synthesis does not take place. The requirement of material of course varies; it depends above all on the composition of the growth medium. When an amino acid is present in the medium, the need for its synthesis does not exist and does not in fact take place (Warner, 1956; Roberts, Abelson, Cowie, Bolton, and Britten, 1955). In other words, the presence of an amino acid suppresses its synthesis. How is this achieved? In some —perhaps many — cases, this is brought about by the inhibition of a crucial step in the synthesis of the cell constituent by this constituent itself. An example is the control of the synthesis of pyrimidines which, thanks largely to the work of Lieberman and Kornberg (1954, 1955, 1956) is known to involve the following stages:

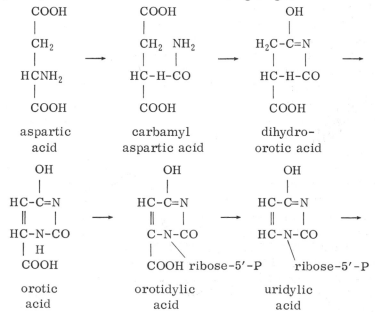

$$
\begin{array}{ccc}
\text{OH} & \text{NH}_2 & \text{NH}_2 \\
| & | & | \\
\text{HC-C=N} & \text{HC-C=N} & \text{HC-C=N} \\
\parallel \quad | \quad \longrightarrow & \parallel \quad | \quad \longrightarrow & \parallel \quad | \quad \longrightarrow \begin{cases} \text{nucleic} \\ \text{acid} \end{cases} \\
\text{HC-N-CO} & \text{HC-N-CO} & \text{HC-N-CO} \\
| & | & | \\
\text{ribose-5'-P-P-P} & \text{ribose-5'-P-P-P} & \text{ribose-5'-P}
\end{array}
$$

uridine	cytidine	cytidine-
triphosphate	triphosphate	5'-phosphate

According to a discovery by Yates and Pardee (1956, 1957) the first step in this sequence, the formation of carbamyl aspartic acid from aspartic acid and carbamyl phosphate, is inhibited in extracts of *E. coli*, by cytidine-5-phosphate. Thus the end product of pyrimidine synthesis can directly prevent the synthesis. Umbarger and Brown (1958) have found a similar situation in the biosynthesis of isoleucine and Wijesundera and Woods (1953, 1960) and Cohn, Cohen, and Monod (1953) in the biosynthesis of methionine in *E. coli*.

In growing microorganisms, the mechanism of this inhibition can be of two different kinds. Either the activity of an existing enzyme is *suppressed* by the metabolite, or the formation of the synthesizing enzymes is prevented by the presence of the metabolite. Vogel (1957) has called the latter type of inhibition "repression." Repression, then, is an inhibition of enzyme synthesis by the end product, while suppression is the control of enzyme activity by end products. It is possible that, in microorganisms at least, both mechanisms exist side by side and are interconnected. Obviously the suppression of enzyme activity is a mechanism which allows for very prompt adjustment while the repression may involve delays to await the synthesis of new enzyme molecules.

An example of repression recently studied by Kornberg and Collins (1960) concerns the enzyme isocitritase. This is a key enzyme in the glyoxylate cycle which represents a mechanism by which certain microorganisms, e.g., Pseudomonads, *Micrococcus denitrificans*, *E. coli*, Aspergillus, form succinate from acetate. It is a modified tricarboxylic acid cycle in which the stages between isocitrate and malate are replaced by the reactions brought about by isocitritase and malate (Scheme 1). If the medium contains adequate quantities of succinate or related dicarboxylic acids, or amino acids like glutamate which on degradation form succinate, then the glyoxalate cycle does not take place because succinate or more likely a substance derived from it (possibly oxaloacetate) prevents the formation of isocitritase (Kornberg and Collins, 1960; Umbarger, 1960).

Whether suppression and repression should be regarded as fundamentally different is perhaps a matter of opinion. Both represent an enzyme inhibition but while suppression is a direct inhibition of the enzyme dealing with the substrate concerned, repression is an inhibition of the system of enzymes concerned with the synthesis of an enzyme, and the synthesis of enzymes, as of all proteins, is known to differ fundamentally from the synthesis of other substances. It cannot be achieved solely through the agency of ordinary enzymes, such as those that catalyse the synthesis of small molecules, or cause the polymerization of, say, glucose to glycogen, but depends on specific macromolecular structures—"templates"—which are concerned with the emergence of a characteristic amino acid sequence ("patternization") of the polypeptide chains.

The examples of specific enzyme inhibition as part of control mechanism given so far refer to microorganisms. There are analogous cases known applying to higher animals. An instance is the formation of bile acids from cholesterol.

Bile acids are formed from cholesterol, and as Scheme 2 (p. 288) indicates, this conversion involves a reduction of ring B, the introduction of α-orientated hydroxyl groups, the transformation of the 8-carbon side chain to a 5-carbon side chain (i.e., the removal of carbon 25, 26, and 27 of cholesterol), the oxidation of carbon 24 to a carboxyl group, and finally the conjugation of the bile acid formed with glycine or taurine. Administration of bile acids to animals prevents the conversion of cholesterol to bile acids (Bergström and Danielsson, 1958). Whitehouse and Staple (1959) have shown that conjugated bile acids control the oxidation of cholesterol by inhibiting an early stage of the long chain of reactions leading from cholesterol to bile acids. 3α, 7α, 12α-trihydroxycoprostane, which has the side chain structure of cholesterol and the nuclear structure of cholic acid and is probably an intermediate in bile acid formation, is still oxidized in the presence of cholic acid conjugates, and this indicates that the rate-determining step in bile acid formation is probably associated with nuclear hydroxylation and that it is this reaction which is inhibited by the conjugated bile acids.

The synthesis of cholesterol is likewise controlled by the amounts of cholesterol in the body. Cholesterol is synthesized from acetate through the stages shown in Scheme 3 (p. 289). Cholesterol itself and some of its immediate precursors (squalene, lathosterol, and mevalonic acid) inhibit an early stage of cholesterol synthesis, probably the reduction of β-hydroxy-β-methyl glutaric acid to mevalonic acid (Langdon and Bloch, 1953; Tomkins, Sheppard and Chaikoff, 1953; Gey et al., 1957).

Scheme 1. Tricarboxylic Acid and Gloxylate Cycles

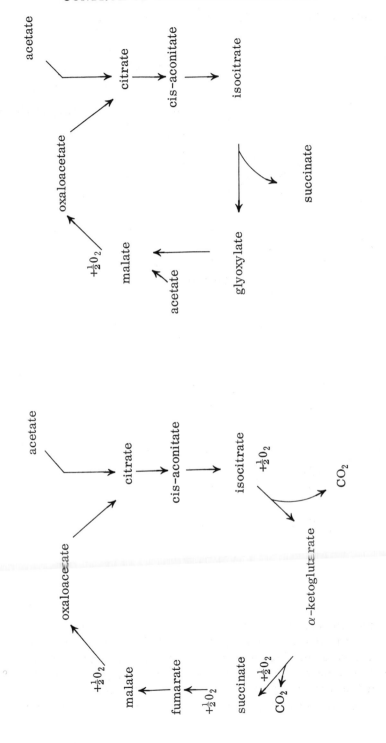

Tricarboxylic acid cycle

Net effect: $acetate - 2O_2 \rightarrow 2CO_2 + 2H_2O$

Glyoxylate cycle

Net effect: $2\ acetate + \tfrac{1}{2}O_2 \rightarrow succinate + H_2O$

Scheme 2. Conversion of Cholesterol to Cholic Acid

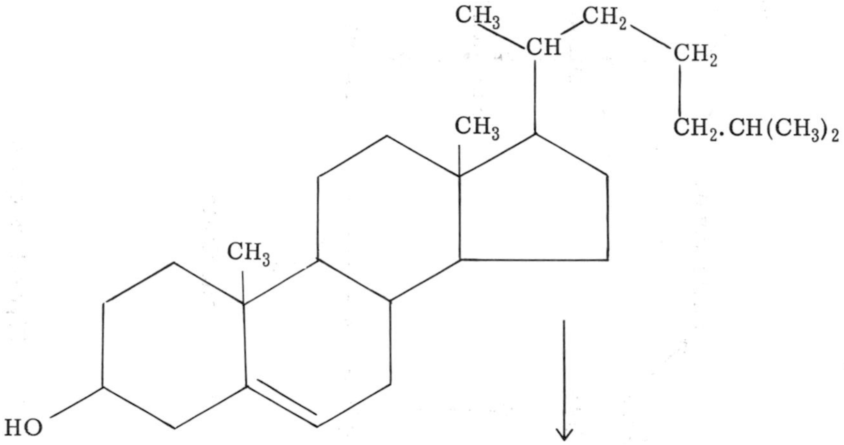

Cholesterol

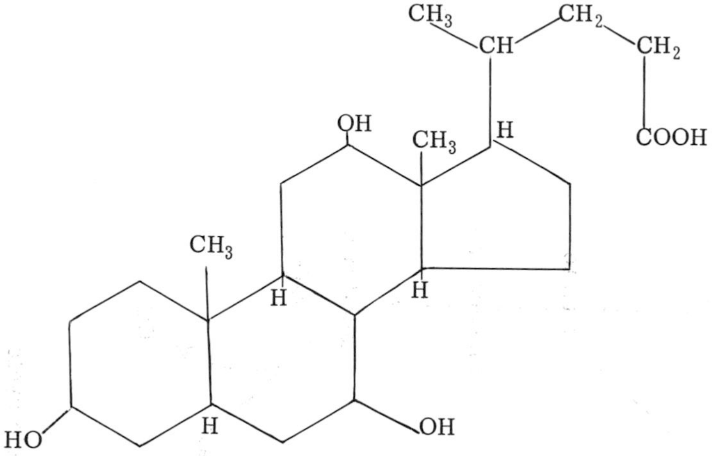

Cholic acid

An analogous case of control of specific enzyme inhibition is the inhibition of purine synthesis by nucleotides. The synthesis of nucleotides involves some thirteen stages (Scheme 4, p. 290). Wyngaarden and Ashton (1959) have reported experiments on pigeon liver which suggest that the first irreversible and specific step of this sequence is inhibited by inosine monophosphate, adenosine phosphates, and guano-

Scheme 3. Intermediary Stages of the Synthesis of Cholesterol*

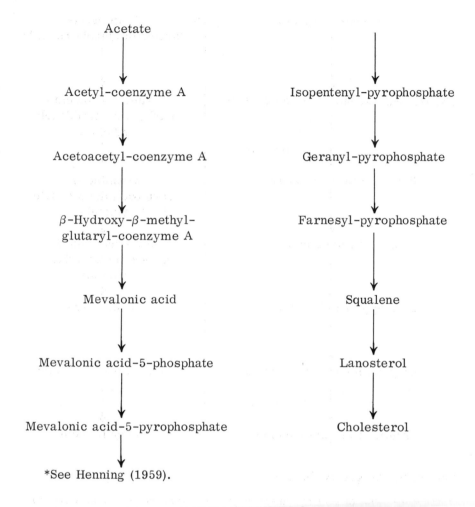

*See Henning (1959).

sine phosphates. This is the reaction in which ribosylamine-5-phosphate is generated from ribose-5-phosphate-1-pyrophosphate and glutamine.

A further case of the inhibition of enzymes by metabolites is the inhibition of hexokinase by sugar phosphates first demonstrated by Weil-Malherbe and Bone (1951) and by Crane and Sols (1953). Glucose-6-phosphate is a noncompetitive inhibitor of hexokinase in concentrations as low as $0.5 \times 10^{-3}M$. It is very likely, though not yet certain, that this inhibition plays a part in controlling the first step, and thereby the over-all rate, of glycolysis.

Scheme 4. Intermediary Stages of the Synthesis of Purines

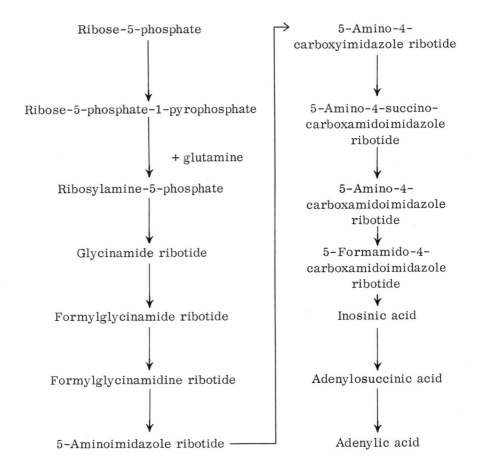

Control by Obligatory Coupling

Another type of control mechanism is employed by living cells in order to adjust to changing needs the rate of oxygen consumption, i.e., the rate at which energy is liberated by combustion. In view of the key position of ATP in energy transformation, energy requirements can be equated to ATP requirements, and owing to the obligatory coupling between electron transport from substrate to oxygen and oxidative phosphorylation (illustrated by Scheme 5), oxygen cannot be used unless phosphate and ADP are available. The supply of ADP and phosphate in turn depends on the expenditure of energy through fission of ATP. When a tissue—say muscle—changes from rest to activity, the rate of ATP hydrolysis increases and the concentrations of ADP and phosphate rise. This causes an increase of the rate of respiration because the factors limiting electron transport are the ADP or inorganic phosphate required for the obligatory coupling.

Experimentally it is now easy to demonstrate the ADP or phosphate control of respiration in isolated mitochondria (Lardy and Wellman, 1953; Aldridge, 1957). Table 2 shows that the rate of respiration is very much accelerated when hexokinase or potato ATPase or dinitrophenol are added. Hexokinase in the presence of glucose causes a conversion of ATP to ADP. Potato-ATPase hydrolyzes ATP to ADP. Dinitrophenol prevents a removal of ADP. Thus all these agents increase the ADP level, which in turn increases the rate of oxygen consumption. In these experiments, ADP rather than phosphate was the controlling factor because the medium contained an excess of phosphate. Racker and Wu (1959) have recently shown that in the isolated ascites tumor cells the concentration of inorganic phosphate rather than the concentration of ADP is the controlling factor.

A similar type of rate control exists in anaerobic glycolysis where the rate of the triose phosphate dehydrogenase reaction also depends on the supply of inorganic phosphate and ADP. The inhibition of fermentation by oxygen—the Pasteur effect—employs in all probability phosphates as the controlling agents although specific enzyme inhibitions by sugar phosphates may be additional factors (see Lynen, 1957; Balazs, 1959; Lynen, Hartmann, Netter, and Schuegraf, 1959).

Scheme 5. Obligatory Coupling between Electron Transport from Substrate to O_2 with Synthesis of ATP from ADP and Phosphate.

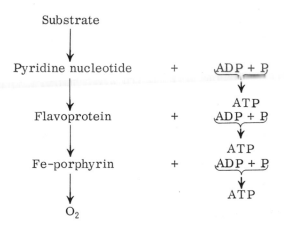

TABLE 2

ADP Control of Respiration of Liver Mitochondria

4 ml liver mitochondria with pyruvate (0.01M), fumarate (0.001M), glucose (0.06M), ATP (0.001M). 30°. O_2. 45 min. Mitochondria prepared according to Aldridge (1957); 4 ml suspension contained the mitochondria obtained from 0.2 g liver.

Additions:	0	Hexokinase	Apyrase	Dinitrophenol 1.25×10^{-5} M
O_2 used (μmoles):	3.52	8.30	6.60	7.68

Control through Shared Cofactors

When cells are offered a mixture of substrates of respiration, these are usually not oxidized at the same time. In most tissues carbohydrate burns first, followed by fat and later by amino acids. As all substrates of respiration require common cofactors for their oxidation, the choice of substrate means competition of several substrates for the same catalyst. Which substrate is oxidized depends on definable physicochemical properties such as the relative rates at which the substrates interact with the common agent.

A special aspect of this competition for common cofactors is the competition between intermediates of metabolism and starting materials. As a rule intermediates do not accumulate in appreciable quantities. Once the degradation of the substance, say a long-chain fatty acid or a sugar molecule, has been started, it is oxidized to completion before a new molecule is attacked. This can be accounted for by the assumption that the intermediates win over the starting materials in the competition between the catalysts of the electron transport chain.

Apart from the catalysts of the electron transport chain, other types of cofactors, such as coenzyme A and pyridoxal phosphate, may also play a role in controlling reaction rates by virtue of being shared cofactors.

Shared cofactors represent a bottleneck which regulates a steadiness in the flow of reactants. The capacity of dehydrogenases to degrade substrate is much greater than is normally needed, as demonstrated by the increases which occur on addition of the substrates. This bottleneck is one of the factors which prevent the simultaneous oxidation of many different substrates.

Feedback Control

Three of the different types of control mechanisms discussed here—specific enzyme inhibition, obligatory coupling, and shared cofactors—have in common a feature which has been compared with the feedback systems of the electronic engineers. In feedback systems the process, as it progresses, creates conditions unfavorable for further progress. The process therefore stops until, because of secondary changes, the environment has changed. In other words, the input—in chemical systems the rate of reaction—is controlled by the output—in chemical systems the product. In the case of the specific enzyme inhibition, the final product inhibits an early stage of a reaction sequence leading to this product. In the obligatory coupling, the availability of one of the final products, ADP, controls the initial stages of oxidation. Competition for joint cofactors may also be looked upon as a feedback system inasmuch as several substrates, when competing for a common catalyst, by their presence create unfavorable conditions for the reactivity of the other substrates. As one of the substrates disappears another is automatically 'fed' to the catalyst, so that an approximate constancy of catalytic activity is achieved.

CONCLUDING REMARKS

Apart from the four mechanisms discussed so far, no doubt many other principles are employed in the regulation of metabolic processes. The supply of key chemicals, for example, may be a controlling factor. Thus a fall of the oxaloacetate level in the liver could reduce the rate of the tricarboxylic acid cycle and divert acetyl coenzyme A to the synthesis of ketone bodies. Hormones like insulin and adrenalin may also be looked upon as key chemicals which can limit reaction rates. The two hormones can control, each by an entirely different mechanism, the amounts of glucose available to animal tissues. Another important factor in the control of reaction rates is the structural organization of the cells and their organelles. Structure is responsible for compartmentation, and can either prevent or facilitate contact between potential reactants. This was discussed by Dr. Siekevitz in his lecture of this series.

REFERENCES

Aldridge, W. N. (1957), Liver and brain mitochondria. *Biochem. J.*, 67:423-431.

Balázs, R. (1959), The point of the aerobic inhibition of glycolytic activity associated with brain mitochondria. *Biochem. J.*, 72:561-574.

Bergström, S., and H. Daniellson (1958), On the regulation of bile acid formation in the rat liver. *Acta Physiol. Scand.*, 43:1-7.

Bourgeois, S., J. M. Wiame, and H. Lelouchier-Dagnelie (1960), Étude du "rétrocontrôle" des synthèses d'enzyme par des acides amines au cour de la croissance de *P. morganii*. *Biochim. Biophys. Acta*, 38:136-144.

Brady, R. O., and S. Gurin (1952), Biosynthesis of fatty acids by cell-free or water-soluble enzyme systems. *J. Biol. Chem.*, 199:421-431.

Cardini, C. E., L. F. Leloir, and J. Chiriboga (1955), The biosynthesis of sucrose. *J. Biol. Chem.*, 214:149-155.

Cohn, M., G. N. Cohen, and J. Monod (1953), L'effet inhibiteur spécifique de la méthione dans la formation de la méthionine-synthèse chez *Escherichia coli*. *Compt. Rend. Acad. Sci. Paris*, 236:746-748.

Cori, Gerty T., C. F. Cori, and G. Schmidt (1939), The role of glucose-1-phosphate in the formation of blood sugar and synthesis of glycogen in the liver. *J. Biol. Chem.*, 129:629-639.

Crane, R. K., and A. Sols (1953), The association of hexokinase with particulate fractions of brain and other tissue homogenates. *J. Biol. Chem.*, 203:273-292.

Gey, F. K., A. Pletscher, O. Isler, R. Rüegg, and J. Würsch (1957), Zur Beeinflussung des Acetat-Einbaues in Cholesterin durch isoprenartige C_{5-} und C_{6-} Verbindungen. *Helv. Chim. Acta*, 40:2354-2368.

Gibson, D. M., E. B. Titchener, and S. J. Wakil (1958), Studies on the mechanism of fatty acid synthesis. V. Bicarbonate requirement for the synthesis of long-chain fatty acids. *Biochim. Biophys. Acta*, 30:376-383.

Green, D. E. (1960), The synthesis of fat. *Scientific American*, 202:46-51.

Hanes, C. S. (1940), The reversible formation of starch from glucose-1-phosphate catalysed by potato phosphorylase. *Proc. Roy. Soc.* (London), Series B. 129: 174-208.

Henning, U. (1959), Die Biosynthese des Cholesterins. *Deut. med. Wochschr.*, 84: 760-764.

Klein, H. P. (1957), Some observations of a cell-free lipid synthesising system from *Saccharomyces cerevisiae*. *J. Bact.*, 73:530-537.

Kornberg, H. L., and J. F. Collins (1960), The influence of growth substrates on metabolic pathways in *Micrococcus denitrificans*. *Biochim. Biophys. Acta*, 39: 9-24.

Krebs, H. A., and D. Bellamy (1960), The interconversion of glutamic and aspartic acid in respiring tissues. *Biochem. J.* (in press).

Langdon, R. G., and K. Bloch (1953), The effect of some dietary additions on the synthesis of cholesterol from acetate in vitro. *J. Biol. Chem.*, 202:77-81.

Lardy, H. A., and H. Wellman (1952), Oxidative phosphorylation; role of inorganic phosphate and acceptor systems in the control of metabolic rates. *J. Biol. Chem.*, 195:215-224.

Leloir, L. F., and C. E. Cardini (1957), Biosynthesis of glycogen from uridine diphosphate glucose. *J. Am. Chem. Soc.*, 79:6340-6341.

—— and Sara H. Goldemberg (1960), Synthesis of glycogen from uridine diphosphate glucose in liver. *J. Biol. Chem.*, 235:919-923.

Lieberman, I. (1956), Enzymatic amination of uridine triphosphate to cytidine triphosphate. *J. Biol. Chem.*, 222:765-775.

—— and A. Kornberg (1954), Enzymatic synthesis and breakdown of a pyrimidine, orotic acid. II. Dihydroorotic acid, ureidosuccinic acid and 5-carboxymethyl-hydantion. *J. Biol. Chem.*, 207:911-924.

——, ——, and E. S. Simms (1955), Enzymatic synthesis of pyrimidine nucleotides oritidine-5'-phosphate and uridine-5'-phosphate. *J. Biol. Chem.*, 215:403-427.

Lynen, F. (1952-53), Acetyl coenzyme A and the "fatty acid cycle." *Harvey Lectures*, 48:210-244.

—— (1957), Phosphatkreislauf und Pasteur Effekt. *Proc. Intn. Symposium on Enzyme Chemistry in Tokyo and Kyoto*, 1957, 2:25-34.
—— (1959), Participation of Acyl-CoA in carbon chain biosynthesis. *J. Cellular Comp. Physiol.*, 54, Suppl. 1:33-49.
——, G. Hartmann, K. F. Netter, and A. Schuegraf (1959), Phosphate turnover and Pasteur effect, in *Ciba Foundation Symposium on Regulation of Cell Metabolism*, pp. 256-273.
Peters, J. C., and D. D. Van Slyke (1931), *Quantitative Clinical Chemistry, Interpretations*, vol. I. (1st ed.). Baillière, Tindall & Cox, London.
Racker, E., and R. Wu (1959), Limiting factors in glycolysis of Ascites tumour cells and the Pasteur effect, in *Ciba Foundation Symposium on Regulation of Cell Metabolism*, G. E. W. Wolstenholme and Cecilia M. O'Connor, eds., J. & A. Churchill, Ltd., London, pp. 205-209.
Roberts, R. B., P. H. Abelson, D. B. Cowie, E. T. Bolton, and R. J. Britten (1955), Studies in Biosynthesis in *Escherichia coli*. Carnegie Institution, Washington, D. C., Publ. 607.
Robbins, P. W., R. R. Traut, and F. Lipmann (1959), Glycogen synthesis from glucose, glucose-6-phosphate and uridine diphosphate glucose in muscle preparations. *Proc. Natl. Acad. Sci. U.S.*, 45:6-12.
Stadie, W. C. (1954), Current concepts of the action of insulin. *Physiol. Rev.*, 34:52-100.
Tomkins, G. M., H. Sheppard, and I. L. Chaikoff (1953), Cholesterol synthesis of liver. IV. Suppression by steroid administration. *J. Biol. Chem.*, 203:781-786.
Umbarger, H. E. (1960), Feedback control of the action of isocitratase in *Escherichia coli*. *Federation Proc.*, 19:52.
Umbarger, H. E., and B. Brown (1958), Isoleucine and valine metabolism in *Escherichia coli*. VII. A negative feedback mechanism controlling isoleucine biosynthesis. *J. Biol. Chem.*, 233:415-420.
Vogel, H. J. (1957), Repression and induction as control mechanisms of enzyme biogenesis; the "adaptive" formation of acetylornithinase, in *The Chemical Basis of Heredity*, W. D. McElroy and B. Glass, eds. Johns Hopkins Press, Baltimore, pp. 276-296.
Wakil, S. J. (1958), A malonic acid derivative as an intermediate in fatty acid synthesis. *J. Am. Chem. Soc.*, 80:6465.
——, E. B. Titchener, and D. M. Gibson (1958), Evidence for the participation of biotin in the enzymic synthesis of fatty acids. *Biochim. Biophys. Acta*, 29:225-226.
Warner, A. C. I. (1956), The actual nitrogen sources for growth of heterotrophic bacteria in non-limiting media. *Biochem. J.*, 64:1-6.
Weil-Malherbe, H., and A. D. Bone (1951), Studies on hexokinase. I. The Hexokinase activity of rat brain extracts. *Biochem. J.*, 49:339-347.
Whitehouse, M. W., and E. Staple (1959), Regulation of cholesterol oxidation by liver in vitro. *Proc. Soc. Exp. Biol. Med.*, 101:439-441.
Wijesundera, S., and D. D. Woods (1953), The effect of growth on a medium containing methionine on the synthesis of this amino acid by *Bacterium coli*. *Biochem. J.*, 55:viii.
—— and —— (1960), Suppression of methionine synthesis in *Escherichia coli* by growth in the presence of this amino acid. *J. Gen. Microbiol.*, 22:229-241.
Wyngaarden, J. B., and D. M. Ashton (1959), The regulation of activity of phosphoriboxylpyrophosphate aminotransferase by purine ribonucleotides: the potential feedback control of purine biosynthesis. *J. Biol. Chem.*, 234:1492-1496.
—— and —— (1959), Feedback control of purine biosynthesis by purine ribonucleotides. *Nature*, 183:747-748.

Yates, R. A., and A. B. Pardee (1956), Pyrimidine biosynthesis in *Escherichia coli*. *J. Biol. Chem.*, 221:743-756.

—— and —— (1956), Control of pyrimidine biosynthesis in *Escherichia coli* by a feed-back mechanism. *J. Biol. Chem.*, 221:757-770.

—— and —— (1957), Control of uracil of formation of enzymes required for crotate synthesis. *J. Biol. Chem.*, 227:677-692.

Chapter Thirteen

The Role of Steroid Hormones in the Control of Metabolic Activity*

CLAUDE A. VILLEE

Department of Biological Chemistry, Harvard Medical School; Research Laboratories, Boston Lying-in Hospital, Boston

Some aspects of metabolic control have been considered in earlier lectures in this series. The rate of any given enzyme system is determined by the concentration of the enzyme, and of its substrates and cofactors, by the association constants of the enzyme for its substrate and cofactors, and by certain intrinsic properties of the enzyme system which are expressed as its "turnover number." In a series of enzymes such as those which comprise a metabolic cycle in which the product of each reaction becomes the substrate for the next, the rates of these reactions are necessarily geared together and are controlled by whichever enzyme is rate-limiting. Metabolic rates in the lower organisms are controlled simply by these basic mechanisms, which are characteristic of the enzymes within the cells. In the higher organisms this type of metabolic control may be augmented by a variety of nervous and hormonal mechanisms. In this lecture we shall consider only the latter.

The many different hormones which have been discovered to date have quite different chemical structures and there is no reason to believe that they must all have a similar mechanism of action. Each hormone affects certain cells in the body to a greater extent than other cells. Even insulin and thyroxine, which have wide-spread effects on tissues, do not affect metabolic rates in all cells to an equal extent. Those tissues which respond dramatically to a given hormone have been termed its "target organs." Just what may differentiate, at the molecular level, a target organ from the other tissues of the body cannot be rigorously defined. However, it is well known

*The experimental work of the author is supported by grants from the Charles A. King and Marjorie King Fund, by grant C-2400 of the National Institutes of Health, U.S. Public Health Service, and by a grant from the Association for the Aid of Crippled Children.

that each type of tissue is characterized by a particular pattern of enzymes which is established in the course of embryonic differentiation. Both qualitative and quantitative differences in the pattern of enzymes in the several tissues of the body have been demonstrated. Thus it is reasonable to postulate that one of the characteristics that may distinguish a target organ of a given hormone from other tissues is the presence of an enzyme system which is specifically stimulated or inhibited by that hormone. The phosphorylases of liver and skeletal muscle catalyze the same reaction yet they have been shown to be antigenically distinct proteins with different molecular weights and subject to stimulation by different hormones.

The specific relations between a hormone and its target organ can be seen clearly when the latter undergoes growth in response to the secretion or administration of the former, or alternatively, when the target organ undergoes atrophy in response to the ablation of the hormone-producing gland. The hormone alters the pattern of metabolism in the target organ in such a way that growth results. The steroid hormones, and the estrogens and androgens in particular, provide excellent examples of such relations between hormone and growth of specific target organs.

To explain the mechanism underlying such hormonally induced growth responses it must first be demonstrated that the hormone can affect either directly or indirectly an enzyme system which is uniquely present in the target organ; that this effect can be produced by the very small concentration of hormone which is present in the tissue under physiologic conditions; and that this reaction can be rate-limiting for growth so that an increase in its rate will result in an increased rate of growth. Then the evidence from experiments at the molecular level must be related both quantitatively and qualitatively to the events which occur in vivo when the hormone is administered.

The phenomenon of growth involves the synthesis of additional molecules of protein, of nucleic acids, and perhaps of lipids, terpenes, and carbohydrates as well. Most of the enzymatic reactions by which each of these molecules is synthesized from simpler precursors require the input of energy. If a hormone were to regulate the rate at which biologically useful energy, in the form of energy-rich phosphate or thioester bonds, is made available to a given cell, it could regulate the rate of all of these energy-requiring biosynthetic reactions and thus regulate growth. This is a simpler theory than the hypothesis that the hormone stimulates each of the biosynthetic reactions directly.

Each enzyme system includes the specific protein enzyme, one or more substrates and products, and one or more cofactors and acti-

vators. The over-all rate of the enzyme system may be regulated
by altering the amount or activity of the protein enzyme, or by altering the availability of some substrate or cofactor at the enzyme site.
Hormonal control of metabolic processes might be effected by any of
the following mechanisms:

1. The hormone might alter the rate at which new enzyme molecules are produced from smaller precursors. By increasing the
number of active enzyme molecules per unit mass of tissue, the over-
all activity of the enzyme system could be increased. Convincing
evidence that such a phenomenon may occur in mammalian tissue
was provided by Knox and Auerbach (1955) who found that the amount
of tryptophan pyrrolase in the liver of the rat can be increased by
the injection of cortisone.

2. The hormone may alter the activity of a preformed protein
molecule, that is, it might convert an inactive protein to one that has
full enzyme activity. There is evidence that glucagon and epinephrine
affect the enzyme which produces cyclic adenylic acid for the reac-
tivation of phosphorylase in the liver (Sutherland and Rall, 1957) and
the effect of estradiol on the estrogen sensitive enzyme of the placenta investigated in our laboratory appears to be brought about in
this way (Hagerman and Villee, 1957).

3. The hormone may alter the permeability of the cell membrane
or of the membranes around the mitochondria and other subcellular
structures. In this way, the hormone would make substrate or cofactor molecules more readily available to the enzyme and thus increase the rate of a specific enzyme system. The action of insulin
in regulating the uptake of glucose by muscle cells has been explained in this fashion by Levine and Goldstein (1955) and by Krahl
(1957).

4. The hormone may be involved as a coenzyme or cosubstrate
in the enzyme system. The synthesis and degradation of each hormone involve a number of enzymatic steps, and some investigators
have been attracted by the possibility that the physiologic action of
the hormone involves some reaction in which the hormone itself is
changed. In other words, the physiological action of the hormone
and its metabolism are regarded as two aspects of the same process.
This mechanism has been invoked by Talalay and Williams-Ashman
(1958) who suggested that the physiological effects of steroid hormones involve their reversible oxidation and reduction by enzymes
with dual pyridine nucleotide specificity.

5. The hormone may compete with one of the cofactors for a specific site on the enzyme molecule. By displacing one of the essential cofactors, the hormone would depress the over-all activity of
the enzyme system. Wolfe and Ball (1957) have shown that thyroxine

may compete with an essential divalent cation such as zinc for a site on the enzyme malic dehydrogenase. The inhibition of malic dehydrogenase decreases the production of oxalacetic acid, which is a powerful inhibitor of the enzyme succinic dehydrogenase. In this way, the addition of thyroxine leads to an increased activity of succinic dehydrogenase.

The evidence that any given hormone acts at one site does not necessarily contradict other evidence that the hormone may affect a different metabolic reaction. Each hormone may well have more than one site of action and it may even have more than one mechanism of action.

Work in our laboratory over the past eight years (Hagerman and Villee, 1952, Villee and Hagerman, 1953, and Villee, Hagerman, and Joel, 1960) has produced evidence which indicates that estrogens promote growth and increase the functional capacities of certain tissues because those cells contain a specific enzyme, an estrogen-dependent pyridine nucleotide transhydrogenase, which catalyzes the reaction $DPN^+ + TPNH \longrightarrow DPNH + TPN^+$. The increased activity of this enzyme which results when estrogen is added to the system leads to an increase in the supply of biologically useful energy and secondarily to an increase in the rate of the endergonic steps in the biosynthesis of proteins, nucleic acids, fats, and terpenes. This hypothesis involves the assumption that the supply of biologically useful energy is rate-limiting for the synthetic reactions in the absence of estradiol.

The estrogen-dependent enzyme has been shown to be present in human endometrium, placenta, mammary gland, and pituitary, but it is not present in liver, heart, lung, kidney, and brain. It is thus present in tissues usually considered to be target organs of estrogens but absent from those which are not. This estrogen-dependent transhydrogenase is located in the nonparticulate fraction of the cell and is distinct from the mitochondrial transhydrogenases which have been investigated by Kaplan and his colleagues (1952, 1953) and by Ball and Cooper (1957). The placenta like most other tissues contains a mitochondrial transhydrogenase whose activity is not modified by estrogens.

The estrogen-dependent transhydrogenase is stimulated by equilin and equilenin as well as by estradiol and estrone. Recent experiments (Glass and Villee, 1961) have shown that the synthetic estrogen, diethyl stilbestrol, will also stimulate the enzyme at low concentrations (10^{-7} M) but inhibits it at higher concentrations.

Two theories have been presented regarding the mechanism of action of estrogens in stimulating the transhydrogenation reaction. The first states that estrogen combines with an inactive protein and changes it to an enzymatically active form. This hypothesis was formulated originally because it best explained the kinetic data obtained from a series of experiments. A number of analogous situations are now known in which a cell has been shown to contain a protein molecule which is antigenically identical to a given enzyme and yet does not have enzymatic activity.

The second theory states that the estrogen functions as a coenzyme and is alternatively oxidized and reduced by a single estradiol dehydrogenase with dual pyridine nucleotide specificity (Talalay and Williams-Ashman, 1958). The mass of experimental evidence which renders this hypothesis unlikely has been considered in detail elsewhere (Villee, Hagerman, and Joel, 1960) and will be reviewed only briefly here. First, the estradiol dehydrogenase is found in a number of tissues such as liver which do not show an estrogen-dependent transhydrogenation reaction. Secondly, the dehydrogenase and the transhydrogenase reactions are differentially inhibited by thyroxine (Villee, 1958), by adenosine-2' phosphate and adenosine-2', 5'-diphosphate (Hollander, Hollander and Brown, 1959), and by the sulfhydryl inhibitor p-chloromercuriphenyl sulfonic acid. The enzymes have different rates of thermal inactivation and have been separated physically by electrophoresis on starch block and on paper curtain, and by adsorption onto and elution from DEAE cellulose columns (Hagerman and Villee, 1959). When certain analogues of estradiol were tested for activity in these two systems it was found that estradiol-17β monomethyl ether is dehydrogenated more rapidly than estradiol itself but is less effective than estradiol in stimulating the transhydrogenase (Table 1). In contrast, 17β-hydroxy androstan-3-one and 17β-hydroxy etiocholan-3-one are not dehydrogenated by estradiol

TABLE 1

Activities of Steroids Relative to Estradiol*

Compound	Transhydrogenase	Dehydrogenase	
		DPN(H)	TPN(H)
None	43	0	0
Estradiol-17β or estrone	100	100	100
17β-Hydroxyandrostan-3-one	89	nil	nil
17β-Hydroxyetiocholan-3-one	93	nil	nil
18-Nor-D-homoestrone methyl ether	100	82	232
Δ4-Androstene-3, 17-dione	68	13	29
Estradiol-17β-3-monomethyl ether	61	145	144
Testosterone	51	1	—
Diethyl stilbestrol	100	nil	nil

*Each value is the mean of three determinations with three different enzyme preparations.

dehydrogenase but do have some stimulatory effect on the transhydrogenase.

In the course of separating the transhydrogenase and dehydrogenase it was found that there are two different estradiol dehydrogenases, one of which specifically requires DPN as hydrogen acceptor and the second specifically requires TPN as hydrogen acceptor. A mixture of these two enzymes was unable to carry out a transhydrogenation reaction at physiological levels of substrate and pyridine nucleotides (Hagerman and Villee, 1959).

Further confirmatory evidence has come from experiments by Jensen and his colleagues at the University of Chicago who have synthesized estradiol labeled with tritium of very high specific activity (Flesher, Gupta, Jacobson, and Jensen, 1960). The radioactivity of the estradiol is high enough to be detectable in the tissues when the substance is injected into an animal in very small, physiological doses. When 0.1 microgram of the labeled estrogen was injected into a rat, 0.25 per cent of the total dose was accumulated in the uterus in fifteen minutes. All the tissues except muscle showed a greater accumulation of radioactivity than that present in the blood. The radioactivity isolated from the uterus was largely ether-soluble whereas the radioactivity isolated from the liver was in part water-soluble, representing conjugated forms of the estradiol. The estrogen isolated from the uterus was identified as estradiol alone whereas the estrogen isolated from the liver was in part estradiol and in part estrone. This is evidence that the estrogen taken up by the uterus does not undergo any chemical change while it is producing its effect. In contrast, the estrogen taken up by the liver does undergo chemical changes in preparation for its excretion.

If hydrogen transfer from one pyridine nucleotide to another involves a reduction of the enzyme-hormone complex, either the hormone or the enzyme portion of the complex might be the site of the reduction. If the hormone portion of the complex is reduced the transhydrogenation reactions might be written as follows:

$$\text{Enz} + \text{EST} \longleftrightarrow \text{Enz} - \text{EST}$$
$$\text{Enz} - \text{Estradiol} + \text{DPN} \longleftrightarrow \text{Enz} - \text{Estrone} + \text{DPNH}$$
$$\text{Enz} - \text{Estrone} + \text{TPNH} \longleftrightarrow \text{Enz} - \text{Estradiol} + \text{TPN}$$
$$\text{Sum: DPN} + \text{TPNH} \longleftrightarrow \text{DPNH} + \text{TPN}$$

The fact that even in prolonged incubation the purified transhydrogenase does not dehydrogenate estradiol renders this interpretation unlikely. If the protein part of the enzyme-hormone complex accepts the hydrogen and is reduced the reactions would be written as follows:

$$Enz + EST \longleftrightarrow EST - Enz$$
$$EST - Enz_{ox} + TPNH \longleftrightarrow EST - Enz_{red} + TPN$$
$$EST - Enz_{red} + DPN \longleftrightarrow EST - Enz_{ox} + DPNH$$
$$Sum: DPN + TPNH \longleftrightarrow TPN + DPNH$$

However, if the hydrogen is transferred directly from one pyridine nucleotide to another, both would have to be bound to the enzyme simultaneously:

$$Enz + EST \longleftrightarrow Enz - EST$$
$$Enz - EST + DPN \longleftrightarrow Enz - EST - DPN$$
$$Enz - EST - DPN + TPNH \longleftrightarrow Enz - EST - DPN - TPNH$$
$$Enz - EST - DPN - TPNH \longleftrightarrow Enz - EST - DPNH - TPN$$
$$Enz - EST - DPNH - TPN \longleftrightarrow Enz - EST - DPNH + TPN$$
$$Enz - EST - DPNH \longleftrightarrow Enz - EST + DPNH$$
$$Sum: DPN + TPNH \longleftrightarrow TPN + DPNH$$

Since there are two different orders in which the pyridine nucleotides may be attached to the enzyme and two orders in which they may be released, the kinetics are rather complex. The hormone might facilitate the binding of the nucleotides to the enzyme as suggested by the experiments of Engel and Scott (1960) with corticosterone and glutamic dehydrogenase. The experimental evidence presently available does not permit a clear decision from among these possible mechanisms.

The key role of transhydrogenase in metabolism is illustrated in Fig. 1. There are two kinds of pyridine nucleotides in the cell, DPN and TPN, and in general, each dehydrogenase will react specifically with one or the other but not with both. Three dehydrogenases, isocitric, glucose-6-phosphate, and 6-phosphogluconate dehydrogenase, all specifically require TPN as hydrogen acceptor. The amount of oxidized TPN present in the cell at any given moment is rather small. The investigations of Glock and McLean (1955) have shown this for liver and for a number of other tissues, and we have found that the same is true in the human placenta (Villee, Joel, Loring, and Spencer, 1960). Thus the rate at which these dehydrogenases operate will be limited by the amount of oxidized TPN available. The concentration of reduced TPN in the cell is considerably greater than the concentration of oxidized TPN. Reduced TPN may be reoxidized by any one of three pathways as indicated in the diagram. Most cells contain a TPNH cytochrome-c reductase which transfers electrons from the pyridine nucleotide to cytochrome c. However, oxidation of TPNH by this pathway is not coupled with phosphorylation and does not lead to the synthesis of energy-rich phosphate. TPNH is also specifically required as hydrogen donor in the synthesis of fatty acids, steroids,

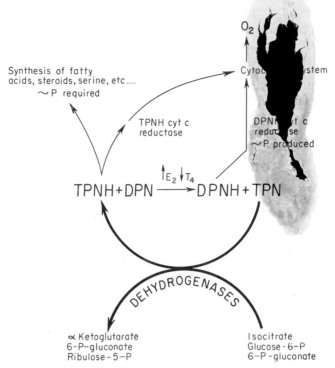

FIG. 1. Diagram illustrating the key role of the transhydrogenase reaction in controlling the rate of energy production.

(I should like to express my deep indebtedness to Drs. Dwain D.
Hagerman, Edwin E. Gordon, Gerald Gaull, and Peteranne Joel,
who have participated in the investigation of this problem, and
to the Misses Janet Loring, Anita Sarner, Joyce Spencer, and
Frederica Wellington for their expert and careful technical assistance.)

purines, and certain other compounds. These reactions result in the
oxidation of the reduced TPNH. The third pathway involves the
transfer of hydrogen from TPNH to DPN by a transhydrogenase and
the subsequent oxidation of the DPNH by a specific DPNH cyto-
chrome-c reductase. This reaction is coupled to phosphorylation
and does result in the formation of about three energy-rich phosphate bonds per pair of electrons transported to oxygen. Thus an
increased concentration of estrogens, by increasing the rate of this
estrogen-dependent transhydrogenase, would result in more of the
TPNH being oxidized by the transhydrogenase-DPNH cytochrome-c
reductase system and less by the direct oxidation of TPNH. This
would result in more energy-rich phosphate being produced per mole
of substrate metabolized. It might also increase the amount of oxidized TPN available and thus lead to an increase in the rates of the

TPN-specific dehydrogenases, to an increase in the amount of substrate metabolized per unit time, and to greater production of biologically useful energy.

Since the placental cell contains two transhydrogenases, one in the mitochondria which is not affected by estrogen, and a second in the nonparticulate fraction of the cell which is stimulated by estrogen, the theory requires that the activation of the latter would provide a significant increase in the total amount of transhydrogenation occurring in the cell. When the mitochondrial and soluble enzymes are tested in vitro under similar conditions, the mitochondrial enzyme has approximately twice the activity of the stimulated enzyme of the nonparticulate fraction (Table 2). The values of these activities were normalized to unit weight of tissue from which the two preparations were derived. In the absence of estrogen there is no activity in the nonparticulate enzyme. Thus stimulation by estradiol results in approximately a 50 per cent increase in the total amount of transhydrogenation carried on by the placental cell.

The table also reveals that, as in other cells, two of the important TPNH generating systems of the placental cell, isocitric dehydrogenase and glucose-6-phosphate dehydrogenase are present to a much greater extent in the nonparticulate fraction of the cell than in the mitochondria. The activity of the TPN specific isocitric dehydrogenase is ten times greater in the nonparticulate fraction than in the mitochondria, and there is more than 100 times as much glucose-6-phosphate dehydrogenase in the nonparticulate fraction than in the mitochondria. Pyridine nucleotides do not readily pass through mitochondrial or cell membranes and hence TPN reduced by the isocitric or glucose-6-phosphate dehydrogenase of the nonparticulate fraction may be much more readily available as substrate for

TABLE 2

Enzyme Activities in Mitochondrial and Nonparticulate Fractions
of Human Placenta*

Enzyme	Mitochondria	Nonparticulate fraction
Transhydrogenase, DPNH + APDPN§	41.2	3.85[†]
Transhydrogenase, coupled with G6PDH‡	6.8	3.72[†]
Glucose-6-phosphate dehydrogenase	10.4	1,280
Isocitric dehydrogenase	250	1,891

*Values are means of five determinations, normalized to unit wet weight of tissue from which the fractions were obtained

[†]Estrogen-stimulated

‡G6PDH, glucose-6-phosphate dehydrogenase

§Acetylpyridine, DPN.

the estrogen-stimulable enzyme than for the mitochondrial enzyme. For this reason, it is likely that at any given moment within the intact cell, the amount of transhydrogenation mediated by the soluble enzyme may be considerably more than the 30 to 50 per cent of the total indicated by these estimates from in vitro experiments simply because of the greater availability of its substrate, TPNH, in that localized region.

Evidence is now accumulating that there is an increase in the rate of energy metabolism of the placental cell upon stimulation by estrogens and that this is reflected in concomitant increases in the biosynthetic activities of that cell. Our early experiments with slices of endometrium and placenta revealed an estrogen-induced increase in oxygen consumption, which is evidence of an increased rate of energy metabolism.

Homogenates of human placenta were incubated one hour at 37° C in a medium containing citrate and inorganic P_{32} with or without estradiol added to a final concentration of 4×10^{-6} M. As shown in Table 3 the homogenates containing estradiol had significantly greater rates of oxygen consumption and citrate utilization, an increased rate of production of alpha-ketoglutarate, and an increased rate of incorporation of inorganic P_{32} into adenosine triphosphate. The ATP was isolated from a trichloroacetic acid extract of the incubation medium by adsorption onto activated charcoal by the method of Crane and Lipmann (1953). The pyrophosphate bonds of ATP were split by acid hydrolysis, the inorganic phosphate was measured chemically, and its radioactivity was determined. On the average, the specific activity of the ATP produced in a system stimulated by estradiol was 2.5 times greater than that produced in the controls

TABLE 3

Effect of Estradiol on Metabolism of Placental Homogenate

	Control	Estradiol 1 mcg/ml
Oxygen consumption μ moles/vessel/hr	0.812* ± 0.025	0.979 ± 0.045
Production of α-ketoglutarate μ moles/vessel/hr	0.621 ± 0.041	0.840 ± 0.039
Incorporation of P^{32} into ATP cpm × 10^{-3}/mg P/hr	82.5 ± 15	205. ± 28

Complete system: phosphate buffer, pH 7.4; citrate, 10μ moles/ml; DPN, 0.15 μ moles/ml; inorganic P^{32}

Number of experiments, 15

*Mean ± standard error

without added estradiol. This was a proportionately greater increase than the increase in citrate utilization or in oxygen consumption.

Other experiments in our laboratory by Hagerman and Robertson have shown that placental slices will accumulate amino acids intracellularly when incubated in vitro in a suitable medium and that the rate of accumulation of amino acids is increased when estradiol is added. This was demonstrated both with natural amino acids and with C^{14}-α-amino isobutyric acid, the nonutilizable amino acid used extensively by Christensen and colleagues (1955) in their pioneering studies of the accumulation of amino acids in cells. The ratio of intracellular to extracellular amino acid was 2.8 in the absence of estrogen and 3.8 in the presence of 4×10^{-6} M estradiol. The accumulation of amino acids requires energy and this increase, we believe, reflects the increased availability of biologically useful energy.

In another series of experiments, slices of human placenta were incubated with carbon-14 labeled substrates, and proteins, lipids, and nucleic acids were isolated from the tissues after incubation. The amount of labeled carbon incorporated into each of these fractions was then measured. Table 4 presents the results of one of the experiments with acetate. The addition of estradiol increased oxygen consumption, it increased the rate of incorporation of acetate carbon into protein, and it increased the rate of incorporation of labeled carbon into lipid, and into the adenine and guanine isolated from the nucleic acids of the cell. The figures are the averages of five determinations. In a second experiment only protein synthesis was measured. The average of the ten determinations showed an increase in the incorporation of acetate carbon into protein in the estradiol vessels over the controls which was significant at the 5 per cent level.

TABLE 4

Effects of Estradiol on the Metabolism of Human Placenta Slices

Substrate: Acetate-2-C^{14} 1.44×10^{8} cpm/μmole	Control	Estradiol 4×10^{-6} M	Per cent increase	Probability
Q_{O_2}, μL O_2/mg dry wt/hr	1.78	1.95	9.5	0.11
C^{14} in protein, cpm/mg protein/hr	676	855	26	0.03
C^{14} in lipid, cpm/mg lipid/hr	305	347	14	0.2
C^{14} in nucleic acid adenine cpm/μM adenine/hr	7.00	8.96	28	0.09
C^{14} in nucleic acid guanine, cpm/μM guanine/hr	7.11	8.83	24	0.09
Acetate to CO_2, μM/gm wet wt/hr	0.386	0.494	28	0.18

Each value is the mean of five determinations.

In a comparable experiment with glycine-1-C^{14} as substrate (Table 5) the addition of estradiol increased the rate of synthesis of proteins and of nucleic acids. The effect on protein synthesis was significant at the 3 per cent level but the increases in nucleic acid synthesis were not statistically significant. In two other experiments with glycine as substrate, in which only protein synthesis was measured, no effect of estradiol was observed. The response of tissue slices and homogenates to estradiol appears to depend on certain constituents in the incubation medium and on other factors which are not yet clear. The incubation medium must contain inorganic phosphate and magnesium and potassium in a certain ratio, yet these are not required by the purified transhydrogenase.

The stimulation by estrogen of this transhydrogenation system would tend to decrease rather than increase the amount of TPNH in the cell. It is known that certain of the reductive steps in the biosynthesis of fatty acids, steroids, purines, and other substances specifically require reduced TPN and not reduced DPN as the hydrogen donor. The investigations of Glock and McLean had shown that the liver cell and certain other cells contain most of their TPN in the reduced state and most of their DPN in the oxidized state. We have carried out measurements of the concentration of oxidized and reduced di- and tri-phosphopyridine nucleotides in suitable extracts of fresh human placenta.

Two independent methods were employed. The first used a DPN specific alcohol dehydrogenase and a TPN specific glucose-6-phosphate dehydrogenase, each coupled with diaphorase and the dye, dichlorophenol indophenol. The other method takes advantage of the strong fluorescence of the oxidized pyridine nucleotides when they are treated with strong alkali. The two methods give very similar results (Table 6). Fresh human placenta contains its DPN largely in

TABLE 5

Effects of Estradiol on the Metabolism of Human Placenta Slices

Substrate: Glycine-1-C^{14} 4.88×10^5 cpm/μmole	Control	Estradiol 4×10^{-6} M	Per cent increase	Probability
Q_{O_2}, μL O_2/mg dry wt/hr	1.64	1.88	15	0.08
C^{14} in protein, cpm/mg prot/hr	171	217	27	0.03
C^{14} in lipid, cpm/mg lipid/hr	67	66		
C^{14} in nucleic acid adenine, cpm/μM ad/hr	6.28	6.79	8	
C^{14} in nucleic acid guanine, cpm/μM gu/hr	9.49	11.19	18	
Glycine to CO_2, μM/gm wet wt/hr	0.0485	0.0507	4	

Each value is mean of five determinations.

TABLE 6

Pyridine Nucleotide Content of Tissues
Micromoles per Gram Fresh Tissue

	Rat liver*	Rat placenta*	Human placenta
DPN	0.504	0.122	0.224
DPNH	0.278	0.015	0.055
TPN	0.0072	<0.0024	0.0056
TPNH	0.298	0.0036	0.0095

*Data of Glock and McLean (1955), *Biochem. J.*, 61:388.

the oxidized state and its TPN largely in the reduced state. This would tend to favor the transfer of hydrogen from TPN to DPN by the estrogen-dependent pyridine nucleotide transhydrogenase.

The transhydrogenase reaction is not readily reversible and attempts to link it with a DPNH generating system such as lactic dehydrogenase have not been successful (Villee and Hagerman, 1958). It appears that oxidized TPN is a potent inhibitor of the transhydrogenase. Under artificial conditions in vitro, however, the transhydrogenase reaction was linked to the TPNH-requiring steps of fatty acid synthesis and an estrogen stimulation of the process could be demonstrated (Hosoya, Hagerman, and Villee, 1960).

The effects of estradiol on placental metabolism which have been demonstrated in vitro, that is, the increased rate of turnover of ATP, the increased rate of uptake of amino acids by the cell, and the suggestion that the synthesis of protein, nucleic acids, and fats is increased, parallel the findings of Mueller (Mueller, Herranen, and Jervell, 1958) who incubated rat uteri in vitro following the injection of estradiol in vivo. These results support the hypothesis that estrogen stimulation of the pyridine nucleotide transhydrogenase leads to an increase in biologically useful energy which is evident secondarily as an increased rate of synthesis of protein, nucleic acids, and fats, reactions which are fundamental to growth.

Another test of the theory that steroid dehydrogenases may function as transhydrogenases has been made by Bloom (1960) who used rat-liver slices, known to contain both 3 α-hydroxy steroid dehydrogenase and estradiol-17β dehydrogenase. Bloom incubated the slices with lactate-2-tritium, which should lead to the production of reduced pyridine nucleotide labeled with tritium. The amount of tritium incorporated into a product which requires DPNH for its synthesis, for example hexose, or a product requiring TPNH for its synthesis, for example fatty acids, was measured in the presence and absence of estradiol-17β, androstan-3, 17-dione or etiocholane-3, 17-dione. In all of these experiments the amount of tritium incorporated into water, lipids, and glycogen in the presence and absence of hormone was the same. This is further proof that steroid dehydrogenases are unable to serve physiologically in transhydrogenation reactions. Our experiments had shown previously that there is no estrogen-dependent transhydrogenase in the liver and we would have predicted that Bloom's experiments would not lead to increased transhydrogenase activity. Our hypothesis would predict, however, that if comparable experiments were carried out with placental tissue a hormonally increased rate of transfer of tritium from substrate to product would be induced. Experiments are now under way to test this hypothesis.

Although there is a considerable body of literature regarding the responses at the biological level to administered androgens and progestins, much less is known about the site or mechanism of action of these sex hormones than is known about estrogens. The rapid growth of the capon comb following the administration of testosterone involves a pronounced increase in the amount of mucopolysaccharide present, but it is not known whether the androgens act by increasing the activity of one of the enzymes involved in the synthesis of polysaccharides or whether it increases the availability of some required cofactor. Many of the other biological effects of androgens do not appear to involve polysaccharide synthesis and the relation of these observations to other roles of androgens is unclear.

Mann and his colleagues (1957) have shown that castration reduces the concentration of fructose, citric acid, and ergothioneine in the semen and that the subcutaneous implantation of a pellet of testosterone results in the return of these constituents to normal concentrations. A satisfactory biochemical explanation for these findings is not yet at hand.

An increase in the activity of β-glucuronidase in the kidney results when androgens are administered (Fishman, 1951). This finding might be interpreted as an adaptive increase in the enzyme induced by the increased concentration of substrate or by a direct effect of the steroid on the synthesis of the enzyme. The respiration of slices of seminal vesicles was shown by Rudolph and Samuels (1949) to decrease following castration and to be restored to normal within ten hours after the injection of testosterone. The ventral prostate gland of the rat shows a similar decrease in the rate of respiration following castration and increase when testosterone is administered.

Williams and his colleagues (Baron, Gore, and Williams, 1960) have recently provided evidence of an androgen-activated transhydrogenase in rat and human prostate gland. Cell-free fractions of prostate obtained by ultracentrifugation were tested for transhydrogenase activity with and without added hormone, using the acetyl pyridine analogue of DPN. The transfer of hydrogen from DPNH to APDPN was increased twofold by the addition of catalytic amounts of androsterone but not of estrogen. The prostatic extracts were tested for hydroxy steroid dehydrogenase activity using stoichiometric amounts of the steroid but none was detected.

The effects of injected androgens on the metabolism of muscles of castrate rats have been investigated in our laboratory (Villee, Loring, and Spencer, 1961). The perineal, temporal, and masseter muscles of the rat decrease in size following castration and increase in size following the administration of androgens. To investigate the sequence of enzyme changes underlying these phenomena, young male rats were castrated and subsequently were injected with testosterone, androsterone, or progesterone dissolved in propylene glycol, or with propylene glycol alone. After four injections the rats were sacrificed; liver, kidney, and masseter muscles were excised for pyridine nucleotide analyses, and perineal, temporal and masseter muscles were homogenized. After centrifugation at low speed to remove cellular debris the preparation was incubated for an hour at 37° C with citrate, succinate, malate, or lactate as substrate in the presence of inorganic P_{32}. The rates of oxygen consumption of the homogenates of control and hormone-treated rats were essentially equal with succinate as substrate (Table 7). This observation confirms the finding of Leonard (1952) that the succinate oxidase activity of muscle is unaffected by castration or by the administration of testosterone. However, the oxygen consumption of homogenates of testosterone-treated muscle was 175 per cent of the controls with malate as substrate and 130 per cent of the controls with citrate

TABLE 7

Metabolism of Muscle Homogenates from Castrate Rats
Control versus Testosterone-treated

Substrate	O_2 Consumption	α-Keto acid produced	Lactate produced	$P^{32} \rightarrow ATP$
Citrate control	0.18	0.03	0.08	324
testosterone	0.25	0.14	0.53	435
Succinate control	2.12	0.05	0.14	347
testosterone	2.06	0.08	0.83	346
Malate control	0.24	0.08	0.14	367
testosterone	0.44	0.12	0.59	466

All values expressed as micromoles/mgm nitrogen/hr, except P^{32}, which are expressed as cpm $\times 10^{-3}$/mgm P/hr.

or lactate as substrate. With all substrates there was a greater accumulation of lactic and alpha-keto acids in the incubation of homogenates of testosterone-treated muscle than in the control. The rate of incorporation of P_{32} into ATP was equal in homogenates of control and testosterone-treated muscle incubated with succinate, but greater in testosterone-treated muscle than in control tissues incubated with malate, citrate, or lactate as substrates.

These results would be consistent with the hypothesis that testosterone increases the activity of DPNH-cytochrome-c reductase in these responsive muscles. The total amount of pyridine nucleotides in the liver was essentially the same in control and testosterone treated animals. The ratio of DPN to DPNH did not differ significantly but the ratio of TPN to TPNH was consistently greater in treated than in control tissues (Table 8).

Attempts to clarify the role of progesterone in metabolism have been hampered by the fact that most tissues must be stimulated by estrogen prior to any effective action of progesterone. The experiments of Wade and Jones (1956) demonstrated effects of progesterone on several aspects of metabolism in rat-liver mitochondria, but the question of the relationship between these observations and the physiologic function of the hormone remains to be answered. Progesterone but not estradiol, testosterone, or any of several other steroids tested stimulated the adenosine triphosphatase activity of rat-liver mitochondria. This was not the result of an altered permeability of the mitochondrial membrane, for the stimulatory effect was demonstrable with mitochondria that had been repeatedly frozen and thawed to rupture the membranes. Higher concentrations of progesterone (10^{-4} M) inhibit the utilization of oxygen by rat-liver mitochondria with DPNH as substrate. Similar inhibitions were produced by estradiol, testosterone, and several other steroids. The inhibition of respiration by these high, unphysiologic concentra-

TABLE 8

Tissue Levels of Pyridine Nucleotides in
Castrate Rats Injected with Testosterone*

	DPN	DPNH	TPN	TPNH
Liver, control	.393	.170	.0149	.348
testosterone	.45	.147	.025	.330
Kidney, control	.719	.408	.036	.217
testosterone	.592	.402	.072	.187
Muscle, control	.510	.064	<.005	.025
testosterone	.429	.036	<.005	.017

*Values given as micromoles per gram fresh tissue.

tions of steroids added in vitro has been reported many times and with several different kinds of tissues; this appears to be a relatively unspecific action of steroids.

Elder, Segal, Maxwell, and Topper (1960) reported that the metabolism of galactose by rat liver is stimulated by progesterone but not by other steroids, and that this effect can be duplicated by adding menthol instead of progesterone. These substances appear to accelerate galactose utilization by increasing the rate of the UDP galactose-4-epimerase, but the physiologic significance of these findings is not yet clear.

The effects of progesterone on uterine muscle have been investigated by Csapo (1956) who was unable to demonstrate any effect of progesterone on a purified, contractile, actomyosin-ATP system obtained from the myometrium. He explained the well-known effect of progesterone in decreasing the contractility of myometrium as occurring in some step of the excitation process. In the presence of progesterone, myometrial cells have a decreased intracellular concentration of potassium ions and an increased concentration of sodium ions. Csapo postulates that the change in ionic gradient across the cell membrane is responsible for the altered action potential and partial depolarization of the cell membrane. This results in decreased conductivity or decreased reactivity of the myometrial cell. Csapo has suggested that progesterone might decrease the over-all rate of cellular metabolism, and that this would be reflected in a decreased rate of the sodium pump in the cell membrane. Under the influence of progesterone, the actomyosin-ATP system is capable of full contraction but because of the partial block in the mechanism for the excitation and propagation of impulses, the muscle cells do not operate effectively and the contractility remains localized.

There have been many attempts to demonstrate some effect of corticosteroid hormones on intermediary metabolism—attempts to explain the fact that the addition of these hormones in vivo leads to an increased rate of gluconeogenesis from proteins. The attempts to analyze this reaction by the addition of corticoids to tissue slices or tissue preparations in vitro have been generally unsuccessful. A brilliant series of observations recently reported by Engel and Scott (1960) has gone far to provide a reasonable explanation for this phenomenon. They began with the observation made by Weil-Malherbe (1946) and by Weber (1950) that certain aromatic polycyclic substances will form complexes with caffein and other purines.

Engel and his colleagues found that a comparable molecular interaction occurs between testosterone and adenosine. Testosterone is solubilized by buffer solutions containing adenosine but not by solutions containing pyrimidines. This phenomenon was explained as due to a binding of testosterone and certain other steroids with adenine and certain other purines. The molecular requirements for this binding were shown to include a group at carbon-17 of the molecule in the alpha configuration and a certain orientation at carbon-11 in the C ring. There are a number of bits of evidence which indicate that the adenine molecule does not interact with ring A but reacts primarily with the alpha side of carbons 11 and 17 in rings C and D. From a model of the testosterone molecule they concluded that the hydrogen atoms on the alpha side of rings D and C and part of ring B form a flat layer, with nearly the same area as that of the adenine molecule which, because of the double bonds in its two rings, is also rather flat. Substituents on the beta side of the steroid molecule may influence the equilibrium constants by interacting with other beta substituents and thus distorting the molecule so that the alpha side is less flat.

The next link in this series of observations was provided by Weber (1957) who demonstrated that there is an intramolecular transfer of energy between the adenine and the pyridine units of reduced diphosphopyridine nucleotide. He did this by showing that light, which is absorbed by the adenine moiety at 260 millimicrons, is reemitted as fluorescent light with a wave length of 460 millimicrons. This is the exact wavelength at which emission occurs when the substance is irradiated at 340 millimicrons, the wavelength of maximum absorption of the dihydronicotinamide portion of DPNH. Weber showed that for this transfer to occur the two portions of DPNH must be close together. If the DPN is hydrolyzed to split off the adenylic acid from the dihydronicotinamide mononucleotide, energy transfer no longer occurs although the two fragments are present in the same molar concentrations as they were before hydrolysis. When the DPNH molecule is drawn in the folded form, the two nitrogen-containing rings are close together. The binding experiments suggest that a complex is formed between the steroid hormone and the adenine moiety of the coenzyme; thus the steroid hormone will be placed close to the locus of hydrogen transfer.

These observations led Engel and Scott to study the effects of steroid hormones upon the rates of reactions mediated by DPN. They first added testosterone to a system containing purified yeast alcohol dehydrogenase. Despite a series of experiments in which a host of conditions was varied, they were unable to demonstrate any effect of testosterone on the activity of this enzyme. Then the work of Vennesland (1958) pointed up the fact that dehydrogenases using DPNH fall into two classes: those which transfer the so-called alpha hydrogen on one side of the nicotinamide ring, and those which transfer the so-called beta hydrogen on the other side of the ring.

Alcohol dehydrogenase is an enzyme which utilizes the alpha hydrogen of DPN, whereas the bacterial beta hydroxysteroid dehydrogenase described by Talalay, Loewus, and Vennesland (1955) is a beta enzyme with respect to DPNH.

For a second series of experiments they turned to glutamic dehydrogenase, which is available commercially in a highly purified form from beef liver, and which does transfer the beta hydrogen of DPNH. They tried a corticosteroid instead of testosterone because of the known effect of the corticoids in the stimulation of gluconeogenesis, which could be mediated at least in part by an effect on glutamic dehydrogenase. They chose corticosterone for their tests because it is known to be an important corticoid in the cow.

By varying separately the relative amounts of enzyme, substrate, and coenzyme, so that each in turn became the limiting reagent, they carried out a series of experiments with corticosterone present at a concentration of about 10^{-6} M. It was found that when the concentration of DPN was the limiting reagent, the addition of corticosterone at concentrations of 10^{-6} to 10^{-5} M exerted a significant stimulation of the initial velocity of the reaction (Table 9). The amount of the stimulation is small, on the order of 10 per cent, but it is reproducible and they have been able to observe this with several different preparations of enzyme, coenzyme, substrate, and steroid. The stimulating effect of corticosterone was demonstrable over a thousandfold range of concentrations but disappeared somewhere between 10^{-8} and 10^{-9} M. The stimulation is not, however, proportional to the concentration of steroid.

Testosterone had no effect upon the rate of this reaction by itself, but when added to a reaction system containing corticosterone it

TABLE 9

Effect of Corticosterone on Beef-liver Glutamic Dehydrogenase

DPN conc. $M \times 10^{-6}$	DPNH produced Moles/liter/min $\times 10^{-7}$ No corticosterone	Corticosterone 0.5×10^{-5} M	Per cent Increase	Probability
18	6.88	7.38	+7.2	> 0.1
25	9.29	10.3	+10.1	< 0.005
30	10.2	11.0	+8.0	< 0.01
40	12.5	13.8	+10.4	< 0.005
50	17.6	17.5	—	
100	31.8	30.9	—	

L. L. Engel and J. F. Scott (1960), *Rec. Prog. Hormone Research*, 16.

blocked the corticosterone effect. The inference is that both steroids are bound to the enzyme-nucleotide complex but only the binding of corticosterone results in an increase in the rate of reaction. A close relative of corticosterone, 11-epicorticosterone, which is devoid of biological activity in vivo, was found not to affect the reaction rate under the conditions and in the concentrations in which corticosterone is effective. When triphosphopyridine nucleotide was used in place of diphosphopyridine nucleotide in the system, no effect of corticosterone was observed, even though the glutamic dehydrogenase can use TPN as hydrogen acceptor.

The concentration of steroid which could elicit the response is low, on the order of 10^{-6} to 10^{-8} M and is in the range in which such a compound might conceivably be circulating in the body. The level of hydrocortisone in plasma has been estimated to be about 10 micrograms per 100 milliliters of blood, which is between 10^{-6} and 10^{-7} M. However, at the present time the true concentration of any hormone at its ultimate site of action is unknown and any estimate based on its concentration in the plasma may be misleading. As Engel points out, the effect of the steroid upon the reaction rate is evident at concentrations where there are roughly the same number of molecules of hormone and of enzyme. Although the increase observed upon the addition of hormone is only 10 per cent, a 10 per cent increase in the rate of a single reaction under steady-state conditions may have profound effects on the over-all metabolic situation. This effect of a corticosteroid on a purified enzyme system could explain at least some of the effects of cortical hormones observed in vivo.

Most investigators who have speculated upon the mode of action of steroids—whether they believe the effect is by activating an enzyme, by altering the permeability of a membrane, or by serving as coenzyme in a given reaction—have emphasized the binding of steroid to protein as an essential part of the mechanism of action or a preliminary step to that action. The specificities, synergisms, and antagonisms of the several steroids have been explained in terms of the formation of specific steroid-protein complexes. The differences between different target organs—for example, those that respond to androgens and those that respond to estrogens—may be attributed to differences in the distribution of the specific cellular proteins that are involved in such binding reactions. Viewed in this light the problem of the mode of action of steroid hormones becomes one aspect of the larger problem of the biochemical basis of embryonic differentiation of tissues.

REFERENCES

Ball, E. G., and O. Cooper (1957), Oxidation of reduced triphosphopyridine nucleotide as mediated by the transhydrogenase reaction and its inhibition by thyroxine. *Proc. Natl. Acad. Sci. U.S.*, 43:357-364.

Baron, D. N., M. B. R. Gore, and D. C. Williams (1960), An androgen activated pyridine nucleotide transhydrogenase in prostatic tissue. *Biochem. J.*, 74:20P.

Bloom, B. (1960), An evaluation of hormonal augmented transhydrogenase activity in rat liver cells. *J. Biol. Chem.*, 235:857-858.

Christensen, H. N. (1955), Mode of transport of amino acids into cells, in *Amino Acid Metabolism*, W. D. McElroy and B. Glass, eds., Johns Hopkins Press, Baltimore, pp. 63-106.

Crane, R. L., and F. Lipmann (1953), Effect of arsenate on aerobic phosphorylation. *J. Biol. Chem.*, 201:235-243.

Csapo, A. (1956), The mechanism of effect of the ovarian steroids. *Rec. Prog. Hormone Res.*, 12:405-427.

Elder, T. D., S. Segal, E. S. Maxwell, and Y. J. Topper (1960), The progesterone-like effects of menthol on galactose metabolism. *Federation Proc.*, 19:53.

Engel, L. L., and J. F. Scott (1960), Effects of steroid hormones upon diphosphopyridine nucleotide mediated enzymatic reactions. *Rec. Prog. Hormone Res.*, 16:79-91.

Fishman, W. H. (1951), Effects of androgens on β glucuronidase of the kidney. *Vitamins and Hormones*, 9:213-234.

Flesher, J. W., G. N. Gupta, H. I. Jacobson, and E. V. Jenson (1960), Fate of steroid estrogens in target tissues. *Federation Proc.*, 19:170.

Glass, R. and C. A. Villee (1961), The estrogen properties in vitro of diethyl-stilbestrol and substances related to estradiol. *Endocrinology*, 68:327-333.

Glock, G., and P. McLean (1955), A preliminary investigation of the hormonal control of the hexose monophosphate oxidative pathway. *Biochem. J.*, 61:390-402.

Hagerman, D. D., and C. A. Villee (1952), Effects of estradiol on the metabolism of human endometrium *in vitro*. *Arch. Biochem. Biophys.*, 40:481-482.

—— and —— (1957), Estrogen-sensitive isocitric dehydrogenase. *J. Biol. Chem.*, 229:589-597.

—— and —— (1959), Separation of human placental estrogen-sensitive transhydrogenase from estradiol-17β dehydrogenase. *J. Biol. Chem.*, 234:2031-2036.

Hollander, V. T., N. Hollander, and J. D. Brown (1959), Inhibition of steroid mediated pyridine nucleotide transhydrogenase and 17β hydroxysteroid dehydrogenase by 2′adenylic acid. *Proc. Soc. Exp. Biol. Med.*, 101:475-477.

Hosoya, N., D. D. Hagerman, and C. A. Villee (1960), Stimulation of fatty acid synthesis by estradiol *in vitro*. *Biochem.*, 76:297-301

Kaplan, N. O., S. P. Colowick, and E. F. Neufeld (1952), Pyridine nucleotide transhydrogenase. II. Direct evidence for mechanism of the transhydrogenase reaction. *J. Biol. Chem.*, 195:107-119.

——, ——, ——, and M. M. Ciotti (1953), Pyridine nucleotide transhydrogenase. IV. Effect of adenylic acid a on the bacterial transhydrogenase. *J. Biol. Chem.*, 205:17-29.

Knox, W. E., and V. H. Auerbach (1955), The hormone control of tryptophane peroxidase in rats. *J. Biol. Chem.*, 214:307-313.

Krahl, M. E. (1957), Speculations on the action of insulin, with a note on other hypoglycemic agents. *Perspectives Biol. Med.*, 1:69-96.

Leonard, S. L. (1952), A glycostatic effect of testosterone on the perineal muscles of the rat. *Endocrinology*, 50:199-205.

Levine, R., and M. S. Goldstein (1955), On the mechanism of action of insulin. *Rec. Prog. Hormone Res.*, 11:343-375.

Mann, T. (1957), *The Biochemistry of Semen.* Cambridge University Press, London.

Mueller, G. C., A. M. Herranen, and K. F. Jervell (1958), Studies on the mechanism of action of estrogens. *Rec. Prog. Hormone Res.*, 14:95-129.

Rudolph, G. G., and L. T. Samuels (1949), Early effects of testosterone propionate on the seminal vesicles of castrate rats. *Endocrinology*, 44:190-196.

Sutherland, E. W., and T. W. Rall (1957), The properties of an adenine ribonucleotide produced with cellular particles, ATP, Mg^{++} and epinephrine or glucagon. *J. Am. Chem. Soc.*, 79:3608.

Talalay, P., F. A. Loewus, and B. Vennesland (1955), The enzymatic transfer of hydrogen. IV. The reaction catalyzed by a β-hydroxysteroid dehydrogenase. *J. Biol. Chem.*, 212:801-809.

—— and H. G. Williams-Ashman (1958), Activation of hydrogen transfer between pyridine nucleotides by steroid hormones. *Proc. Natl. Acad. Sci. U.S.*, 44:15-26.

Vennesland, B. (1958), Stereospecificity of hydrogen transfer in pyridine nucleotide dehydrogenase reactions. *Federation Proc.*, 17:1150-1155.

Villee, C. A., and D. D. Hagerman (1953), Effects of estradiol on the metabolism of human placenta *in vitro. J. Biol. Chem.*, 203:863-882.

—— (1958), Antagonistic effects of estrogens and thyroxine on an enzymatic system *in vitro. Proc. Intern. Congr. Biochem., 4th Congr., Vienna*, 1:115.

—— and D. D. Hagerman (1958), On the identity of the estrogen-sensitive enzyme of human placenta. *J. Biol. Chem.*, 233:42-48.

——, P. B. Joel, J. M. Loring, and J. M. Spencer (1960), Stimulation of ATP production and protein synthesis by estrogens. *Federation Proc.*, 19:53.

——, D. D. Hagerman, and P. B. Joel (1960), An enzymatic basis for the physiologic functions of estrogens. *Rec. Prog. Hormone Res.*, 16:46-69.

——, J. M. Loring, and J. M. Spencer (1961), Effects of androgens on intermediary metabolism in muscle. *Endrocrinology*, 68:501-506.

Wade, R., and H. W. Jones, Jr. (1956), Effect of progesterone on mitochondrial adenosine triphosphatase. *J. Biol. Chem.*, 220:547-552.

Weber, G. (1950), Fluorescence of riboflavin and flavin-adenine dinucleotide. *Biochem. J.*, 47:114-121.

—— (1957), Intramolecular transfer of electronic energy in dihydrodiphosphopyridine nucleotide. *Nature*, 180:1409.

Weil-Malherbe, H. (1946), The solubilization of polycyclic aromatic hydrocarbons by purines. *Biochem. J.*, 40:351-363.

Wolfe, E. C., and E. G. Ball (1957), The action of thyroxine on the oxidation of succinate and malate. *J. Biol. Chem.*, 224:1083-1098.

Index

Numbers in italic type indicate pages on which there are
illustrations or tables